HARDEN'S

London
Restaurants
1999

© Harden's Guides, 1998

ISBN 1-873721-20-X (paperback)
ISBN 1-873721-23-4 (bonded leather)

British Library Cataloguing-in-Publication data:
a catalogue record for this book is available from
the British Library.

Printed and bound in Finland by
Werner Söderström Osakeyhtiö

Research and editorial assistants:
Antonia Russell, Charles Cain

Harden's Guides
29 Villiers Street
London WC2N 6ND

Distributed in the United States of America by
Seven Hills Book Distributors,
49 Central Avenue, Cincinnati, OH 45202

CONTENTS

Ratings & prices

RATINGS & PRICES

Ratings

Our rating system is unlike those found in other guides (most of which tell you nothing more helpful than that expensive restaurants are, as a general rule, better than cheap ones).

What we do is to compare each restaurant's performance with other restaurants in the same price-bracket.

This system has the advantage that it helps you find – whatever your budget for any particular meal – where you will get the best "bang for your buck".

The following qualities are assessed:

> **F** — Food
> **S** — Service
> **A** — Ambience

The rating indicates that, *in comparison with other restaurants in the same price-bracket*, performance is ...

> **❶** — Exceptional
> **❷** — Very good
> **❸** — Good
> ④ — Mediocre
> ⑤ — Disappointing

Prices

The price shown for each restaurant is the cost for one (1) person of an average three-course *dinner* with half a bottle of house wine and coffee, any cover charge, service and VAT. Lunch is often cheaper. With BYO restaurants, we have assumed that two people share a £5 bottle of off-licence wine.

Map reference – shown immediately after the telephone number.

Last orders time – the first entry in the small print (Sunday may be up to 90 minutes earlier).

Opening hours – unless otherwise stated, restaurants are open for lunch and dinner seven days a week.

Credit and debit cards – unless otherwise stated, Mastercard, Visa, Amex and Switch are accepted.

Dress – where appropriate, the management's preferences concerning patrons' dress are given.

Smoking – cigarette smoking restrictions are noted. Pipe or cigar smokers should always check ahead.

Special menus – if we know of a particularly good value set menu we note this (eg "set weekday L"), together with its formula price (FP) calculated exactly as in 'Prices' above. Details change, so always check ahead.

FROM THE EDITORS

This is the eighth edition of our annual guide, designed to help you find the right London restaurant for any particular occasion and then, as briefly as possible, to tell you everything you need to know about it.

The Survey

Once again this year, the guide has been compiled with the benefit of a much-enlarged survey. This year over 3,400 people participated (some 24 per cent more than last year). We are very grateful to all who did so, and also to those who have helped enlarge the survey by introducing friends and colleagues.

Reporters eat out, on average, 3.5 times a week. Thus the survey reflects the experiences of some 600,000 meals eaten in the preceding 12 months.

Whose views?

We have ourselves visited every restaurant, or chain, listed in this book – always anonymously and at our own expense. But, for the most part, we use these personal experiences only to help us to interpret and explain the results of the survey – we do not seek to superimpose our personal views. Rather, we seek from our informed starting-point, to analyse and comment on the views and ratings from our 'reporters'. In the rare cases we feel that we can add something by noting our dissent from the general view, we do so in the text. The numerical ratings reflect the survey results.

The survey however can provide no useful information on the 'hot' summer openings (upon which we receive little or no commentary), and it is of only limited assistance where there has been a recent major chef or ownership change. In these cases, our own opinions are, of necessity, more to the fore, and, in these cases only, any numerical rating reflects our personal opinions alone.

We believe that it is this pragmatic combination of the views of thousands of people with the impressions from our own personal visits which enables the production of an up-to-date guide of unequalled reliability.

Please help us to make the next edition even more accurate. If you register for the free updates (by returning the reply-paid card at the back of the book) you will be invited, in the summer of 1999, to take part in our next survey. **If you take part in the survey, you will, on publication, receive a complimentary copy of _Harden's London Restaurants 2000_.**

Richard Harden   **Peter Harden**

SURVEY – MOST MENTIONED

These are the restaurants which were most frequently mentioned by reporters. (Last year's position is given in brackets. An asterisk* indicates a first appearance in the list of a recently opened or re-launched restaurant.)

1 Oxo Tower (1)
2 The Ivy (4)
3 Bluebird (22)
4 Bank (5)
5 Le Pont de la Tour (6)
6 Quaglino's (3)
7 Aubergine (7)
8 Mezzo (2)
9 The Criterion (9)
10 Le Palais du Jardin (8)

11 Blue Elephant (11)
12 Le Caprice (10)
13 The River Café (15)
14 Livebait (13)
15 Bibendum (12)
16 L'Oranger (18)
17 Belgo (28=)
18 The Square (40)
19 City Rhodes (-)
20 Vong (17)

21 Wagamama (16)
22 La Tante Claire (20)
23 Nobu (32)
24 Momo (-)
25 Le Gavroche (39=)
26 Zafferano (-)
27 Café Spice Namaste (38)
28 Kensington Place (23)
29 Oak Room Marco Pierre White (30)
30 Langan's Brasserie (-)

31 Pharmacy*
32 Andrew Edmunds (35)
33 Mash*
34 Atlantic Bar & Grill (27)
35 Chutney Mary (26)
36 The Avenue (25)
37 L'Odéon (14)
38 The Sugar Club (34)
39 Coast (19)
40 Circus*

SURVEY – NOMINATIONS

Ranked by the number of reporters' votes for:

Best meal of the year

1. Aubergine (*see Gordon Ramsay*) (1)
2. The Ivy (5=)
3. La Tante Claire (2)
4. The Square (-)
5. L'Oranger (7)
6. Le Gavroche (5=)
7. Oak Room Marco Pierre White (10)
8. The River Café (3)
9. Le Pont de la Tour (8)
10. Chez Nico at Ninety (7)

Favourite

1. The Ivy (1)
2. Le Caprice (2)
3. Aubergine (*see Gordon Ramsay*) (4)
4. Le Palais du Jardin (3)
5. Oxo Tower (6=)
6. Zafferano (-)
7. The River Café (5)
8. Chez Bruce (-)
9. Le Pont de la Tour (10)
10. L'Oranger (-)

Best for business

1. City Rhodes (6)
2. Le Pont de la Tour (1)
3. Oxo Tower (4)
4. Bank (5)
5. Savoy Grill (2=)
6. The Square (8)
7. The Ivy (2=)
8. Quaglino's (7)
9. Rules (-)
10. L'Oranger(-)

Best for romance

1. La Poule au Pot (1)
2. Andrew Edmunds (3)
3. Oxo Tower (8=)
4. The Blue Elephant (6)
5. Launceston Place (5)
6. The Ivy (7)
7. Julie's (1=)
8. The Criterion (8=)
9. Aubergine (4)
10. Le Caprice (10)

SURVEY – HIGHEST RATINGS

Rankings are determined from reporters' average ratings:

Money no object (£55+)

Food		Service	
Food		**Service**	
1	Aubergine (Gordon Ramsay)	1	Dorchester Grill
2	La Tante Claire	2	Connaught
3	Tatsuso	3	La Tante Claire
4	Le Gavroche	4	Le Gavroche
5	Pied à Terre	5	Aubergine

Expensive (£45-£54)

Food		**Service**	
1	Clarke's	1	Goring Hotel
2	Salloos	2	The Ivy
3	Nobu	3	Rib Room
4	City Rhodes	4	Clarke's
5	Matsuri	5	Lanesborough

Upper mid-price (£35-£44)

Food		**Service**	
1	Chez Bruce	1	Oslo Court
2	Zafferano	2	Assaggi
3	Al San Vincenzo	3	Le Caprice
4	Assaggi	4	Chezmax
5	Chezmax	5	Odin's

Lower mid-price (£25-£34)

Food		**Service**	
1	Inaho	1	Antipasto e Pasta
2	Rasa	2	Hujo's
3	Chez Liline	3	Soulard
4	Royal China W1, W2	4	Marquis
5	Tentazioni	5	Vasco & Piero's Pavilion

Budget (£24 or less)

Food		**Service**	
1	Brilliant	1	Tandoori Lane
2	The Gate	2	Topsy Tasty
3	Luigi's Delicatessen	3	Old School Thai
4	Shree Krishna	4	Halepi
5	Lahore Kebab House	5	Emile's

Ambience
1 Blakes Hotel
2 The Ritz
3 Aubergine
4 Windows on the World
5 Connaught

Overall
1 Aubergine
2 La Tante Claire
3 Connaught
4 Dorchester Grill
5 Le Gavroche

Ambience
1 The Ivy
2 Landmark
3 Lanesborough
4 Rib Room
5 Atlantic Bar & Grill

Overall
1 The Ivy
2 Clarke's
3 Rib Room
4 Landmark Hotel
5 City Rhodes

Ambience
1 La Poule au Pot
2 Dan's
3 Momo
4 L'Aventure
5 Blue Elephant

Overall
1 Le Caprice
2 Chez Bruce
3 L'Aventure
4 Assaggi
5 Chezmax

Ambience
1 Julie's Bar
2 Sarastro
3 Andrew Edmund's
4 Café Bohème
5 Cantaloupe

Overall
1 Soulard
2 Quincy's
3 Elistano
4 Brass. du Marché aux P.
5 Hujo's

Ambience
1 Troubadour
2 Gordon's Wine Bar
3 Bar Italia
4 Gastro
5 Iznik

Overall
1 The Gate
2 Brilliant
3 Pizza Metro
4 Le Sacré-Coeur
5 Iznik

SURVEY – HIGHEST RATINGS

Highest average ratings by cuisine

These are the restaurants which received the best average food ratings, listed by cuisine. (A few equally deserving restaurants are excluded because they are too little known to generate a sufficient number of reports.)

Each section is divided into '£30 and over', and 'under £30'. Within each section, restaurants are ranked by rating.

Modern British

£35 and over
1. Chez Bruce
2. Clarke's
3. City Rhodes
4. The Ivy
5. Halcyon Hotel
6. Le Caprice
7. The Sugar Club
8. The Canteen

Under £35
1. Quincy's
2. The Chelsea Ram
3. Mesclun
4. The Mason's Arms
5. The Havelock Tavern

Steaks & Grills

£35 and over
1. The Rib Room

Under £35
1. Popeseye

Fish & chips

Under £35
1. Faulkner's
2. Two Brothers
3. Toff's

East/West

£35 and over
1. Nobu
2. Vong

Under £35
1. The Birdcage

French

£35 and over
1. Aubergine
2. La Tante Claire
3. Le Gavroche
4. Pied à Terre
5. The Square
6. Chezmax
7. L'Oranger
8. Chinon
9. Oslo Court
10. Chez Nico

Under £35
1. Sacré-Coeur
2. The White Onion

Italian/Mediterranean

£35 and over
1. Zafferano
2. Al San Vincenzo
3. Assaggi
4. The River Café

Under £35
1. Luigi's Delicatessen
2. Tentazioni
3. Del Buongustaio

Vegetarian

Under £35
1. The Gate
2. Mildred's

Pizza

Under £35
1. Pizza Metro
2. Eco

Indian

£35 and over
1 Salloos
2 Tamarind
3 Star of India

Under £35
1 Brilliant
2 Rasa
3 Shree Krishna
4 Lahore Kebab House
5 Khyber Pass
6 Babur Brasserie
7 Ma Goa
8 Diwana Bhel Poori House
9 Malabar
10 Kastoori

Chinese

£35 and over
1 Dorchester, Oriental

Under £35
1 Royal China W1, W2
2 Hunan
3 Mandarin Kitchen
4 Joy King Lau
5 Fung Shing
6 Gung Ho
7 Mao Thai

Japanese

£35 and over
1 Tatsuso
2 Matsuri
3 Suntory

Under £35
1 Inaho

Thai

£35 and over
1 Blue Elephant

Under £35
1 Chiang Mai
2 Churchill

Fish & seafood

£35 and over
1 Jason's
2 The Lobster Pot

Under £35
1 Chez Liline
2 Bibendum Oyster Bar
3 Back to Basics

Lebanese

£35 and over
1 Maroush
2 Phoenicia

Nepalese

Under £35
1 Great Nepalese

Snacks

Under £35
1 Brick Lane Beigel Bake
2 Seattle Coffee

TOP SPECIAL DEALS

Menus which are included in the following lists give you the chance to eat in the restaurants concerned at a significant discount compared to the evening à la carte prices.

The price in brackets is calculated in accordance with our formula (ie three courses with house wine, coffee and tip).

Special menus are by their nature susceptible to change – please call ahead to check that they are still available.

Weekday lunch

Chez Nico *(£53)*
Oak Room MPW *(£53)*
Connaught *(£48)*
The Ritz *(£44)*
Halcyon Hotel *(£41)*
Aubergine *(£40)*
Capital Hotel *(£40)*
Le Gavroche *(£40)*
Gordon Ramsay *(£40)*
Suntory *(£40)*
Windows on the World *(£40)*
Pied à Terre *(£38)*
Savoy River Restaurant *(£38)*
The Halkin *(£37)*
1837 at Brown's Hotel *(£36)*
La Tante Claire *(£36)*
The Landmark Hotel *(£35)*
Neal Street *(£33)*
Chavot *(£33)*
Santini *(£33)*
Bentley's *(£32)*
L'Incontro *(£32)*
L'Odéon *(£31)*
Poissonnerie de l'Avenue *(£29)*
Teatro *(£29)*
Bank *(£28)*
Leith's Soho *(£28)*
Mr Chow *(£28)*
Bluebird *(£27)*
Café Royal Grill *(£27)*
Cibo *(£27)*
The Criterion *(£27)*
Launceston Place *(£27)*
Mirabelle *(£27)*
Turner's *(£27)*
Atlantic Bar & Grill *(£26)*
Bombay Brasserie *(£26)*
L'Escargot Doré *(£26)*
Mezzo *(£26)*
Pharmacy *(£26)*
Salloos *(£26)*
English Garden *(£25)*
La Porte des Indes *(£25)*
Frederick's *(£24)*
Kensington Place *(£24)*
Lobster Pot *(£24)*

Manzi's *(£24)*
La Poule au Pot *(£24)*
Zen Garden *(£24)*
English House *(£23)*
Icon *(£23)*
Momo *(£23)*
Mon Plaisir *(£23)*
Orsino *(£23)*
Tamarind *(£23)*
192 *(£22)*
Chezmax *(£22)*
Dakota *(£22)*
Café du Jardin *(£21)*
Chiswick *(£21)*
Joe Allen *(£21)*
Montana *(£21)*
Stratford's *(£21)*
Le Suquet *(£21)*
Tandoori of Chelsea *(£21)*
Wódka *(£21)*
Jindivick *(£20)*
Odette's *(£20)*
The Cross Keys *(£19)*
Gresslin's *(£19)*
Leonardo's *(£19)*
Lou Pescadou *(£19)*
Snows by the Pond *(£19)*
Thai on the River *(£19)*
Verbanella *(£19)*
Beach Blanket Babylon *(£18)*
Bombay Palace *(£18)*
La Bouchée *(£18)*
Le Bouchon Bordelais *(£18)*
The Brackenbury *(£18)*
Café Lazeez *(£18)*
Maggie Jones's *(£18)*
Palio *(£18)*
Phoenicia *(£18)*
Cantinetto Venegazzú *(£17)*
Carnevale *(£17)*
Malabar Junction *(£17)*
Le P'tit Normand *(£17)*
Singapore Garden *(£17)*
Vama *(£17)*
Banners *(£16)*
Bengal Clipper *(£16)*
Busabong Tree *(£16)*

Café des Arts *(£16)*
Arancia *(£15)*
Lemonia *(£15)*
Naked Turtle *(£15)*
The Polish Club *(£15)*
Toff's *(£15)*
Bonjour Vietnam *(£14)*
Caravan Serai *(£14)*
Globe Restaurant *(£14)*
New World *(£14)*
Pasha *(£14)*
San Daniele *(£14)*
Bu San *(£13)*
Gecko *(£13)*
Inaho *(£13)*
Khan's of Kensington *(£13)*
Le Sacré-Coeur *(£13)*
San Martino *(£13)*
Galicia *(£12)*
Le Shop *(£12)*
Vegia Zena *(£12)*
Chutneys *(£10)*
Mandalay *(£10)*
Mandeer *(£10)*
Soho Brewing Company *(£10)*
Diwana Bhel-Poori House *(£9)*
Daquise *(£7)*

Pre/post theatre (and early evening)

Savoy Grill *(£43)*
Savoy River Restaurant *(£38)*
Neal Street *(£35)*
The Waldorf Meridien *(£34)*
Bentley's *(£32)*
L'Odéon *(£31)*
Simpsons-in-the-Strand *(£31)*
The Avenue *(£29)*
Teatro *(£29)*
Bank *(£28)*
Leith's Soho *(£28)*
Bluebird *(£27)*
Café Royal Grill *(£27)*
Christopher's *(£27)*
The Criterion *(£27)*
Launceston Place *(£27)*
Mirabelle *(£27)*
Mezzo *(£25)*
Luigi's *(£23)*
Orso *(£23)*
Café des Amis du Vin *(£22)*
Chezmax *(£22)*
Joe Allen *(£22)*
Café du Jardin *(£21)*
Chiswick *(£21)*
Mezzonine *(£21)*
Stratford's *(£21)*
Cantina del Ponte *(£20)*

L'Estaminet *(£20)*
Magno's Brasserie *(£20)*
Manzi's *(£20)*
Boudin Blanc *(£19)*
La Bouchée *(£18)*
Café des Arts *(£18)*
Carnevale *(£17)*
Hujo's *(£17)*
Malabar Junction *(£17)*
Mon Plaisir *(£15)*
The Polish Club *(£15)*
Nayab *(£14)*
Kartouche *(£11)*

Sunday lunch

Connaught *(£54)*
The Ritz *(£44)*
Savoy River Restaurant *(£38)*
Turner's *(£34)*
Wiltons *(£32)*
Greenhouse *(£30)*
Cibo *(£28)*
English Garden *(£28)*
Mr Chow *(£28)*
The Criterion *(£27)*
Blue Elephant *(£26)*
Bombay Brasserie *(£26)*
The Ivy *(£26)*
Kensington Place *(£26)*
Mezzo *(£26)*
Chutney Mary *(£25)*
La Porte des Indes *(£25)*
192 *(£24)*
Beach Blanket Babylon *(£24)*
Orso *(£24)*
Prego *(£24)*
Tamarind *(£23)*
Lou Pescadou *(£22)*
Wilson's *(£22)*
The Butlers Wharf Chop-house *(£21)*
Café du Jardin *(£21)*
Maggie Jones's *(£21)*
Chor Bizarre *(£20)*
Odette's *(£20)*
Le Pont de la Tour Bar & Grill *(£20)*
Bradley's *(£19)*
Café Lazeez *(£19)*
Bengal Clipper *(£18)*
Bombay Palace *(£18)*
Naked Turtle *(£16)*
Townhouse Brasserie *(£16)*
The Polish Club *(£15)*
Veeraswamy *(£15)*
Globe Restaurant *(£13)*
Galicia *(£12)*
Soho Brewing Company *(£10)*

THE CHAIN GANG

Your guide to the groups

London's restaurants are more and more dominated by group ownership. If proof is needed, look at the list (p10) of establishments most often mentioned in our survey. Of the top 20, only one (the River Café) is in any real sense a 'stand-alone' – five years ago, about half would have answered to that description.

Until recently, groups have usually grown by evolution rather than major acquisition. That may be changing (see p20) and, if the trend continues, it may have a major effect on Londoners' favourite haunts.

How good (or bad) the respective groups are is therefore a matter of growing importance, and we are pleased to present what we believe is the first ever group-by-group overview of consumer satisfaction.

We have analysed the major groups represented in the 'most-mentioned' list by averaging the ratings achieved by the individual restaurants making up each group. These are set out below in descending order of food ratings.

(The ratings we have used for this analysis are derived from the ratings awarded by our 3,400 reporters. The rating of each group is based on between 500 'votes' (Oliver Peyton) and 2,250 (Conran Restaurants).

F S A

A-Z Restaurants ❷❷❸

The three restaurants for which the group is best known (*Aubergine, L'Oranger, Zafferano*) are among the very best in London (and, on their own, would be rated 1-1-2). They are all characterised by real culinary endeavour, good service, pleasant (but not ostentatious) settings and reasonable prices. The lesser-known establishments in their portfolio (*Ken Lo's, Spiga* and *Spighetta*) are not so exciting, but still perform creditably.

Marco Pierre White ❸❸❸

MPW specialises in relaunching classic restaurant sites. His ventures therefore often benefit from a fantastic setting (*Criterion, Mirabelle, Café Royal*), with food which, though competent-to-good, plays second fiddle. Reasons for the 'flat' overall ratings shown include the stilted ambience at the restaurant which wins MPW his three-Michelin-star culinary reputation – the *Oak Room* – and the dreadful service at *The Criterion*. The mediocre *Quo Vadis* depresses ratings across the board.

Groupe Chez Gerard

F S A
❸❸❸

As reflected by its ratings, the bulk of GCGs businesses (*Chez Gérard, Bertorelli's, Café Fish*) are worthy-but-dull, middle-of-the-road eateries. With the exception of one good performer across the board (*Scotts*), its more bespoke products (*Livebait, Soho Soho, Brasserie St Quentin*) tend to be something of a curate's egg, where strength in one respect is cut away by failings in another.

Harvey Nichols

④④❷

As you might expect of retailers, this is a group which understands presentation, and the creation of a good atmosphere is the great success of their two main restaurants (*Fifth Floor* and *Oxo Tower*), helped in each case by elevated and unusual locations. Neither food nor service seems to be a high priority.

Conran Restaurants

④④❸

Given this group's media profile and endorsements as 'London's Leading Restaurant Chain', it is amazing how poor most of its offerings are. Some (*Mezzo, Mezzonine, Cantina del Ponte, Zinc*) are quite extraordinarily bad. Most are just thoroughly mediocre (*Bluebird, Butler's Wharf Chop-house, Quaglino's*, and – one which used to have ambition – *Le Pont de la Tour*). Others (*Orrery, Sartoria*) might be good if they weren't so greedily priced. But aren't Conran restaurants really supposed to be about style and theatre? Perhaps so, but even on that score fewer than half of them make it into the top half of their class! (*Coq d'Argent* opened too late to feature in the survey – but illustrates the deficiencies of the group magnificently.)

Oliver Peyton

④⑤❸

Mr Peyton's restaurants give every appearance of being run like nightclubs – it doesn't seem to matter how bad the food and service are, because the creation of a trendy atmosphere is all. The *Atlantic* has the dubious distinction of achieving the lowest score in its price-category for *both* food *and* service (with *Mash* not far behind). *Coast* is the odd one out – the ambitious food comes off quite well, but the stark style puts people off (and service, again, is poor).

Belgo Group

new

The new kid on the block – put together over the last couple of months or so – is made up of some odd bedfellows – London's best all-rounders (*The Ivy, Le Caprice*), three fashion-driven trendy scenes with mediocre food and service (*Daphne's, The Collection, Pasha*), and the *Belgo* duo of wacky, but so-so moules/frites emporia. What kind of a go they will make of running this disparate empire remains to be seen.

THE RESTAURANT SCENE

All change?

The best and most popular restaurants in London have seen major developments over the past 12 months.

For the last two years, reporters have been in no doubt as to where to find the best meals in town – *Aubergine* (chef, Gordon Ramsay) and *La Tante Claire* (chef, Pierre Koffmann). Both gentlemen moved on in the summer of '98. Koffmann left Chelsea for the bright lights of Knightsbridge, and Ramsay stormed out of Aubergine to set up under his own name … in Koffmann's old premises.

Perhaps a more significant development – though all concerned swear that absolutely nothing will change – is the recent acquisition of reporters' two favourite restaurants, *The Ivy* and *Le Caprice,* by the Belgo Group, whose aspirations now spread well beyond moules and frites. Belgo had already acquired Mogens Tholstrop's fashionable ventures (*Daphne's, The Collection* and *Pasha*), and thus emerges as the most important new force in London restaurants for many years. Can our favourites survive in a group where all else is hype and mediocrity? It is not impossible of course, but the performance of most of the more established groups (see previous pages) hardly gives much cause for optimism.

Meanwhile …

We list 92 openings (see opposite), against 90 last year. This tends to understate the true level of activity, ignoring as it does the expansion of existing groups.

The era of the mega-restaurant is dead. Most openings this year have been small to medium-sized, with almost all newcomers of any quality having fewer than 110 seats.

The market is also maturing in other ways: it is now much more difficult to hype a restaurant into being the talk of the town. Even *Pharmacy* – the year's most talked-about newcomer – comes well down the table of most-mentioned places in the survey (see p10), at number 31.

The number of closures (p22) – 48 this year, down from 58 last – gives no hint of impending global melt-down.

The 'top ten' notable newcomers

In each edition of the guide, we present what appear to us to be the ten most significant openings of the past twelve months. This year, our selection is as follows:

Axis	Mirabelle
The Birdcage	One Lawn Terrace
Le Coq d'Argent	1 Lombard Street
Gordon Ramsay	Pharmacy
Mash	Tentazioni

OPENINGS

a.k.a.
Alphabet
Axis
Bali Sugar
Bar Bourse
The Birdcage
Café Coq
Café Milan
Cantina Italia
Cantinetto Venegazzú
Centuria
Che
Cicada
The Circle
Circus
Club Gascon
Le Colombier
Le Coq d'Argent
Corney & Barrow WC2
County Hall Restaurant
Coyote Café
Cy
Dakota
1837 at Brown's Hotel
Faro
Fishnets
Gaudi
Globe Restaurant
Gordon Ramsay
Gt Eastern Dining Rooms
Havana
Home
The Honest Cabbage
Ibla
The Icon
Indigo
Ishbilia
King's Brasserie
Langan's Coq d'Or
Leith's Soho
Little Havana
Lunch
Mango Room
Mash
Medina's
Mediterranean Café
Mediterraneo
Min's Bar
Mirabelle
Monza
Moxon's
Navajo Joe
Nine Golden Square

No 1 Cigar Club
Noho
The North Pole
1 Lawn Terrace
1 Lombard Street
Orrery
Pasha
Pasta di Milano
Pelham Street
La Perla
Pharmacy
The Purple Sage
Rain
Rasa W1
Restaurant 190
Reubens
RK Stanleys
Rodizio Rico
Rousillon
Saffron
Sartoria
Satsuma
Shanghai
Sixty Two Restaurant
Snows by the Pond
Soho Brewing Company
La Spiga
Sri India
The Stargazer
Suan-Neo
La Tante Claire SW1
Teatro
Teca
10
Tentazioni
The Terrace
Villandry Dining Rooms
Wiz
Zed

CLOSINGS

Ajimura
Al Basha
L'Altro (except W11)
Arisugawa
Atelier
Au Bon Accueil
Bahn Thai
Bar Central
Bistrot Soho
The Blenheim
Brook
Café Jeune
Café Sogo
Caffe Graffiti
Le Champenois
Chelsea Square
Chicago Pizza Pie Factory
Cosmo
Fables
La Finezza
Fisk
Four Seasons W1
Gabriel
Grill St Quentin
Inmala
Jimmy Beez
Kalamaras, Mega
Leith's at the Institute
Lobster Trading Co
Mackintosh's Brass' SW1
Mad Dog Café
Mamta
Marabel's
Noughts 'n' Crosses
Osteria del Parco
Osteria Le Fate
Parson's Nose
Pizza Chelsea
La Pomme d'Amour
San Frediano
Shaw's
La Tante Claire SW3
Three Little Pigs
Tusc
Valhalla
W11
White Tower
Wren at St James's

DIRECTORY

Comments in "double quotation-marks" were made by reporters.

Establishments which we judge to be particularly notable have their NAME IN CAPITALS.

a.k.a. WC1   £28   ❷❷❸
18 West Central Street   0171-836 0110   4–1C
Next to a groovy Bloomsbury-fringe club (The End), this impressively designed newcomer provides modern British fare that is much better than you would expect, and "very personal service". / 1 am, 11.30 pm Wed-Sat; closed Mon & Sat L; Sun D.

The Abingdon W8   £34   ❸❷❸
54 Abingdon Rd   0171-937 3339   5–2A
You "have to book" for this "friendly", "relaxed" and cosily boothed bar/restaurant in a quiet Kensington street; the modern British fare is "competent". / 11 pm.

L'Accento Italiano W2   £29   ④❷④
16 Garway Rd   0171-243 2201   6–1B
Fans find "good food and good value" (the set menus in particular) at this "noisy and echoey", family-run Bayswater Italian. / 11.30 pm; smart casual.

Adams Café W12   £22   ❷❷④
77 Askew Rd   0181-743 0572   7–1B
This greasy spoon, in Shepherd's Bush is "more and more like a traditional restaurant"; it "goes Tunisian in the evenings" and offers some "good, solid", somewhat "different" fare (couscous, and so on); BYO. / 11 pm; D only.

Afghan Kitchen N1   £14   ❷④❸
35 Islington Gn   0171-359 8019   8–3D
The interesting, "tremendous value for money" food "makes up for" the "very slow" service and discomfort at this tiny and "cramped" Islington café. / 11.30 pm; closed Mon & Sun; no credit cards.

Al Bustan SW1   £39   ❸❷⑤
27 Motcomb St   0171-235 8277   2–4A
"Softer lighting" might help the disappointing atmosphere at this otherwise commendable Belgravia Lebanese; the cooking is "fresh and full of flavour", and service "very pleasant". / 11 pm.

Al Hamra W1   £39   ❷④④
31-33 Shepherd Mkt   0171-493 1954   3–4B
For many, this is "the best Lebanese" in town, though it is "very, very expensive", and (even after a refit) has all the ambience of an "airport lounge"; the tables outside, though, are particularly charming. / 11.30 pm; no Switch.

Al San Vincenzo W2   £ 42   ❶❶④

30 Connaught St   0171-262 9623   6–1D
*"Outstanding" cooking makes the Borgonzolo family's
"unpretentious" Bayswater venture one of the best Italians in
town; there are those who find the tiny room – with its "really
personal and attentive" service – "odd", but for others it's just
"the perfect antidote to those large, modern joints". / 10 pm;
closed Sat L & Sun; no Amex & no Switch.*

Al Sultan W1   £ 35   ❸④④

51-52 Hertford St   0171-408 1155   3–4B
*"Quietly located" Lebanese, by Shepherd Market, with a
limited, but loyal following. / 11 pm.*

Al's EC1   £ 20   ④④❸

11-13 Exmouth Mkt   0171-837 4821   8–4D
*Once rather studenty, this all-day Clerkenwell café – with
generally "sound grub and beer" – has "gone a bit more
upmarket", but is still best known as a breakfast and brunch
place; (there is a door charge of £3 after 11.30 pm). / Midnight,
Wed–Sat 2am (bar 2am).*

Alastair Little W1   £ 47   ④⑤⑤

49 Frith St   0171-734 5183   4–2A
*Some are "surprised at the low ratings" awarded to this
famous modern British chef's minimalist Soho HQ; for many,
though, a visit here is just "too awful" – a "waste of money"
for food that's "tired, unimaginative and poorly executed".
/ 11 pm; closed Sat L & Sun.*

Alastair Little, Lancaster Road W11 £ 36   ❸❸⑤

136a Lancaster Rd   0171-243 2220   6–1A
*Mr Little's "cramped" Portobello outpost is "cruising on his
reputation"; some still proclaim it "a continuing pleasure",
but a report of "bland food and no service to speak of" is
far from being a one-off. / 11 pm; closed Sun.*

Alba EC1   £ 29   ❸④④

107 Whitecross St   0171-588 1798   9–1B
*"Regional Italian cooking at its best" (especially "very good
pastas") still win praise for this rather "chilling" Piedmontese
near the Barbican, but the number who think it "nothing
special" is on the up. / 11 pm; closed Sat & Sun.*

Albero & Grana SW3   £ 47   ⑤⑤❸

89 Sloane Ave   0171-225 1048   5–2C
*"With redecoration, it lost its buzz and Spanishness" –
post-refit the dining room at this smart and expensive
("overpriced") Brompton Cross Iberian is "without
personality", and its once-innovative cooking lacks interest.
/ 11 pm.*

Albero & Grana Tapas Bar SW3 £28 ❸❸❷
89 Sloane Ave 0171-225 1048 5–2C
"Great fun (if a bit of a pick-up joint)" – the bar wears its
new look better than the restaurant at this Brompton Cross
Spaniard, and serves tapas that are *"a little expensive,
but very good"*. / Midnight; D only ex Sat, when open all day.

Alfred WC2 £34 ❷❷④
245 Shaftesbury Ave 0171-240 2566 4–1C
"Delicious" English food (together with *"lots of beers and
English wines"*) makes this *"idiosyncratic"* spot – decorated
like a '50s kitchen – a continuing success with today's
Bloomsbury Set. / 11.30 pm; closed Sun.

Ali Baba NW1 £18 ❷❷④
32 Ivor Pl 0171-723 5805 8–4A
"Hidden away" in a brightly lit room behind a take-away near
Marylebone station, this *"cheap and cheerful"* spot serves up
some *"superb Egyptian dishes"*. / 11.30 pm; no credit cards.

All Bar One £24 ④④❸
289-293 Regent St, W1 0171-467 9901 3–1C
3-4 Hanover St, W1 0171-518 9931 3–2C
36-38 Dean St, W1 0171-479 7921 4–2A
7-9 Paddington Street, W1 0171-487 0071 2–1A
108 New Oxford Street, WC1 0171-307 7980 4–1A
19 Henrietta Street, WC2 0171-557 7941 4–3C
48 Leicester Sq, WC2 0171-747 9921 4–4A
58 Kingsway, WC2 0171-269 5171 2–1D
587-591 Fulham Rd, SW6 0171-471 0611 5–4A
152 Gloucester Road, SW7 0171-244 5861 5–2B
126-128 Notting Hill Gate, W11 0171-313 9362 6–2B
197-199 Chiswick High Rd, W4 0181-987 8211 7–2A
1 Liverpool Rd, N1 0171-843 0021 8–3D
1-3 Hampstead Ln, N6 0181-342 7861 8–1B
60 St John's Wood High St, NW8 0171-483 9931 8–3A
30 London Bridge Street, SE1 0171-940 9981 9–4C
32-38 Northcote Road, SW11 0171-801 9951 10–2C
7-9 Battersea Square, SW11 0171-326 9831 10–1C
527-529 Old York Rd, SW18 0181-875 7941 10–2B
42 Mackenzie Walk, E14 0171-513 0911 1–3D
91-93 Charterhouse Street, EC1 0171-553 9391 9–1B
63 Threadneedle St, EC2 0171-614 9931 9–2C
16 Byward St, EC3 0171-533 0301 9–3D
3 Cannon St, EC4 0171-220 9031 9–3C
44-46 Ludgate Hl, EC4 0171-653 9901 9–2A
"Good snacks, for a chain" contribute to the success of these
"friendly" and *"happening"* wine bars; (proof, incidentally,
that big brewers – Bass, in this case – are quite capable of
producing *"reliable"* dining concepts if they put their mind to
it). / Mon-Thu 10 pm, Fri-Sun 9 pm; Hanover St, Kingsway, City and E14
branches close part of weekend; no booking.

Alma SW18 £ 23 ④④❸
499 Old York Rd 0181-870 2537 10–2B
Benefiting from a "great pub atmosphere", this large and
characterful Wandsworth boozer serves some OK brasserie
staples in its dining annexe. / 10.30 pm; closed Sun D.

Alounak W14 £ 20 ❶❷④
10 Russell Gdns 0171-603 1130 7–1D
"Cheap beyond belief, especially for the size of portions
and the brilliant flavours" – this duo of "superb Iranian"
BYO restaurants make "cheerful", "cosy", "fantastic value"
venues to "go with friends" (Olympia being the better of
the two). / Midnight; no Amex.

Alphabet W1 £ 26 ❸④❷
61-63 Beak St 0171-439 2190 3–2D
A "tops Soho bar", say twentysomething fans of this "fun",
funky, but "cramped" hang-out, which offers "good, fresh"
food. / 10.30 pm; closed Sat L & Sun; no Amex; no booking.

L'Altro W11 £ 31 ④❸④
210 Kensington Pk Rd 0171-792 1066 6–1A
Briefly the cradle of a short-lived group, this small, theatrically
designed Notting Hill Italian (specialising in seafood) has
lost its way; some do still report "high quality", "reasonably
priced" cooking, but overall it's "nothing special" and "lacks
ambience". / 11.30 pm; no Amex.

Anarkali W6 £ 25 ❸④④
303-305 King St 0181-748 1760 7–2B
"Decent local Indian" which has graced Hammersmith with
its presence for over a quarter of a century; we hope the
recent refurbishment has not removed the wonderfully
sinister tinted windows. / Midnight.

Andrew Edmunds W1 £ 25 ❸❷❶
46 Lexington St 0171-437 5708 3–2D
"Newcomers return as regulars" to this "quirky", "cramped",
"candle-lit" Soho townhouse, whose "unpretentious",
"intimate" and "friendly" style has won it a huge following;
the modern British food is "good value", but arguably the
"interesting wines" are a greater attraction. / 10.45 pm.

Anglesea Arms W6 £ 25 ❷⑤❸
35 Wingate Rd 0181-749 1291 7–1B
"Resign yourself to the bizarre and wholly ineffective service"
– this "pleasant" 'Brackenbury Village' boozer delivers
"yummy" English cooking which is "worth waiting for".
/ 10.30 pm; no Amex; no booking.

Anglo Asian Tandoori N16 £20 ❸❸❸
60-62 Stoke Newington Ch St 0171-254 9298 1–1C
"Well established" Stoke Newington Indian, providing superior curry in dated, low-lit comfort. / 11.45 pm, Fri & Sat 12.30 am; no Switch.

Anna's Place N1 £30 ❸❷❷
90 Mildmay Pk 0171-249 9379 1–1C
"Anna sold out to her chefs, so standards should be maintained" – and they have been – at this "tiny", "warm and friendly" Swede in Islington; the "light and airy conservatory" has long helped make this a top local choice, and you "must book". / 10.45 pm; closed Mon & Sun D; no credit cards.

Anonimato W10 £32 ❷❷❸
12 All Saints Rd 0171-243 2808 6–1B
"Delicious", "eclectic" cooking (and staff who are "friendly and helpful, without being ingratiating") helps makes this "unpretentious" and "good value" yearling (on the "trendier-than-trendy" North Kensington front line) an excellent all-rounder. / 11 pm; D only except Sun, L only.

Antipasto & Pasta SW11 £26 ❶❶❸
511 Battersea Park Rd 0171-223 9765 5–3D
"Exceptional value on the half-price food nights" (Mon, Thu, Sun) – not to mention "above-average pasta" – create quite a stir at this "basic", but "consistently good" Battersea Italian, with "very helpful" service. /—

The Apprentice SE1 £26 ❶⑤⑤
31 Shad Thames 0171-234 0254 9–4D
"Great things will emanate from here", say patrons of this South Bank chefs' school, where "lovingly prepared" cooking that's "almost as tasty as Le Pont de la Tour" comes at a fraction of the price; service is only "just passable", though, and there's "no atmosphere". / 8.30 pm; closed Sat & Sun; no smoking area.

Aquarium E1 £32 ❸❸❷
Ivory Hs, St Katharine-by-the-Tower 0171-480 6116 1–2D
"Fresh, well cooked fish" – from a "varied menu" – and a "pretty setting" (in a quiet marina by Tower Bridge) are slowly raising the profile of this modernistic restaurant, which is still relatively "little known". / 11 pm; closed Sun, Mon D.

Arancia SE16 £24 ❷❸❸
52 Southwark Park Road 0171-394 1751 1–3D
The "dodgy neighbourhood" is no reason to avoid this cosy Italian – on a corner opposite Bermondsey's Southwark Park; cooking which is notably good, in parts, comes very reasonably priced. / 11 pm; no Amex; set weekday L £15(FP).

F S A

Archduke Wine Bar SE1   £29   ④④④
Arch 153, Concert Hall Appr. 0171-928 9370 2–3D
*Though "very handy before or after South Bank concerts
and plays", this well known wine bar in a railway arch serves
"uninspiring" and "pricey" food. / 11 pm; closed Sat L;
no smoking area.*

Arkansas Café E1   £19   ❸④⑤
Unit 12, Old Spitalfield Market 0171-377 6999 9–1D
*Fans laud the "great BBQ ribs" and "good burgers" dished up
by patron Bubba at this "fun", if "very basic", market café;
others, though, are less impressed with the nosh, and find the
place plain "tacky". / L only; closed Sat; no Amex.*

L'Arte W1   £24   ❸❸⑤
126 Cleveland St 0171-813 1011 2–1B
*"Go for the culinary experience rather than comfort" to
this "small", "adventurous" Italian, obscurely located on the
fringe of Fitzrovia; some find the "soulless", decidedly
"uncomfortable" setting makes the whole meal a let-down.
/ 11 pm; closed Sat L & Sun.*

L'Artiste Musclé W1   £23   ④❷❷
1 Shepherd Mkt 0171-493 6150 3–4B
*"Feels like a real bistro", say fans of this useful Shepherd
Market spot – "a great place for sitting outside"; the cooking
is basic, but "well priced". / 11.30 pm; winter closed Sun L.*

Ashtons EC3   £41   ④④❸
13-15 Leadenhall Mkt 0171-929 2022 9–2D
*"Good food" – but only by City standards – makes this
"small and intimate" fish restaurant near Lloyds useful for
business lunches. / L only; closed Sat & Sun.*

Ask! Pizza   £19   ❸❸❸
160-162 Victoria St, SW1 0171-630 8228 2–4B
121-125 Park St, W1 0171-495 7760 2–2A
48 Grafton Way, W1 0171-388 8108 2–1B
345 Fulham Palace Rd, SW6 0171-371 0392 10–1B
1 Gloucester Arcade, SW7 0171-835 0840 5–2B
145 Notting Hill Gt, W11 0171-792 9942 6–2B
Whiteleys, 151 Queensway, W2 0171-792 1977 6–1C
219-221 Chiswick High Rd, W4 0181-742 1323 7–2A
222 Kensington High Street, W8 0171-937 5540 5–1A
Bus' Design Ctr, Upper St, N1 0171-226 8728 8–3D
216 Haverstock Hill, NW3 0171-433 3896 8–2A
103 St John Street, EC1 0171-253 0323 9–1A
*Increasingly, this fast-expanding chain is "a contender for the
PizzaExpress crown" as the best pizza-chain in London;
its "modern cool interiors" are much praised, as are the
"interesting and different toppings". / 11.30 pm.*

Assaggi W2 £38 ❶❶❷
39 Chepstow Pl 0171-792 5501 6–1B
"Simple and gorgeous Italian cooking" in "generous portions" attracts a cult foodie following to this "basic, but attractive" room above a Bayswater pub; service is "knowledgeable and friendly", too – "shame you have to book so far in advance". / 11 pm; closed Sun.

Les Associés N8 £29 ❸❸❸
172 Park Rd 0181-348 8944 1–1C
It may be a "funny place" – in a row of houses, opposite a swimming pool – but residents of Crouch End love not only the "excellent, bourgeois French cooking" at this "homely" local, but also its "friendly and unfussy" service. / 10 pm; closed L; closed Sat & Sun L; no Amex.

Atlantic Bar & Grill W1 £45 ⑤⑤❶
20 Glasshouse St 0171-734 4888 3–3D
"Standards are sinking faster than the Titanic" at this cavernous basement, near Piccadilly Circus; the place may offer "a great night out, if you're after a party" (with "lots of beautiful people about"), but, if you want to eat, then the "evil" food and "snotty and disinterested" service are major drawbacks. / 11.30 pm; bar food until 2.30 am; closed Sat L & Sun L; set weekday L £26(FP).

Atrium SW1 £36 ⑤⑤④
4 Millbank 0171-233 0032 2–4C
That this "political hot spot" (near Westminster) is "full of New Labourites" is, we hope, no indication of the standards acceptable to our new masters – both the modern British cooking and the service are "poor". / 10 pm; closed Sat & Sun; no smoking area.

Au Bon Pain £9 ④❸④
52 Piccadilly, W1 0171-499 5253 3–3C
227 Strand, WC2 0171-353 6425 2–2D
60 Cheapside, EC1 0171-489 7905 9–2B
Notwithstanding a few knowing comments from those who have encountered it Stateside, this coffee and made-to-order sandwich chain has, to date, generated little local enthusiasm for its rather overpriced offerings. /—

Au Jardin des Gourmets W1 £30 ❸❷❸
5 Greek St 0171-437 1816 4–2A
"Why is this place never packed?", ask loyal fans of this "stolid" Soho stalwart – whose extensive wine-list is the top attraction, and whose set lunch is "good value"; as a comfortable central rendezvous, it's worth considering. / 11.15 pm; closed Sat L & Sun; smart casual; no smoking area.

Aubergine SW10   £58   – – –

11 Park Wk 0171-352 3449 5–3B

In September '98, what has famously been the toughest place in town to get a booking for the past three years was relaunched after an unexpected closure – the result of Gordon Ramsay (see entry under that name) having stormed out, taking his whole team with him; new chef William Drabble could not have a harder act to follow.
/ 10.30 pm; closed Sat L & Sun; set weekday L £40(FP).

Aurora W1   £24 ❸④❶

49 Lexington St 0171-494 0514 3–2D

"Shabby chic" Soho café providing a very "characterful" setting (and with a "sweet courtyard" at the back) for a "cheap and cheerful" lunch, or a candlelit dinner; BYO.
/ 10.30 pm; closed Sun; no Amex.

L'Aventure NW8   £39 ❶❷❶

3 Blenheim Ter 0171-624 6232 8–3A

The discreet "jewel of St John's Wood" – "hidden away, and long may it remain so" – offers "really good" French food in "romantic" and "intimate" surroundings; the outside terrace is "superb on a summer evening". / 11 pm; closed Sat L and, in Winter, Sun; no Switch.

The Avenue SW1   £44 ④④❸

7-9 St James's St 0171-321 2111 3–4D

This large, "light" and "spacious" venture in St James's won wider support this year for its "reliable" cooking – at least by the standards of the hangars of the West End – and for its "trendy, smart and fun" atmosphere; "snotty" service, however, let the side down more than ever. / Midnight; set pre-th. £29(FP).

Axis WC2   £43 ❷❷❷

1 Aldwych 0171-300 0300 2–2D

Dominated by a Futuristic mural, the basement restaurant at Aldwych's swanky new hotel is one of the more atmospheric West End spaces to have opened in recent years; first-week visits can deceive, but we took to both the menu – modern British, with some traditional twists – and to the smart and welcoming service. / 11.15 pm; closed Sat L & Sun.

Aykoku-Kaku EC4   £45 ❸④④

9 Walbrook 0171-248 2548 9–3C

"Great Japanese food on the run" makes the "excellent-value lunch" (served in the 'canteen' section) the top attraction of this dated City basement; the "flawless presentation" and professional service of the grander restaurant also win praise.
/ 10 pm; closed Sat & Sun; no booking at L.

Babe Ruth's E1 £28 ⑤⑤⑤
172-176 The Highway   0171-481 8181   1–2D
*This "rowdy" and "tacky" "American baseball-theme joint in
Wapping" is hailed by some as "the best trough in E1", but it
really does "need to try harder"; "what a waste of money –
go West!"* / Midnight; no smoking area; no booking.

Babur Brasserie SE23 £25 ❶❶❸
119 Brockley Rise, Forest Hill   0181-291 2400   1–4D
*"Always varied, always delicious", the "fresh-tasting" Indian
fare at this Forest Hill curry house is "the best for miles
around", especially if you visit during one of the "special
festivals of exotic cuisine"; service is unusually "friendly"
and well-informed, too.* / 11.15 pm; Fri L; no smoking area.

Back to Basics W1 £30 ❶❸④
21a Foley St   0171-436 2181   2–1B
*"Good fresh fish", "interestingly cooked" and in "large
portions", make these "simple" Fitzrovia premises worth
seeking out, but "get there early as the lunch specials
run out"; service tends to the "Teutonic".* / L only; closed Sat & Sun.

Bah Humbug SW2 £25 ④④❶
St Matthew's Peace Garden   0171-738 3184   10–2D
*The "romantic, Gothic atmosphere" makes this Brixton
church crypt a smash hit with trendy local twentysomethings,
many of whom also laud the "delicious and beautifully
presented veggie and fish dishes"; we're with those who say
"wonderful setting, shame about the food".* / 10.30 pm; D only
Mon-Fri, Sat & Sun open L & D; no Amex.

Balans £29 ❸❷❶
60 Old Compton St, W1   0171-437 5212   4–3A
239 Old Brompton Rd, SW5   0171-244 8838   5–3A
*"Always lively and laid back, whoever you are", these "busy
and vibrant" Miami Beach-style all-day brasseries are the top
place for "cute boys" and "girls who don't want to be leered
at" – the Soho branch, in particular, is "too gay" for some.*
/ W1 Mon-Sat 3 am, Sun 1 am – SW5 1 am; W1 no booking – SW5 Sat &
Sun no booking.

Bali Sugar W11 £40 ❸❸❸
33a All Saints Rd   0171-221 4477   6–1B
*August '98 opening in the cramped former North Kensington
premises of the Sugar Club (see also) under the same owners;
'fusion' cooking is also the style here, but our early-days visit
found variable results at invariably high prices (though others
have fared better); the "nice garden" remains.* / 11 pm;
no smoking area.

F S A

Bangkok SW7   £ 26   ②④⑤
9 Bute St   0171-584 8529   5–2B
"Good flavours" and *"reliable"* cooking at relatively *"modest prices"* make this old-established South Kensington canteen *"still the best Thai"* for diehard regulars; the setting and the service, though, are *"going down"*. / 11 pm; closed Sun; no Amex.

BANK WC2   £ 45   ③④❸
1 Kingsway   0171-379 9797   2–2D
Two years on, the scale of this "colourful" "canteen for suits", on the City-side fringe of Covent Garden, still seems "impressive", and, for the many who tip it for business (or for breakfast) it remains the "best of the big places". / 11 pm;
no Switch; set pre-th. £28(FP).

Banners N8   £ 25   ④④❷
21 Park Rd   0181-348 2930   1–1C
"Nice, if revoltingly trendy", "casual and very friendly" Crouch End bar-diner which is *"excellent, for the type of place it is"*; in particular, there's a *"great choice of breakfast/brunch material"*. / 11.30 pm, Fri & Sat midnight; no Amex & no Switch; set weekday L £16(FP).

Bar Bourse EC4   £ 39   ❸④❸
67 Queen St   0171-248 2200   9–3C
"Lively", "stylish and attractive" ("flash") new City basement, serving modern British fare which is "interesting" by local standards; "great sandwiches" at the bar. / L only; closed Sat & Sun.

Bar Gansa NW1   £ 19   ❷④❷
2 Inverness St   0171-267 8909   8–3B
It's "a bit ramshackle" in terms of staff organisation, "but you can eat cheaply and get very full" at this "buzzy", younger-scene Camden Town tapas bar. / Midnight; no Amex.

Bar Italia W1   £ 5   ④❸❶
22 Frith St   0171-437 4520   4–2A
"You can't beat the atmosphere" at this *"scruffy, but cool"* Soho coffee shop which serves a mean espresso at all hours of day and night – it's *"still the best post-clubbing hang-out"*.
/ 4 am, Fri & Sat 24 hours; no credit cards; no booking.

Bar Japan SW5   £ 20   ❸❸❸
251 Old Brompton Rd   0171-370 2323   5–3A
Simple Earl's Court café serving "cheap, good sushi"; "service slows when full". / 10.45 pm.

Barcelona Tapas £ 20 ❷❷❷

Ia Bell Ln, EI 0171-247 7014 9–2D
I Beaufort Hs, St Botolph St, EC3 0171-377 5222 9–2D
*"Great tapas and good fun" are to be had at this "friendly"
and "cheap" pair of City-fringe bars – the original in a
crowded cellar, the second in a glitzy office block;
(a new branch opens in Dulwich as we go to press).
/ 10 pm; closed Sat & Sun D.*

Basil St Hotel SW3 £ 34 ④❸❸

8 Basil St 0171-581 3311 5–ID
*For those wishing to escape all this Cool Britannia nonsense,
the "very traditional", "wonderfully comforting" atmosphere
of this "quintessential" Knightsbridge hotel dining room has
much to commend it; "great for Sunday lunch". / 10 pm;
jacket & tie.*

Battersea Barge Bistro SW8 £ 17 ④❸❷

Nine Elms Ln 0171-498 0004 10–ID
*Oddball barge (down a small lane opposite New Covent
Garden Market) from which "it's nice to look over the river";
it can be "good for parties", when the standard of the "poor
and dated" cooking is less important. / 11 pm; closed Sun D.*

Battersea Rickshaw SW11 £ 23 ❸❸④

15-16 Battersea Sq 0171-924 2450 5–4C
*There's "always a good curry", at this smarter than average
subcontinental – and "the maître d' is brilliant at concocting
a menu for you"; the place "lacks atmosphere", though.
/ 11.30 pm; D only.*

Beach Blanket Babylon W11 £ 35 ⑤④❷

45 Ledbury Rd 0171-229 2907 6–IB
*It may be only five years old, but the "camp" design of this
"fantasy"-Gothic Notting Hill bar/restaurant looks set to
become a classic; the cooking is "very poor", though, and
best sampled at brunch. / 11 pm; set Sun L £24(FP).*

Beauchamp's EC3 £ 42 ④④④

23-25 Leadenhall Mkt 0171-621 1331 9–2D
*Proponents of Captain Beauchamp Blackett's traditional
parlour may enthuse about "fantastic fresh fish" and the
"good setting in Leadenhall Market", but the place has too
many opponents who say it's "awful" and "ridiculously
overpriced". / Mon & Fri L only, Tue-Thu 9 pm; closed Sat & Sun.*

Bedlington Café W4 £ 19 ❷⑤⑤

24 Fauconberg Rd 0181-994 1965 7–2A
*"Super Thai cooking at very low prices helps you to forget
everything else is lacking" at this "famous" Chiswick café
(by day a 'greasy Joe'); falling ratings across the board,
though, suggest that they are beginning to take life too
easily. / 10 pm; no credit cards; no smoking area.*

Beirut Express W2   £ 18   ❷❷❸
112-114 Edgware Rd   0171-724 2700   6–1D
*"The finest mango juice this side of the Red Sea" and
"delicious", "cheap" Lebanese grub "served swiftly and priced
fairly" makes this Bayswater "pit stop" ideal for "quick food".
/ 1.45 am; no credit cards.*

Beiteddine SW1   £ 31   ❸❷④
8 Harriet St   0171-235 3969   2–3A
*Reliable Lebanese, just off Sloane Street, with "authentic"
cooking and professional service. / Midnight.*

Belair House SE21   £ 39   ❸❸❷
Gallery Road, Dulwich Village   0181-299 9788   1–4C
*The "beautiful setting (especially on a balmy summer
evening)" is not the only reason to visit this Dulwich yearling,
which occupies a listed Georgian house by the Picture Gallery
– the modern British cooking is "super", if somewhat
"expensive". / 10.30 pm.*

Belgo   £ 30   ④④❸
50 Earlham St, WC2   0171-813 2233   4–2C
72 Chalk Farm Rd, NW1   0171-267 0718   8–2B
*The "dynamic" and "fun" environment is the only real
attraction of these strikingly designed Belgian moules and
beer emporia – they're "very expensive, for the quality",
service is too often "stroppy", and, at Covent Garden,
diners endure "hot" and "cramped" conditions. / 11.30 pm.*

La Belle Epoque SW3   £ 40   ④⑤④
151 Draycott Ave   0171-460 5000   5–2C
*"Service which makes Fawlty Towers look competent",
expensively "tacky" décor and occasional servings-up of
"disgusting" Gallic fare combine to make this 800-seat
Brompton Cross fiasco the fitting final whimper of the craze
for oversize brasseries. / Midnight.*

Bellinis SW13   £ 16   ④❸❸
2-3 Rocks Ln   0181-255 9922   10–1A
*"Jolly", bright Barnes Italian roundly praised – especially by
the locals – for its "tasty" pizza and other fare. / 11.30 pm.*

Belvedere W8   £ 35   ❸❸❷
Holland Hs, off Abbotsbury Rd   0171-602 1238   7–1D
*"Food better than before" – it used to be dire – is the general
theme of reports on this "excellently located" modern British
restaurant, whose "superb balcony", overlooking Holland
Park, is many people's idea of a perfect summer location.
/ 11 pm; closed Sun D.*

Ben's Thai W9 £21 ❷④❸
93 Warrington Cr   0171-266 3134   8–4A
Though the setting is "a bit noisy and pubby" (and it can be "smoky"), the "delicious" and "authentic" Thai cooking in this characterful first-floor room of a Maida Vale landmark (the Warrington Castle) is worth seeking out. / 10 pm; D only; no Amex & no Switch.

Bengal Clipper SE1 £31 ❷❸④
Shad Thames   0171-357 9001   9–4D
"A good range of traditional and unusual cuisine" – "always of high quality" – makes this smart, if colourless, South Bank Indian worthy of a visit; Sunday buffet is a top attraction. / 11 pm; set Sun L £18(FP).

Benihana £45 ④④❸
37-43 Sackville St, W1   0171-494 2525   3–3D
77 King's Rd, SW3   0171-376 7799   5–3D
100 Avenue Rd, NW3   0171-586 9508   8–2A
Swanky "American-style", international Japanese chain, where ninja chefs cooking at your table offer an "entertaining spectacle" (which kids love); the food is decidedly "overpriced", however. / 10 pm, Fri & Sat Midnight.

Bentley's W1 £48 ❸❸❷
11-15 Swallow St   0171-734 4756   3–3D
"Good traditional fish" (and "excellent oysters") win renewed approval for this long-established and rather charming English restaurant near Piccadilly Circus; service can sometimes jar. / 11.30 pm; closed Sun; smart casual; set pre-th. £32(FP).

Beotys WC2 £36 ④❶❸
79 St Martin's Ln   0171-836 8768   4–3B
"It's good that some places never change – we are always well looked after here" typifies the devotion of regulars to this "clubby" Theatreland stalwart, who find compensation for the "overpriced" Franco–Greek cooking in the very "warm" welcome. / 11.30 pm; closed Sun; no smoking area.

Bersagliera SW3 £28 ❸❷❸
372 King's Rd   0171-352 5993   5–3B
Perennially packed and noisy World's End Italian, whose regulars praise "friendly" service and reliable, "cheap" pizza and pasta. / Midnight; closed Sun; no Amex.

Bertorelli's £31 ❸❸❸
19-23 Charlotte St, W1   0171-636 4174   2–1C
44a Floral St, WC2   0171-836 3969   4–2D
"Improving" (though still rather "average") food and better service make these large, middle-of-the-road Italians quite useful West End stand-bys. / W1 11 pm, WC2 11.30 pm; WC2 closed Sun; no smoking area.

Beyoglu SW11 £19 ❷❶④

50 Battersea Pk Rd 0171-627 2052 10–1C

"Cheap, but amazingly friendly and unrushed" Battersea Turk frequented not just by locals for its *"excellent"*, basic grub; *"sit upstairs"*. / 11 pm; closed Sun; no Amex & no Switch.

Bibendum SW3 £57 ❸④❸

81 Fulham Rd 0171-581 5817 5–2C

"Beautiful", *"light"* and *"airy"* it may be, but this Brompton Cross fixture rests ever more heavily on *"old laurels"*; that it's *"expensive"* (especially the *"horrific"* wine mark-ups) is hardly news, but nowadays the *"precise"* modern French cooking rarely sets the pulse racing, and service is below par. / 10.30 pm.

Bibendum Oyster Bar SW3 £32 ❶❷❸

81 Fulham Rd 0171-589 1480 5–2C

"The quality of the seafood and oysters always impress" at this excellent parlour, off the foyer to the Conran Shop – it's *"worth the wait for a seat"*. / 10 pm; no booking.

Bice W1 £42 ④❸④

13 Albemarle St 0171-409 1011 3–3C

"Everything's fine, but there's nothing to get excited about" at this Mayfair basement branch of a swanky international Italian chain (which couldn't make a duller contrast to its glitzy New York cousin); the *"good-value business lunch menu"* is the main reason to go. / 10.45 pm; closed Sat L & Sun; smart casual.

Big Easy SW3 £33 ④❸❷

334 King's Rd 0171-352 4071 5–3C

"Great for kids", this *"noisy"* and *"fun"* American 'crabshack' in Chelsea is at least pretty *"predictable"*; *"don't go unless you could eat a horse"*. / Midnight, Fri & Sat 12.30 am; no smoking area; Fri & Sat, no booking after 7 pm.

Billboard Café NW6 £24 ⑤❸④

280 West End Ln 0171-431 4188 1–1B

Though loyal regulars are "never disappointed" by this Italianate West Hampstead local, there is a general feeling that it has "gone downhill", with reports of "adequate, but boring food", and worse. / 11.30 pm; Mon-Fri closed L.

The Birdcage W1 £29 ❶❸❶

110 Whitfield St 0171-383 3346 2–1B

"Mesmerizing, Aladdin's cave" décor combines with *"exquisitely presented"* and *"sensationally spiced"* fusion cooking to make this *"refreshingly original"* newcomer (near Warren Street tube) *"a revelation"*. / 10.30 pm; closed Sun; no Amex; no smoking.

Bistrot 190 SW7 £ 32 ④④❸
189-190 Queen's Gt 0171-581 5666 5–1B
"It used to be great", but this South Kensington "former
favourite" is now at best "a good old stand-by"; the brasserie
fare is "not amazing", the service can be "slow", and the
principal vestige of its previous self is the "good buzz".
/ 12.30 am; no booking.

Bistrot 2 Riverside SE1 £ 33 ❸④④
Oxo Tower Wharf 0171-401 8200 9–3A
It may be "a typical brasserie with an untypically stunning
view", but, surprisingly, the strongest point of this large
outfit (six floors below the Oxo Tower) is its "good value"
(if "unexceptional") modern British fare – the large and
characterless room is "noisy", and service can be "slow".
/ 11.30 pm; closed Sun.

Blah! Blah! Blah! W12 £ 22 ❷❸❷
78 Goldhawk Rd 0181-746 1337 7–1C
"You would never know you were eating veggie", say
proponents of the "incongruously good" grub served at this
commendable Shepherd's Bush all-rounder; BYO. / 11 pm;
closed Sun; no credit cards.

Blakes Hotel SW7 £ 85 ④④❶
33 Roland Gdns 0171-370 6701 5–2B
"It always makes me feel like a Bond girl" – this "sexy",
"back-to-the-70s" South Kensington basement still works its
magic, especially "with the ladies"; prices for the eclectic
cooking are, as ever, "highway robbery". / Midnight.

Bleeding Heart EC1 £ 29 ❷❷❶
Bleeding Heart Yd, Greville St 0171-242 8238 9–2A
"A bugger to find" it may be, but this "delightful" and
"characterful" (if "cramped") cellar wine bar-cum-restaurant
(off a small yard, near Holborn) repays the effort with
"attentive" service, "excellent wines" and good Gallic cooking;
the place is "businessy at lunch, romantic in the evening".
/ 10.30 pm; closed Sat & Sun.

BLUE ELEPHANT SW6 £ 44 ❷❷❶
4-6 Fulham Broadway 0171-385 6595 5–4A
"It's so lovely just to sit there", gush admirers of this
"incredible" Fulham institution, whose "romantic"
pond-and-jungle décor is like "a magic garden";
perhaps surprisingly, the Thai food is "yummy", if, of course,
no bargain. / 12.30 am, Sun 10.30 pm; closed Sat L; smart casual; set
Sun L £26(FP).

Blue Jade SW1 £ 24 ❸❸④
44 Hugh St 0171-828 0321 2–4B
Popular Pimlico "neighbourhood Thai", where the "food is
undoubtedly fresh, but a bit pricey". / 11 pm; closed Sat L & Sun.

Blue Print Café SE1   £40   ❸❸❷

Design Mus, Butler's Whf   0171-378 7031   9–4D

It's "worth arriving early for a window-side table" to enjoy the "great river view" at the Design Museum's first floor café, not far from Tower Bridge; the modern British cooking generally satisfies, but it's been somewhat "inconsistent" this year. / *11 pm; closed Sun D.*

BLUEBIRD SW3   £41   ④④❸

350 Kings Rd   0171-559 1000   5–3C

"Robotic" service and "insipid" modern British cooking have done little to incite affection for this prominently housed and much commented-on Chelsea yearling; it offers "Conran on a grand scale" – "bland" and "formulaic". / *11.30 pm; set pre-th. £27(FP).*

Blues W1   £30   ❸❸❷

42 Dean St   0171-494 1966   4–2A

"Lively" ("extremely noisy") modern British venture in Soho, praised by a younger crowd for its "fun" atmosphere and "obliging" attitude, though service can be "slow". / *11.30 pm, Thu-Sat midnight; closed Sat L.*

Blythe Road Restaurant W14   £29   ❸❸❷

71 Blythe Rd   0171-371 3635   7–1C

"Steady, but well presented" modern British food and "good" service are on offer at this quite "stylish" Brook Green local. / *10.30 pm; closed Sat L & Sun.*

Boiled Egg & Soldiers SW11   £17   ❸④❸

63 Northcote Rd   0171-223 4894   10–2C

It's popular with the good people of Wandsworth, but some wonder whether this "small cosy caff serving brilliant fry-ups" is not "a bit overpriced for an upmarket greasy spoon". / *6 pm; no credit cards; no booking.*

Boisdale SW1   £39   ❸④❸

15 Eccleston St   0171-730 6922   2–4B

"One of a kind", this fashionable Victoria wine bar/restaurant offers "surprisingly good" modern British food (albeit at "unbelievably high prices"); service can be "surly", though, and those whose faces do not 'fit' may find the atmosphere "slightly frosty". / *10.30 pm; closed Sat L & Sun.*

Bombay Bicycle Club SW12   £30   ❷❷❷

95 Nightingale Ln   0181-673 6217   10–2C

"Different", "light, interesting and tasty" subcontinental cooking makes this Wandsworth "favourite" one of the most popular places with south-of-the-river dwellers. / *11.30 pm; D only; closed Sun.*

Bombay Brasserie SW7   **£ 40**   ❷❸❷
Courtfield Clo, Glouc. Rd   0171-370 4040   5–2B
The "wonderful room" (plus large conservatory) is the
special strength of this upmarket ("posey and expensive")
South Kensington subcontinental; that's not to overlook the
fact that the food is of "high quality". / Midnight; no Amex
& no Switch; smart casual; set Sun L £26(FP).

Bombay Palace W2   **£ 30**   ❷❷❸
50 Connaught St   0171-723 8855   6–1D
"Some of the freshest and tastiest Indian food" in town is to
be found at this "clinical, but consistent" spot, just north of
Hyde Park. / 11.15 pm; no smoking area; set Sun L £18(FP).

Bonjour Vietnam SW6   **£ 24**   ⑤④④
593-599 Fulham Rd   0171-385 7603   5–4A
Though its fans swear that this is a "lively", "informal" venue
that's "good if you are really hungry", many others write off
the all-you-can-eat concept of this once-stylish Fulham oriental
as an excuse for "poor" food and "rude" service. / 11 pm; set
weekday L £14(FP).

La Bouchée SW7   **£ 29**   ④⑤❸
56 Old Brompton Rd   0171-589 1929   5–2B
"Wildly popular" South Kensington bistro – but thanks to the
"fun" atmosphere, rather than the "average cooking and
decidedly sloppy service"; the pre-8pm set meal offers the
best value. / 11 pm; no Amex & no Switch; set pre-th. £18(FP).

Le Bouchon Bordelais SW11   **£ 29**   ④④❷
9 Battersea Rs   0171-738 0307   10–2C
Despite its somewhat "excessive price tag", this Battersea
bistro remains a popular local "stand-by". / 11.30 pm; set
weekday L £18(FP).

Boudin Blanc W1   **£ 30**   ❷❷❶
5 Trebeck St   0171-499 3292   3–4B
With its "authentic French food and atmosphere", this
"cosy and comforting" Shepherd Market bistro is always
"excellent value" – but especially with the "fantastic set
menu" available before 8pm. / 11 pm; set pre-th. £19(FP).

La Bouffe SW11   **£ 28**   ④❸❷
13 Battersea Rs   0171-228 3384   10–2C
To its large (and largely local) fan-club, this is an "underrated"
Battersea favourite – a "superb, informal French restaurant
with a good bar"; the cooking remains too variable, though,
to win wider acclaim. / 11 pm.

Boulevard WC2   **£ 25**   ④④❸
40 Wellington St   0171-240 2992   4–3D
Generally "good food at reasonable prices" makes this
"fun" brasserie a superior stand-by, at least by the standards
of Covent Garden. / Midnight.

The Bow Wine Vaults EC4   **£29**   ④❸④
10 Bow Church Yd   0171-248 1121   9–2C
*The English cooking "may not be that great", but this
"reliable" City venue, nicely tucked away in the shadow of
St Mary-le-Bow, "never disappoints or surprises".* / L only;
closed Sat & Sun.

Boyd's W8   **£36**   ⑤⑤④
135 Kensington Ch St   0171-727 5452   5–1A
*After a promising start a year or so ago, the post-Boyd
Gilmour régime is "stumbling" at this modern British
restaurant in Kensington; it does receive compliments, but
also far too many complaints of the "absolutely appalling",
"tasted-as-if-it-had-been-microwaved" variety.* / 11 pm;
closed Sat L & Sun.

The Brackenbury W6   **£30**   ❷❷❸
129-131 Brackenbury Rd   0181-748 0107   7–1C
*It looks just like a "nice little neighbourhood" place, but this
well known Shepherd's Bush outfit still "impresses" its
diverse following with "excellent", "value-for-money"
modern British cooking and general "attention to detail".*
/ 10.45 pm; closed Sat L & Sun D; set weekday L £18(FP).

Bradley's NW3   **£35**   ❷❷❸
25 Winchester Rd   0171-722 3457   8–2A
*A "lovely find in Swiss Cottage", this quality neighbourhood
venture offers an "interesting, well balanced menu"
(with "especially good" fish) in a tasteful modern setting.*
/ 11 pm; closed Sat L; set Sun L £19(FP).

Brady's SW18   **£19**   ❸④④
513 Old York Rd   0181-877 9599   10–2B
*"Very tasty" fish, "superb" chips and "good puds" make this a
Wandsworth formula that's "excellent in its simplicity";
however, "the service seems better when Mr Brady is there",
and a lick of paint would not go amiss.* / 10.30 pm; closed Sun;
no credit cards; no booking.

Brass. du Marché aux Puces W10   **£29**   ❷❶❶
349 Portobello Rd   0181-968 5828   6–1A
*"Simple" and "convincing" North Kensington bistro, whose
"friendly and honest service" and dependable Gallic cooking
make it "great for brunch", and, indeed, many other
occasions.* / 11.30 pm; closed Sun D; no Amex.

La Brasserie SW3   **£34**   ④④④
272 Brompton Rd   0171-584 1668   5–2C
*Long-established, "authentically French" Brompton Cross
stand-by, whose breakfasts are the key attraction for a
"Eurotrashy" crowd; "it's a wonderful place to sit about at
the weekend, but don't go for the food".* / Midnight; no booking
Sat/Sun L.

Brasserie 24 EC2   £ 38   ④⑤④
International Financial Centre   0171-877 7703   9–2C
*A new experience in the City – try this function-room eyrie
(now pressed into service by Roux Catering) on the 24th floor
of what many still call the NatWest tower; amateur staff and
simple food that is far too expensive for what it is, limit one's
desire to return.* / L only; closed Sat & Sun; no Amex.

Brasserie Rocque EC2   £ 35   ④④❸
37 Broadgate Circle   0171-638 7919   9–2D
*"Functional for business", this Broadgate brasserie wins many
City nominations as a "good meeting point", and the outside
tables are "great on a hot day"; the modern British cooking is
borderline.* / brasserie 8.30 pm; closed Sat & Sun; book only in restaurant.

Brasserie St Quentin SW3   £ 37   ④❸④
243 Brompton Rd   0171-589 8005   5–2C
*An object-lesson in what a disaster chain-ownership can be;
only two years ago, we noted "top quality food in a genuinely
Parisian atmosphere" at this Knightsbridge brasserie – it's
been "awful" since Groupe Chez Gérard took over, however,
with the Gallic cooking now "mundane" and "overpriced".*
/ 11 pm.

Brick Lane Beigel Bake E1   £ 4   ❷❶④
159 Brick Ln   0171-729 0616   1–2D
*"Most excellent value" and the "best bagels in London" – not
to mention mean salt beef sandwiches – keep this celebrated
24-hour East End institution permanently packed.* / 24 hr;
no credit cards.

Brilliant UB1   £ 19   ❶❷④
72-76 Western Rd   0181-574 1928   1–3A
*"The best Indian food in the UK" is not a rare claim on
behalf of this celebrated, cavernous curry-house, lost in
distant Southall; for our money that's slightly over-egging it,
but, it's definitely, er, brilliant.* / 11 pm; closed Mon; closed Sat & Sun L.

Brinkley's SW10   £ 25   ④④❷
47 Hollywood Rd   0171-351 1683   5–3B
*The "nice ambience in the covered rear garden" and the
go-go atmosphere of the cocktail bar at the front are the
highlights at this "inconsistent" modern British restaurant on
the fringe of Chelsea.* / 11 pm; D only; closed Sun; no Amex.

La Brocca NW6   £ 29   ❸④❸
273 West End Ln   0171-433 1989   1–1B
*West Hampstead locals go a bundle on this "few-frills,
but busy and noisy" Italian basement, and proclaim its
"fab pizza" and "charming" (if "slow") service.* / 11 pm.

Browns £30 ④❸❸

47 Maddox St, W1   0171-491 4565   3–2C
82-84 St Martin's Ln, WC2   0171-497 5050   4–4B
114 Draycott Av, SW3   0171-584 5359   5–2C
Atmospherically kitted-out English brasserie chain – now in the hands of Bass – where even those who find "reliably decent" food say it's "somewhat overpriced", and many just feel it's "mediocre and expensive". / 10 pm, midnight WC2; no smoking tables, WC2 & W1.

Bu San N7 £23 ❷❸⑤

43 Holloway Rd   0171-607 8264   8–2D
It's easy to miss this low-key neighbourhood Korean, just around the corner from Highbury and Islington tube; appearancewise it is, admittedly, "a bit of a dump", but foodwise it's usually a "really enjoyable experience". / 11.30 pm; closed Sat L & Sun L; no Amex; set weekday L £13(FP).

Bubb's EC1 £42 ④④④

329 Cent Mkts, Farringdon St   0171-236 2435   9–2A
"Old and dated" fixture, on a corner of Smithfield market, offering "rich", "traditional" French cooking; "OK – but it should be better at this price". / 10 pm; closed Sat & Sun.

Buchan's SW11 £31 ❸❸❷

62-64 Battersea Br Rd   0171-228 0888   5–4C
"Really enjoyable", if sometimes "noisy", wine bar/bistro, just over Battersea Bridge, with "good" modern Caledonian cooking – "fresh Angus beef in the burgers" and "splendid haggis". / 10.45 pm.

Buona Sera SW11 £24 ❸❸❷

22 Northcote Rd   0171-228 9925   10–2C
"Loud, garlicky and friendly", this "cheap" Clapham Italian has a huge local following (especially amongst "pram-pushing thirtysomethings") on account of its "excellent choice" of "good value" grub. / Midnight; no Amex.

Busabong Too SW10 £30 ❸④④

1a Langton St   0171-352 7414   5–3B
Quite characterful World's End Thai liked by its fans for its "relaxing" ambience and tasty grub; as at its sibling, "erratic" standards discourage a wider following. / 11.15 pm; D only.

Busabong Tree SW10 £30 ④❸④

112 Cheyne Walk   0171-352 7534   5–4B
This once-reliable hidden Thai, off Chelsea Embankment, has performed variably of late, and though some still laud the "tasty" cooking, others feel it has "gone off". / 11.15 pm; smart casual; set weekday L £16(FP).

The Butlers Wharf Chop-house SE1 £42 ④❸❸
36e Shad Thames   0171-403 3403   9–4D
This anodyne Tower Bridge-side English restaurant makes "an excellent place to discuss business"; leaving aside the bar menu (which is a steal), the cooking epitomises the mundane level which seems to be the summit of aspiration for any Conran establishment. / 11 pm; closed Sat L & Sun D; set Sun L £21(FP).

Byron's NW3 £29 ④❷❷
3a Downshire Hl   0171-435 3544   8–2A
It's rather a shame that the "interesting" modern British menu of this charming Hampstead side street townhouse "still seems too ambitious for what they can actually deliver". / 11 pm; D only ex Sat & Sun, when open L & D; no smoking area.

Cactus Blue SW3 £31 ④④❷
86 Fulham Rd   0171-823 7858   5–2C
"When the tequila starts flowing", this coolly designed joint (opposite Chelsea's Royal Marsden hospital) is "jumping"; the potentially "interesting and creative" Latin-American inspired scoff is too often "disappointing", though, and service comes and goes. / 11.45 pm; D only ex Sat & Sun, when open L & D; no smoking area.

Café 206 W11 £29 ❷❷❸
206 Westbourne Grove   0171-221 1535   6–1B
"Fun", "friendly" Notting Hill Italian café, with "good breakfasts" and "the best coffee". / 6.30 pm; L only; closed Sat D & Sun D; no Amex.

Café 209 SW6 £15 ④❷❸
209 Munster Rd   0171-385 3625   10–1B
"Mad Thai Fulham café", where the "delightful owner", Joy, is full of "light-hearted abuse" and where the fact you can BYO makes it "great for big groups"; take ear-plugs. / 10.45 pm; D only; closed Sun; no credit cards.

Café Bohème W1 £30 ④④❶
17 Old Compton St   0171-734 0623   4–2A
Its "lovely", "lively" "Soho atmosphere" commends this "loud", "crowded" and "smoky" corner bar-café-bistro to the younger-at-heart; the food's "ordinary" however, and service can be "snotty". / 2.45 am, Thu-Sat open 24 hours, Sun 11.30 pm.

Café Coq WC2 £19 ❸❷④
154-156 Shaftesbury Ave   0171-836 8635   4–2B
Bistro-chain-prototype, just north of Cambridge Circus, whose flame-roasted-chicken formula offers good-value protein, in rather stark surroundings. / 11 pm; closed Sun L; bookings only for 10+.

Café de la Place SW11 £22 ❸④❸
11/12 Battersea Sq   0171-978 5374   5–4C
Unpretentious, "good value" Gallic Battersea bistro. / 11 pm; closed Sun D; no Amex.

Café de Paris W1 £ 47 ④④❷
3 Coventry St   0171-734 7700   4–4A
*"A great cattle market for the rich" – this "inexcusably
pricey" Art Deco nightclub-restaurant, just off Leicester
Square, may be a cool and "romantic" scene, but the modern
British grub can be "terrible", and the service leaves much to
be desired.* / 11 pm (bar 3 am); D only, closed Sun & Mon.

Café Delancey NW1 £ 25 ④④❷
3 Delancey St   0171-387 1985   8–3B
*It's "worth the patchy service for the perfect brunch menu"
at this large and "very, very relaxed" Camden Town brasserie;
at other times, look elsewhere.* / 11.30 pm; no Amex.

Café des Amis du Vin WC2 £ 32 ④❸❸
11-14 Hanover Pl   0171-379 3444   4–2D
*We much prefer the new-look Café des Amis, whose bright,
contemporary design couldn't be in starker contrast to its
old 'Allo 'Allo styling; it now makes a fair bet for a bite in
Covent Garden, but the basement bar (with its "good value
cheeseboard" and "interesting varied wine list") remains the
top attraction.* / 11.30 pm; set pre-th. £22(FP).

Café des Arts NW3 £ 30 ④④❸
82 Hampstead High St   0171-435 3608   8–2A
*What has happened to this once-charming central
Hampstead site? – it's now widely found "completely
underwhelming in every way", thanks to its "unexciting"
cooking (now Mediterranean in slant) and "shambolic"
service.* / 11.30 pm; no smoking area; set pre-th. £18(FP).

Café du Jardin WC2 £ 35 ❸❸④
28 Wellington St   0171-836 8769   4–3D
*Pre-theatre and lunch menus are definitely "good-value"
at this agreeable – but "noisy" and tightly packed –
Covent Garden outfit; at the à la carte prices, it's
questionable whether the cooking shows "enough attention
to detail".* / Midnight; set Sun L £21(FP).

Café du Marché EC1 £ 31 ❷❷❶
22 Charterhouse Sq   0171-608 1609   9–1B
*Tucked away in a quiet corner near Smithfield Market, this
converted warehouse perennially pleases with its "consistent
and interesting" French cooking, its "very pleasant staff" and
its stylish, yet relaxing atmosphere – "great for a more
informal business lunch", or a romantic dinner.* / 10 pm;
closed Sat L & Sun; no Amex.

Café Emm W1 £ 20 ❸❸❸
17 Frith St   0171-437 0723   4–2A
*"Amazingly good value-for-money" – "I haven't finished a
portion yet" – makes this "cheap", "laid back" and loud Soho
spot a useful central resource.* / 10.30 pm, Fri & Sat 12.30 am;
closed Sat L & Sun L; no Amex; book L only.

Café Fish W1 £ 32 ❸④❸
36-40 Rupert Street   0171-287 8989   4–3A
*We prefer Café Fish's new (summer '98) home, just off
Shaftesbury Avenue, to its "crowded" former premises;
the basic proposition remains the same, however – it's a
"pleasant", but "unexciting" fish bistro, "bang in the middle
of town". / 11.30 pm; no smoking area.*

Café Flo £ 27 ④④④
11 Haymarket, SW1   0171-976 1313   4–4A
103 Wardour Street, W1   0171-734 0581   3–2D
13 Thayer St, W1   0171-935 5023   2–1A
51 St Martin's Ln, WC2   0171-836 8289   4–4C
676 Fulham Rd, SW6   0171-371 9673   10–1B
25-35 Gloucester Road, SW7   0171-589 1383   5–1B
127 Kensington Ch St, W8   0171-727 8142   6–2B
334 Upper St, N1   0171-226 7916   8–3D
205 Haverstock Hl, NW3   0171-435 6744   8–2A
38-40 Ludgate Hill, EC4   0171-329 3900   9–2A
*Some hold up this bright-looking Gallic group as being
"reliable" and "good value"; it's certainly "much superior to
Café Rouge" – hardly an earth-shattering achievement – and
most feel that "even a chain should cook better than this".
/ 11.30 pm, Sun 11 pm.*

Café Grove W11 £ 18 ④④❷
253a Portobello Rd   0171-243 1094   6–1A
*"Particularly on sunny mornings" the "excellent coffee" and
"reasonable" light grub make the large terrace of this
Portobello diner a preferred brunch venue (and it has a fine
view of the market, below); in the evening it can be "quiet".
/ winter 5 pm, summer 10.30 pm; winter L only – summer, closed Sat D
& Sun D; no credit cards; need 10+ to book.*

Café Indiya E1 £ 23 ❷❷④
30 Alie St   0171-481 8288   9–3D
*The "different" cooking "packs a good punch" at this
year-old, east-City Indian; "brisk service" and "hi-tech décor
that's not to all tastes" make it "not a place to linger". / 11 pm;
closed Sat & Sun.*

Café Japan NW11 £ 24 ❷❷④
626 Finchley Rd   0181-455 6854   1–1B
*The name says it all at this "authentic", "friendly", "good
value" oriental – across from Golder's Green tube – where
"excellent sushi" is the top attraction. / 10.30 pm; D only; no Amex.*

Café Latino W1 £ 24 ④❷❷
25 Frith St   0171-287 5676   4–2A
*This small, but vibrant Soho bar makes a "great spot for
meeting friends", and boasts notably "friendly" service; on the
food front, "tapas are fine, but main courses are dodgy".
/ 11 pm, Thu-Sat 1 am.*

Café Laville W2 £29 ④④❷
453 Edgware Rd   0171-706 2620   8–4A
*The "amazing view of the canal" – the café is actually on a
bridge – makes this Maida Vale café "perfect for brunch" or
"coffee"; sadly, the general rooms-with-a-view rules apply –
the food can be "awful", and service "sloppy".* / 10 pm; no Amex;
no smoking area.

Café Lazeez SW7 £34 ④④❸
93-95 Old Brompton Rd   0171-581 9993   5–2C
*It "gets lively with bands playing" at this South Kensington
'modern Indian', where the 'evolved' cooking (even if it does
have some "interesting flavours") is "usually not good value";
as we go to press, City workers can enjoy a similar package
at 88 St John Street, tel 0171-253 2224.* / 12.30 am,
Sun 10.30 pm; smart casual; no smoking area; set Sun L £19(FP).

Café Med £29 ④④❸
22-25 Dean St, W1   0171-287 9007   4–2A
2 Hollywood Rd, SW10   0171-823 3355   5–3B
184a Kensington Pk Rd, W11   0171-221 1150   6–1B
320 Goldhawk Rd, W6   0181-741 1994   7–1B
21 Loudon Rd, NW8   0171-625 1222   8–3A
*Complaints of "café food at restaurant prices" depress
enthusiasm for these "unpretentious", "fun" bistros, where
"great grills" top the bill.* / 11.30 pm.

Café Milan SW3 £35 – – –
312-314 King's Road   tel n/a   5–3C
*The owners of the Italian Kitchen aim to bring a high level of
design – from the architect whose credits include the famous
New York branch of Vong – to this ambitious, late-1998
Chelsea restaurant, antipasti bar and pizzeria.*

Café Montpeliano SW3 £25 ❸❸❷
144 Brompton Rd   0171-225 2926   5–1C
*"Super people-watching at lunchtime" is a plus at this
pleasant, upmarket Italian café/bistro, near Harrods.* / 11 pm;
closed Sun D; no Switch.

Café Mozart N6 £18 ❸❸④
17 Swains Lane   0181-348 1384   8–1B
*"A little bit of Vienna", this "mid-European coffee house"
offers "a great breakfast next to Hampstead Heath",
and "good home-made food" (including hearty meat dishes)
throughout the day.* / 10 pm; no Amex; no smoking; no booking at L.

Café O SW3 £31 ❸❷④
163 Draycott Ave   0171-584 5950   5–2C
*This "stylish Greek" deserves to be better known; not only
does it provide "an affordable refuge near Brompton Cross",
but also some "interesting, modern" cooking, delivered by
notably "relaxed, but efficient" staff.* / 11 pm; closed Sun.

Café Pacifico WC2   £27   ④④❸
5 Langley St   0171-379 7728   4–2C
"London's best Mexican" is slipping rather; its jolly Covent Garden premises still provide a good setting "for a lively night out", but the cooking tends to be "uninspired" nowadays, and service continues to deteriorate. / 11.45 pm; no smoking area; book pre 6.30 pm only.

Café Pasta   £21   ④❸④
184 Shaftesbury Ave, WC2   0171-379 0198   4–2B
2-4 Garrick St, WC2   0171-497 2779   4–3C
270 Chiswick High Rd, W4   0181-995 2903   7–2A
229-231 Kensington High St, W8   0171-937 6314   5–1A
8 Theberton St, N1   0171-704 9089   8–3D
200 Haverstock Hl, NW3   0171-431 8531   8–2A
Though fans still say this is a "cheap, cheerful and reliable" chain, too many think its menu "stale", and the pasta itself "revolting"; perhaps PizzaExpress, who bought the group in mid-1998, will pep things up. / 11.30 pm; no Amex; some have no smoking area; book L and early eve only.

Café Portugal SW8   £27   ❷❷④
5a & 6a Victoria Hs, S Lambeth Rd   0171-587 1962   10–1D
"Comforting" and "reliable" Portuguese "home cooking" is provided at the Branco family's "cheap and cheerful" Vauxhall café/tapas bar, which moonlights as a restaurant. / 11 pm; no Amex.

Café Rouge   £24   ⑤⑤④
15 Frith St, W1   0171-437 4307   4–2A
46-48 James St, W1   0171-487 4847   3–1A
34 Wellington St, WC2   0171-836 0998   4–3D
27-31 Basil St, SW3   0171-584 2345   5–1D
390 King's Rd, SW3   0171-352 2226   5–3B
855 Fulham Rd, SW6   0171-371 7600   10–1B
102 Old Brompton Rd, SW7   0171-373 2403   5–2B
31 Kensington Pk Rd, W11   0171-221 4449   6–1A
Whiteleys, W2   0171-221 1509   6–1C
227-229 Chiswick High Rd, W4   0181-742 7447   7–2A
158 Fulham Palace Rd, W6   0181-741 5037   7–2C
98-100 Shepherd's Bush Rd, W6   0171-602 7732   7–1C
2 Lancer Sq, Kensington Ch St, W8   0171-938 4200   5–1A
30 Clifton St, W9   0171-286 2266   8–4A
6 South Grove, N6   0181-342 9797   8–1B
18 Chalk Farm Rd, NW1   0171-428 0998   8–2B
38-39 High St, NW3   0171-435 4240   8–1A
120 St John's Wood High St, NW8   0171-722 8366   8–3A

Café Rouge (continued)

Hay's Galleria, Tooley St, SE1   0171-378 0097   9–4D
39-49 Parkgate Rd, SW11   0171-924 3565   5–4C
248 Upper R'mond Rd, SW14   0181-878 8897   10–2A
200 Putney Br Rd, SW15   0181-788 4257   10–2B
26 High St, SW19   0181-944 5131   10–2B
40 Abbeville Rd, SW4   0181-673 3399   10–2D
140 Fetter Ln, EC4   0171-242 3469   9–2A
Hillgate Hs, Limeburner Ln, EC4   0171-329 1234   9–2A
"Woeful" chain of faux-Gallic bistros with "nothing to
recommend" them – "very drab and poorly presented"
food is served "shockingly" badly in an "incredibly dull"
environment; Whitbread, the owners, run breweries – now,
what's that saying that comes to mind? / 11 pm, City & W2 earlier;
City & W2 closed some or all Sat & Sun.

Café Royal Grill Room W1   £ 42   ❷❷❶

68 Regent St   0171-437 1177   3–3D
"Approachable haute cuisine" makes this "wonderful" and
"intensely rococo" central dining room a "class" act; though
under the Marco Pierre White umbrella for a year now, it
keeps a remarkably low profile, and – notwithstanding slightly
mixed feedback – deserves a wider following. / 11 pm;
closed Sat L & Sun; jacket & tie; set pre-th. £27(FP).

Café Sofra   £ 13   ④⑤④

10 Shepherd Mkt, W1   0171-495 3434   3–4B
33 Old Compton St, W1   0171-494 0222   4–2A
63 Wigmore St, W1   0171-486 7788   3–1A
1-3 New Oxford St, WC1   0171-430 0430   2–1D
15 Catherine St, WC2   0171-240 9991   4–3D
5 Garrick St, WC2   0171-240 6688   4–3C
101 Fleet St, EC4   0171-583 6669   9–2A
"Tasty and varied food" at a moderate price makes these
Turkish cafés useful stand-bys; service is decidedly
"indifferent", though, and conditions are "uncomfortable".
/ Midnight, Old Compton St 2 am, EC4 9 pm; no credit cards; no smoking area;
no booking.

Café Spice Namaste   £ 29   ❷❷❷

247 Lavender Hill, SW11   0171-738 1717   10–2C
16 Prescot St, E1   0171-488 9242   1–2D
"Revolutionising the image of Indian food at very respectable
prices" continues to be the mission at Cyrus Todiwala's
"different", "bright and friendly" east-City mould-breaker;
the new Clapham branch is, however, ordinary in every
respect. / 10.30 pm; closed Sat L & Sun; set weekday L £18(FP).

Caffè Uno £ 23 ⑤④④
28 Binney St, W1 0171-499 9312 3–2A
5 Argyll St, W1 0171-437 2503 3–1C
64 Tottenham Court Rd, W1 0171-636 3587 2–1C
24 Charing Cross Rd, WC2 0171-240 2524 4–3B
37 St Martin's Ln, WC2 0171-836 5837 4–4C
805 Fulham Rd, SW6 0171-731 0990 10–1B
106 Queensway, W2 0171-229 8470 6–1C
11 Edgware Rd, W2 0171-723 4898 6–1D
163-165 Chiswick High Rd, W4 0181-742 1942 7–2A
9 Kensington High St, W8 0171-937 8961 5–1A
62 Upper St, N1 0171-226 7988 8–3D
4 South Grove, N6 0181-342 8662 8–1B
40-42 Parkway, NW1 0171-428 9124 8–3B
122 St John's Wood High St, NW8 0171-722 0400 8–3A
375 Lonsdale Rd, SW13 0181-876 3414 10–1A
*The initial promise has deserted this pasta and pizza chain;
some still vote it a "cheap and cheerful" stand-by, but,
"bland" and "truly dreadful" cooking means many just
"will not go again". / Midnight; some branches have no smoking areas.*

La Cage Imaginaire NW3 £ 28 ④❸❸
16 Flask Wk 0171-794 6674 8–1A
*"An attractive local gem", say fans of this rather clichéed –
but, some find, romantic – Gallic spot, which benefits from a
super-cute Hampstead location. / 11 pm, Sat 11.30 pm; closed Mon.*

Calabash WC2 £ 21 ❸④⑤
38 King St 0171-836 1976 4–3C
*'Daktari' comes to Covent Garden at this musty basement
under the Africa Centre, where the standard of the décor
certainly evokes the Third World; the pan-African cooking is
definitely 'different'. / 10.30 pm; closed Sat L & Sun; no Switch.*

Caldesi W1 £ 30 ❸❷④
15-17 Marylebone Ln 0171-935 9226 3–1A
*"The maître d' is quite a character" at this "cute" old-style
Marylebone Italian, where service is especially friendly "to
known patrons". / 11 pm; closed Sat L & Sun; no smoking area.*

Calzone £ 20 ④❸④
335 Fulham Rd, SW10 0171-352 9797 5–3B
2a Kensington Pk Rd, W11 0171-243 2003 6–2B
35 Upper St, N1 0171-359 9191 8–3D
66 Heath St, NW3 0171-794 6775 8–1A
*"Thin and crispy" pizzas can still make these stark spots
useful stand-bys; it's sad, though, that the once-exemplary
standards have been superseded by "overall mediocrity".
/ Midnight, SW10 Fri & Sat 12.45 am.*

Cam Phat W1 £17 ④❸④
12 Macclesfield St   0171-437 5598   4–3A
Chinatown-fringe Vietnamese whose friendly attitude and clean-tasting (if not particularly punchy) cooking makes it an OK stand-by. / 11 pm; only for groups of 4+.

Cambio de Tercio SW5 £29 ❸❷❷
163 Old Brompton Rd   0171-244 8970   5–2B
South Kensington Spaniard whose growing fan club proclaims the virtues of its "substantial", "rustic" cooking and its "charming and efficient" service. / 11 pm.

Camden Brasserie NW1 £29 ❸❷❷
216 Camden High St   0171-482 2114   8–2B
"Always welcoming and friendly", says the sizeable north London fan club of this "dependable", "laid-back" fixture, whose name says it all. / 11.30 pm; no Amex.

Cantaloupe EC2 £27 ❸❸❶
35-42 Charlotte Rd   0171-613 4411   9–1D
It's the "chilled" and "lively" crowd which makes this "scruffy, but fun" Shoreditch-fringe bar/restaurant a "benchmark" for artier types; there's "real value" to be had from the modern British restaurant at the rear, or you can settle for a (good) bar snack. / Midnight; closed Sat L; no Amex; no smoking area.

THE CANTEEN SW10 £40 ❶❷❷
Chelsea Harbour   0171-351 7330   5–4B
Though no longer in the limelight as it once was, this sophisticated establishment, stuck out on a limb in Chelsea Harbour, has never before delivered such all-round "excellent value", with its "polished" service, "wonderful" modern British cooking and a setting that is "romantic, as well as lively". / 11 pm, Fri & Sat midnight; closed Sat L & Sun.

Cantina del Ponte SE1 £39 ⑤⑤⑤
36c Shad Thames   0171-403 5403   9–4D
"Where do they get such rude staff?"; why is the food so "consistently dreadful?"; how does London's 'leading' restaurant chain (Conran Restaurants) continue to run this potentially pleasant Thames-side pizzeria so badly? / 10.45 pm; set pre-th. £20(FP).

Cantina Italia N1 £24 ❷❸④
19 Canonbury Lane   0171-226 9791   8–2D
"Unpretentious" Islington newcomer, already pleasing locals with its "mammoth pizzas and huge bowls of pasta"; "book a ground-floor table", though – the "really Spartan" downstairs has a "poor" ambience. / 11.30 pm; no Amex.

Cantinetto Venegazzú SW11 £29 ❶❷❸
31–32 Battersea Sq   0171-978 5395   5–4C
"A poky, dark place producing culinary miracles in deepest Battersea" – this *"eager to please"* new Venetian has only recently opened, but is already something of a foodie mecca. / 11.30 pm; set weekday L £17(FP).

La Capannina W1 £33 ❸❷④
24 Romilly St   0171-437 2473   4–3A
"The waiters are always good for a laugh", at this *"solid, constant, old-fashioned"* Soho Italian, which makes *"a good stand-by, even if the cooking is slightly dull"*. / 11.15 pm; closed Sat L & Sun.

Capital Hotel SW3 £73 ❸❷❸
22-24 Basil St   0171-589 5171   5–1D
Philip Britten's *"subtle"* and *"imaginative"* modern French cooking continues to win foodie plaudits for this *"tiny"*, but *"comfortable"* Knightsbridge dining room; prices are *"high"*, though, which makes the *"fabulous value"* lunch worth particular consideration. / 11.15 pm; dinner, jacket & tie; set weekday L £40(FP).

Capital Radio Restaurant WC2 £27 ⑤④❸
29-30 Leicester Sq   0171-484 8888   4–4B
Even supporters admit the food is only *"just about passable"* at this *"noisy"* West End theme-café, whose *"happy and helpful"* service is *"erratic"*; some still manage a *"fun night out"*, but to others *"it's an all round disappointment – even the kids thought so"*. / Midnight; no smoking area.

LE CAPRICE SW1 £41 ❷❶❶
Arlington Hs, Arlington St   0171-629 2239   3–4C
The atmosphere *"glows with excitement"* at this *"sleek"* modern British brasserie near the Ritz, whose *"poetry in motion"* service helps to maintain its position as one of the very top rendezvous in town – *"great for people watching"* (but, for those not on the inside track, *"so difficult to book"*); time will tell whether the new (August '98) owners will keep up standards. / Midnight.

Caraffini SW1 £31 ❷❶❷
61-63 Lower Sloane St   0171-259 0235   5–2D
"Noisy, but worth the ear-drum battering", says the vociferous fan-club of this *"happy"* Chelsea Italian, whose *"faultless and totally charming service"* wins high praise; *"good"* cooking, too, and *"well priced"* by local standards. / 11.30 pm; closed Sun.

Caravaggio EC3 £40 ④④④
107-112 Leadenhall St   0171-626 6206   9–2D
For *"business lunch buzz"*, it's difficult to beat this large Italian near Lloyds; for the *"standard fare"*, though, prices are *"pretty full"* – *"even by City standards"* – and service can be *"chaotic"*. / 10 pm; closed Sat & Sun.

Caravan Serai W1   £ 25   ④❷❸
50 Paddington St   0171-935 1208   2–1A
*A cosy rug-filled setting, "obliging" staff and an "interesting"
menu make this long-established Marylebone Afghan of
note; some now complain of "tired" décor, though, and
"uninspiring" cooking. / 11 pm, Fri & Sat 11.30 pm; no smoking area;
set weekday L £14(FP).*

Carnevale EC1   £ 27   ❷❸④
135 Whitecross St   0171-250 3452   9–1B
*"Scrumptious" and "inventive" nosh makes it worth seeking
out this stylish veggie café near the Barbican, despite
conditions that are "cramped", and "uncomfortable".
/ 10.30 pm; closed Sun; switch only; set pre-th. £17(FP).*

Casale Franco N1   £ 33   ❸④❸
rear of 134-137 Upper St   0171-226 8994   8–3D
*The attraction of "huge, real pizzas" (and "a reliable menu"
of other dishes) means you're quite likely to have to queue for
this characterful Islingtonian, hidden down an alleyway; as
usual, it attracted complaints of "surly" and "rude" service.
/ 11.30 pm, Sun 9 pm; closed Mon ; no Amex; no smoking area; book L only.*

Cave W1   £ 46   ❷❷④
161 Piccadilly   0171-409 0445   3–3C
*"Delicious", "fresh" fish (with "innovative use of caviar, for
those who can afford it") makes the Caviar House's dining
room a "more serious" culinary venue than you might expect;
the setting's "somewhat cold", however, and evenings can be
"quiet". / 10 pm, Thu–Sat 10.30 pm; closed Sun.*

Cecconi's W1   £ 59   ⑤⑤⑤
5a Burlington Gdns   0171-434 1509   3–3C
*"Only the bill is extraordinary" at this "tired", "dowdy" and
"pretentious" Mayfair Italian; "how does it survive?" / 11.30 pm;
jacket; no smoking area.*

Centuria N1   £ 24   ❸⑤④
100 St Paul's Rd   0171-704 2435   1–1C
*Islington pub/restaurant, offering "fresh" Italian cooking "at
reasonable prices"; service can be very slow, though, and
"the bar's atmosphere is better than the restaurant's". / 11 pm;
closed weekday L; no Amex.*

Chada SW11   £ 29   ❸❸④
208-210 Battersea Pk Rd   0171-622 2209   10–1C
*Battersea Thai, whose professional service, but "above all,
its good food" makes it an asset to the area; it can be "quiet"
though. / 11 pm, Fri & Sat 11.30 pm; closed Sat L; smart casual.*

The Chapel NW1   £ 25   ❸❷❷
48 Chapel St   0171-402 9220   6–1D
*"Crowded, noisy, smoky – great", say the twentysomething
fans of this "fun" gastropub, near Edgware Road tube,
who praise "original food and good beer". / 9.50 pm.*

Charco's SW3 £33 ④④④
1 Bray Pl 0171-584 0765 5–2D
The modern British restaurant in the basement of this long established Chelsea wine bar is now rather "quiet", making it more suitable than ever for "illicit assignations". / 10.30 pm; closed Sun.

Chavot SW3 £56 ❸❸❸
257-259 Fulham Rd 0171-351 7823 5–2C
"Dependable" and "nice" are the sort of adjectives heaped on this "serious" modern French Chelsea yearling; yes, it is "consistent", but – for us at least – the reporter who says it's just "another upscale, but unremarkable restaurant" has it absolutely right. / 11 pm; closed Sat L & Sun; parties of 8+; set weekday L £33(FP).

Che SW1 £45 – – –
23 St James's Street 0171-747 9380 3–4D
London has no US-style cigar room-cum-restaurant of any note – a situation this ambitious late-1998 venture (at the base of the prominent '60s building adjoining The Economist, in St James's) hopes to rectify; great things are promised for the lofty ground-floor cocktail bar. /—

Chelsea Bun Diner SW10 £16 ④❸❸
9a Lamont Rd 0171-352 3635 5–3B
"Great breakfasts" – "the portions are huge and it's really cheap" – make this "fun" World's End all-day diner a natural brunch hang-out; it can get "smoky". / 11 pm; no Amex; need 6+ to book.

Chelsea Kitchen SW3 £11 ④❷④
98 King's Rd 0171-589 1330 5–2D
Canteen-style '60s survivor which is "unbeatable", in the environs of Sloane Square, as a purveyor of "tasty", "hearty" and "outrageously cheap" nosh. / 11.30 pm; no credit cards; no smoking area; need 4+ to book.

Chelsea Ram SW10 £25 ❶❸❷
32 Burnaby St 0171-351 4008 5–4B
"A notch above your average revamped pub", this Chelsea-fringe boozer offers a "delicious" "ever-changing" modern British menu to "hearty rugby-players and their molls"; it "gets very busy at weekends". / 10 pm, Sun 9 pm; no Amex; no booking.

Cheng Du NW1 £31 ❸❸❸
9 Parkway 0171-485 8058 8–3B
"A safe bet, even if it's a bit pricey", this quite smart Camden Town Chinese has proved "very reliable over the years". / 11.30 pm; no Amex & no Switch.

CHEZ BRUCE SW17   **£ 37**   **①①②**

2 Bellevue Rd   0181-672 0114   10–2C

"Outstanding value as well as outstanding food" is a potent combination that helps make this "jolly" and "informal", but very professionally run modern British establishment, by Wandsworth Common, one of the best all-rounders in town. / 10.30 pm; closed Sun D.

Chez Gérard   **£ 28**   ④④**③**

31 Dover St, W1   0171-499 8171   3–3C

8 Charlotte St, W1   0171-636 4975   2–1C

119 Chancery Ln, WC2   0171-405 0290   2–2D

45 East Ter, Covent Gdn, WC2   0171-379 0666   4–3D

3 Yeoman's Row, SW3   0171-581 8377   5–2C

84-86 Rosebery Ave, EC1   0171-833 1515   8–4D

64 Bishopsgate, EC2   0171-588 1200   9–2D

"Delicious steak", "excellent frites" and a "good set menu" are the highlights of the offerings at these "reliable" establishments, which make "useful stand-bys" (if "nothing more"); the new Bishopsgate branch is impressive. / 10 pm-11.15 pm; Charlotte St closed Sat L, Dover St closed Sun L, Chancery Ln & EC2 closed Sat & Sun, EC1 closed Sat L & Sun; no smoking areas.

Chez Liline N4   **£ 29**   **①③**④

101 Stroud Green Rd   0171-263 6550   8–1D

"Grim place, but great fish" – this "grottilly located" and "cramped" Finsbury Park Mauritian is well known for the "great innovation" displayed in its cooking, its "really fresh" ingredients and its "excellent value". / 10.30 pm; closed Sun.

Chez Moi W11   **£ 38**   **③①②**

1 Addison Ave   0171-603 8267   6–2A

This "intimate" Holland Park "charmer" would make "a decadent setting for a tryst", so it's "amusing that most of the clientele is middle-aged and firmly faithful"; the Gallic cooking (with the odd exotic flourish) is "steady". / 11 pm; closed Sat L & Sun.

**CHEZ NICO AT NINETY
GROSVENOR HOUSE HOTEL W1**   **£ 87**   **②**④④

90 Park Ln   0171-409 1290   3–3A

Nico Ladenis's "stiff" Mayfair dining room has always seemed more an exercise in classical Gallic perfection than a place to be enjoyed ("brilliant, but a bit sterile"); however, "often mediocre" service has, of late, swelled the ranks of those who find the whole experience "an expensive let-down". / 11 pm; closed Sat L & Sun; no Switch; jacket & tie; set weekday L £53(FP).

Chezmax SW10 £35 **①①②**
168 Ifield Rd 0171-835 0874 5–3A
"Off-beat" and *"intimate"* Earl's Court cellar, where reporters
don't know which to praise more – the *"fantastic"* French
cooking (*"by enthusiasts, for enthusiasts"*) or the *"wonderful"*,
"OTT" performance of the maître d'; *"excellent wines at
sensible prices"* are a further attraction. / 11 pm; closed Mon
& Sun; set pre-th. £22(FP).

Chiang Mai W1 £28 **①③⑤**
48 Frith St 0171-437 7444 4–2A
"A must for Thai fans", this *"underrated"* Soho establishment
has recently been on cracking culinary form; shame it
"lacks atmosphere". / 11 pm; closed Sun L.

Chicago Rib Shack SW7 £26 ④⑤④
1 Raphael St 0171-581 5595 5–1C
A *"great greasy glob"* can variously be taken as a compliment
to or a criticism of the *"obscenely large"* dishes served at this
cavernous Knightsbridge institution, which some endorse for
being *"fantastic as a family restaurant"*. / 11.45 pm;
no smoking area; no booking Sat.

China Blues NW1 £35 ④④**③**
29-31 Parkway 0171-482 3940 8–3B
"It left me blue", bemoan critics of this allegedly *"fun"*
Camden Town oriental, where the *"tasteless and watery food"*
falls short of expectations; a major Mayfair offshoot, China
Jazz, is planned. / 11 pm; smart casual; no smoking area.

China City WC2 £25 **③**④④
25a Lisle St 0171-734 3388 4–3A
"Comfortable surroundings" and *"food that is different from
the bland chow prevalent in Chinatown"* make this huge
Chinese, set back in its own little courtyard, an *"above
average"* choice for the area. / 11.45 pm; no smoking area; Sun, no
lunch bookings.

Chinon W14 £36 **①**④④
23 Richmond Way 0171-602 4082 7–1C
"Absolutely fantastic" and *"original"* Gallic fare, with *"very
pronounced flavours"*, makes this obscure Shepherd's Bush
fixture *"a true find – if you can!"*; *"eccentric"* service,
though, contributes to a *"unique, and sometimes bizarre"*
atmosphere. / 10.45 pm; D only, closed Sun.

Chiswick Restaurant W4 £35 **②③**④
131-133 Chiswick High Rd 0181-994 6887 7–2B
"Great British-eclectic cooking, reasonably priced" makes it
worth braving the slightly *"bleak"* décor of what is otherwise
a *"perfect local restaurant"*. / 11 pm; closed Sat L & Sun D;
set pre-th. £21(FP).

Chor Bizarre W1 £36 ❸❸❷
16 Albemarle St   0171-629 9802   3–3C
*"Interestingly decorated" Mayfair Indian yearling, laden
with bric-a-brac, whose cooking is "tasty" and "authentic",
but "doesn't quite live up to the surroundings".* / 11.30 pm;
no smoking area; set Sun L £20(FP).

Christian's W4 £29 ❸❸❸
1 Station Pde   0181-995 0382   1–3A
*"Welcoming" Chiswick "local" whose ambitious Anglo-French
cooking, prepared in the open-plan kitchen, is hailed by some
locals; those who "always have great expectations, which are
always disappointed" had an experience similar to our own.*
/ 10.30 pm; closed Mon; closed Sun.

Christopher's WC2 £41 ❸❸❸
18 Wellington St   0171-240 4222   4–3D
*"Since the refit", a year or so ago, this "chic" surf 'n' turf
American – impressively housed in an "airy" period building in
Covent Garden – has "improved on all fronts"; it's still "rather
full of itself", though, and "a tad dear for what you get".*
/ 11.45 pm; closed Sun D; smart casual; set pre-th. £27(FP).

Chuen Cheng Ku W1 £25 ❸④④
17 Wardour St   0171-437 1398   4–3A
*"Extremely authentic dim sum" – a "huge choice" served
from criss-crossing trolleys – is the highlight at this enormous,
gaudy Chinatown landmark; at other times, there's no
particular reason to seek it out.* / 11.45 pm; no smoking area.

Churchill W8 £14 ❷④❸
119 Kensington Ch St   0171-792 1246   6–2B
*"Ideal for a quick and cheap Thai bite" – you get "great food
for the price" in the "very busy and smoky" annexe of this
otherwise undistinguished boozer, just off Notting Hill Gate;
you "need to book".* / 9.30 pm; closed Sun D; no Amex; no lunch
bookings.

Chutney Mary SW10 £37 ❷❸❸
535 King's Rd   0171-351 3113   5–4B
*"Excellent" and "unusual" cooking (latterly more regional
Indian, than Anglo–Indian in style) has made this obscurely
located outfit, on the Chelsea/Fulham fringe, one of the
best-reputed subcontinentals in town; a major makeover of its
formerly rather naff décor was completed just before we went
to press.* / 11.30 pm; no smoking area; set Sun L £25(FP).

Chutneys NW1 £16 ❸④❸
124 Drummond St   0171-388 0604   8–4C
*The "great-value buffet" of "basic, but cheap and filling"
veggie fare for a fiver (served at lunch and all day on Sunday)
is the reason to visit this simple Indian café, near Euston.*
/ 11 pm; no Amex & no Switch; not under 10 for Sun; set weekday L £10(FP).

Cibo W14 £41 ❷❷❸

3 Russell Gdns 0171-371 6271 7–1D

It's down to the "poor location", near the Olympia railway tracks, that this quality Italian is "sometimes a bit empty" – those who make the journey are rewarded by "huge plates" of "super" modern Italian cooking. / 11 pm; closed Sat L & Sun D; smart casual; set Sun L £28(FP).

Cicada EC1 £29 ④④❷

132-136 St John St 0171-608 1550 9–1B

"Slightly self-conscious", but agreeable Smithfield café packed with local loft-dwelling trendies; it's a place "not afraid to experiment" with its oriental-inspired cooking – what's "interesting" and "good value" to some is a "dreadful fusion" to others. / 10.45 pm; closed Sat L & Sun; no smoking area.

The Circle SE1 £22 – – –

Unit 13–15, Queen Elizabeth St 0171-407 1122 9–4D

This "featureless", new modern British outfit, located among the trendy flats behind Butler's Wharf, had a much-needed change of formula (from restaurant to brasserie) not long before we went to press. / 10.30 pm.

Circus W1 £41 ④❸④

1 Upper James St 0171-534 4000 3–2D

Expensively designed Soho newcomer which is understated to a fault – its potentially "cool" ambience is too widely thought "minimalist to the point of not having any", and the competent modern British fare is dismissed as being "generic"; great basement cocktail bar, though. / Midnight, Fri & Sat 12.30 am; closed Sun D.

City Brasserie EC3 £51 ④④❸

56 Mark Lane 0171-220 7094 9–3D

"One winces, even on expenses" at bills run up at this "overpriced" City basement; though some think its new Deco-ish setting a "great improvement", we agree with those who feel it's "not quite as cosy as the previous site". / 9 pm; closed Sat & Sun; smart casual; no booking in bar.

City Miyama EC4 £50 ❷❷④

17 Godliman St 0171-489 1937 9–3B

"Go for the sushi bar, but be prepared to pay for it", say fans of this smart, but soulless City establishment; the basement dining room is a lesser attraction. / 10 pm; closed Sat D & Sun.

CITY RHODES EC4 £51 ❶❷❸

New Street Sq 0171-583 1313 9–2A

Gary R's "amazingly competent" and "innovative" treatment of traditional dishes has made his "superbly well oiled" operation – in "bright" and "modern" premises at the foot of an office-block near Fleet Street – the top choice in town for a "special business lunch". / 9 pm; closed Sat & Sun.

Claridges Restaurant W1   £60   ④❷❷
Brook St   0171-629 8860   3–2B
*"Fall in love, with your guest or the place!" – the Art Deco
charms of this classic Mayfair hotel win it many admirers;
the traditional cooking provides "no surprises" (though
breakfasts are "great"). / 10.45 pm; jacket & tie.*

CLARKE'S W8   £46   ❶❶❷
124 Kensington Ch St   0171-221 9225   6–2B
*"Why go to new restaurants, when this one doesn't change"
– "few places match Sally Clarke's cooking" (with, in the
evenings, a no-choice menu) at this "sophisticated" modern
British pioneer; for the best atmosphere, "choose upstairs".
/ 10 pm; closed Sat & Sun; no smoking area.*

The Clerkenwell EC1   £29   ❸❸④
73 Clerkenwell Rd   0171-831 7595   9–1A
*"Designer" City-fringe venture, whose "good" Italianate food,
and "wide range of wines" lead some to recommend it as a
business lunch venue (but there are also warnings about
"designer prices"). / 10.45 pm; L only Mon-Fri; closed Sat & Sun.*

Club Gascon EC1   £30   – – –
57 West Smithfield   0171-253 5853   9–2B
*Mourad Mazouz has already achieved fame in London with
his eponymous yearling, Momo; to sample this new venture,
the beautiful people will have to head for trendy Smithfield,
where a menu of tapas-style dishes from south west France
is promised. / 11 pm; closed Sat L & Sun.*

Coast W1   £44   ❸④⑤
26b Albemarle St   0171-495 5999   3–3C
*Enthusiasm is waning for the "stark" and "incredibly noisy"
environment of this "hip and happening" ("pretentious")
converted car-showroom in Mayfair; "interesting" modern
British cooking provides some solace, but service is "uneven";
"don't eat downstairs at any price". / Midnight.*

Coffee Republic   £9   ❸❷❸
2 South Molton Street, W1   0171-629 4567   3–2B
37 Gt Marlborough Street, W1   0171-734 5529   3–2C
18 Garrick Street, WC2   0171-240 1323   4–3C
234 Strand Law Courts, WC2   0171-583 2456   2–2D
80 Strand, WC2   0171-836 6660   4–2D
8 Pembridge Road, W11   0171-229 6698   6–2B
58 Queensway, W2   0171-792 3600   6–2C
*It doesn't score quite as well overall, but this glossy, luxury
coffee chain has many fans who tout it as "far superior to
Seattle Coffee"; from the ratings, though, it's difficult to tell
them apart.*

Coins W11 £24 ❸④❷

105-107 Talbot Rd 0171-221 8099 6–1B
*"Essential Notting Hillbilly hang-out", with "average"
snack fare, "good coffee" and "great people-watching" –
"for brunch, get there early". / L only.*

The Collection SW3 £43 ④⑤❸

264 Brompton Rd 0171-225 1212 5–2C
*The "great bar" – rather than the mezzanine restaurant –
attracts "younger crowds" to this "lively" Brompton Cross
scene; the modern British cooking is "overpriced and
pretentious", and some experience "truly offensive" service.
/ 11.30 pm; closed Sun.*

Le Colombier SW3 £34 ④❸❸

145 Dovehouse St 0171-351 1155 5–2C
*This Gallic newcomer (on the site of Chelsea Square, RIP) was
launched in spring '98, thus assuring maximum benefit from
its "lovely", "sunny" terrace; it will be interesting, though, to
see whether the ordinary and "overpriced" bistro cooking
sees it through the winter. / 11 pm.*

Como Lario SW1 £34 ❸❷❷

22 Holbein Pl 0171-730 2954 5–2D
*For its fans – and there are many – the "best welcome in
town" makes this "crowded" fixture, off Sloane Square,
"another great Italian"; others (including us) say it's "just
normal". / 11.30 pm; closed Sun; smart casual.*

CONNAUGHT W1 £80 ❸❶❷

Carlos Pl 0171-499 7070 3–3B
*"Traditional cooking at its best" – in an Anglo-French style
extinct elsewhere – and "all-embracing" service make this
"magnificent" panelled Mayfair institution a true benchmark;
you would expect to (over)pay accordingly, and you do.
/ 10.45 pm; Grill closed Sat L; no Switch; jacket & tie for dinner;
jacket for lunch; appreciated if guests try to refrain from smoking; set Sun L
£54(FP).*

Conrad Hotel SW10 £41 ❸❷❸

Chelsea Harbour 0171-823 3000 5–4B
*The "terrace overlooking the Harbour" offers a pleasant
(but oddly "provincial") setting for this distant-Chelsea hotel's
"excellent, if slightly pricey", Sunday brunch (to which our
price and ratings relate). / 10.30 pm; no smoking area.*

The Cook House SW15 £33 ❸❷④

56 Lower Richmond Rd 0181-785 2300 10–1A
*"Short, but imaginative, regularly changing menus" draw
repeat custom to this small, modern British Putney venture,
in spite of décor bordering on "terrible"; BYO. / 11 pm; D only,
closed Sun & Mon; no Amex.*

Coopers Arms SW3 £22 ❸❸❷
87 Flood St 0171-376 3120 5–3C
"They've really got it right" at this *"informal"* Chelsea
pub/restaurant – *"good food", helpful staff"* and *"an
interesting bunch of regulars"; "good wine"*, too. / 10 pm;
no bookings Sun .

Coq d'Argent EC3 £47 ⑤④❸
I Poultry 0171-395 5000 9–2C
*More 'turkey' than coq – Conran Restaurants' flashy new City
eyrie, by Bank, pushes the exaltation of form over function to
the point of parody; given the sky-high prices, the brasserie
fare risibly lacks ambition.* / 11 pm; closed Sat L.

Cork & Bottle WC2 £26 ④❸❷
44-46 Cranbourn St 0171-734 7807 4–3B
*It's long been a favourite "rendezvous", but this cramped
cellar off Leicester Square is pricey, and its simple cooking is
increasingly "variable"; the "extensive" list of interesting wines
remains a feature.* / 11.30 pm; no smoking area; no booking after 6 pm.

Corney & Barrow £26 ❷❶④
116 St Martin's Lane, WC2 0171-655 9800 4–4B
*The area around Trafalgar Square is still something of a black
hole for restaurants, making the new branch of the stylish
City wine bar/restaurant chain, with its very competent
modern British cooking, a welcome local addition;
pity about the arctic setting.* / 11.15pm; closed Sun.

Costa's Fish Restaurant W8 £14 ❷❷④
18 Hillgate St 0171-727 4310 6–2B
*Size wise, it may be eclipsed by its neighbour, Geales, but
the "fresh, down-to-earth, uncomplicated" scoff at this
old-fashioned Notting Hill caff puts it on a par with the
better chippies in town.* / 10 pm; closed Mon & Sun; no credit cards.

Costa's Grill W8 £13 ❸❷❸
12-14 Hillgate St 0171-229 3794 6–2B
*Characterful, very long-established Greek restaurant, just off
Notting Hill Gate, which some say still offers "the best value
in the area".* / 10.30 pm; closed Sun; no credit cards.

Côte à Côte SW11 £17 ④④❸
74-75 Battersea Br Rd 0171-738 0198 5–4C
*For a big group outing on zero budget, this large Battersea
zoo has a rôle; "it's very dark", so some find difficulty
"seeing what you are eating" – no bad thing.* / 11 pm; no Amex.

Cottons NW1 £28 ④④❸
55 Chalk Farm Rd 0171-482 1096 8–2B
*Funky Camden Town Caribbean joint, whose young-at-heart
fans approve of the "enjoyable" (we'd say ordinary) cooking
and, more to the point, the list of cocktails.* / 11 pm, Thu-Sat
11.45 pm; no smoking area.

The County Hall Restaurant SE1   £39   ④❸④

Queens Walk   0171-902 8000   2–3D

In the old GLC building, this new hotel's restaurant (with river/Westminster views) offers modern British cooking which is good only in parts, in a setting of ponderous Edwardian stateliness; we have yet to get over the discovery that we had been charged £13.75 for a glass of champagne. / 11 pm; no smoking at breakfast.

The Cow W11   £36   ❷❸❸

89 Westbourne Park Rd   0171-221 0021   6–1B

"Small and cramped" – but "funky", "cosy" and "fun" – room over an oh-so-trendy Notting Hill pub, where the "very original" menu (particularly the "imaginative fish dishes") is "interestingly realised"; downstairs in the bar the "oysters and mussels are always good, as is the Guinness". / 11.30 pm; D only; no Amex.

Coyote Café W4   £24   ❸❸❸

2 Fauconberg Road   0181-742 8545   7–2A

A good "attempt to be different in suburbia", this deepest Chiswick hang-out (a few doors down from the landmark Bedlington Café) tries hard; the "filling" grub is fair by the dire standards of London Tex-Mexes. / 10 pm; no large bookings on Fri & Sat.

Cranks   £16   ⑤⑤⑤

23 Barrett St, W1   0171-495 1340   3–1B
8 Marshall St, W1   0171-437 9431   3–2D
9-11 Tottenham St, W1   0171-631 3912   2–1B
17-19 Great Newport St, WC2   0171-836 5226   4–3B
Unit 11, 8 Adelaide St, WC2   0171-836 0660   4–4C

"Wholesome" organic offerings win this revamped, long-established chain Brownie points from some; even fans admit it's "expensive", though, and many find its food "dismal", "mediocre", and "tasteless". / 7 pm - 11 pm; some branches closed part of weekend; some branches no credit cards; no smoking; no booking.

The Crescent SW3   £24   ❸❷❸

99 Fulham Rd   0171-225 2244   5–2C

A "most interesting wine list, with huge variety and value" is the highlight at this "trendy" (but "quiet") Brompton Cross bistro/wine bar, which also numbers "charming" service and an "inexpensive" snack menu amongst its attractions. / 11 pm; no booking.

THE CRITERION W1   £40   ❸⑤❶

Piccadilly Circus   0171-930 0488   3–3D

Thanks to its "stunning" neo-Byzantine décor, this is a "palace of a restaurant"; some fans of the generally "well executed" modern French cooking (overseen by Marco Pierre White) "won't go back", though, having encountered one of too many incidents of "outrageously rude" service. / Midnight, Sun 10.30 pm; set Sun L £27(FP).

The Cross Keys SW3   £31   ❸❸❷
1 Lawrence St   0171-349 9111   5–3C
*"Neatly tucked away" in Old Chelsea, this bijou
pub-conversion serves "surprisingly good" modern British fare;
its secret weapon, though, is that it's "always full of interesting
beautiful people who look as if they are enjoying themselves".*
/ 11 pm; set weekday L £19(FP).

Crown & Goose NW1   £23   ❸④❸
100 Arlington Rd   0171-485 8008   8–3B
*"Burgers to die for" are a key feature of this "great Camden
Town stalwart" – one of the first boozers in the locality to be
revamped as a gastropub, and still one of the best.* / 10 pm;
no credit cards.

Cuba Libre N1   £29   ⑤⑤❸
72 Upper St   0171-354 9998   8–3D
*"It's nice to go Cuban, but the food is really not very good",
at this "fun" and "crowded" Islington venue.* / 11 pm, Fri & Sat
12 am; no Amex.

Cucina NW3   £29   ❸❷❸
45a South End Rd   0171-435 7814   8–2A
*Hampstead devotees applaud this "real, buzzing
neighbourhood place" for its "delicious Italian-influenced
cooking" and its "friendly" service; visitors from afar tend to
be less impressed, and find the setting a little "overbright"
and "noisy".* / 10.30 pm, Fri & Sat 11 pm; closed Sun D; smart casual.

Cy W1   £44   ④❸④
3-5 Mill St   0171-629 8877   3–2C
*"Huge variations in the quality of dishes" rob this otherwise
pleasant Provençal newcomer, near Hanover Square, of the
following it might otherwise achieve.* / Midnight; closed Sun L.

Czech Club NW6   £20   ④④④
74 West End Ln   0171-372 5251   1–1B
*Endearingly anachronistic West Hampstead dining room,
which serves cheap, if slightly rough-and-ready, fodder,
washed down with fine Czech beer.* / 9.30 pm; closed Mon (ex bank
hols) Sat D & Sun D; no credit cards.

Da Mario SW7   £25   ❸❸❸
15 Gloucester Rd   0171-584 9078   5–1B
*This "reliable and friendly" stand-by (actually a PizzaExpress
in disguise), just round the corner from the Royal Albert Hall,
wins praise for its "great atmosphere and pizza"; (its disco
cellar also has its attractions for those organising a budget
dine-and-boogie bash).* / 11.30 pm; no Switch; book for disco.

Da Pierino SW7   £20   ❸❸④
37 Thurloe Pl   0171-581 3770   5–2C
*"Consistently good value" is to be had at this very informal,
family-run Italian diner, just by South Kensington tube.*
/ 11.15 pm; closed Mon; no Amex & no Switch.

Dakota W11 £ 35 ❸④❸

127 Ledbury Rd   0171-792 9191   6–1B

*"Imaginative" south west USA cooking wins many plaudits
for this ultra "hip" Notting Hill newcomer (which recently
installed a "great terrace"); gripes include sometimes
"unmemorable" fare, oddly "blank" décor, and service
which, though "friendly", can be "incompetent". / 10.45 pm;
no bookings for 8-8.30 pm; set weekday L £22(FP).*

Dan's SW3 £ 36 ❸❷❶

119 Sydney St   0171-352 2718   5–3C

*The "intimate, dark, and cosy" ambience (and pretty garden)
make devotees of this "romantic" townhouse swoon with joy;
we're with those who say it's "fine if you like that kind of
thing" – "a typical Chelsea haunt" which may have
"excellent" service, but whose cooking is only tolerable.
/ 10.30 pm; closed Sat L & Sun.*

Daphne NW1 £ 24 ❸❷❸

83 Bayham St   0171-267 7322   8–3C

*"Caring" hosts, reliable nosh and a cosy atmosphere make
this long-established Camden Town Greek (with a roof terrace
in summer) "a good local". / 11.30 pm; closed Sun; no Amex.*

Daphne's SW3 £ 42 ④④❷

110-112 Draycott Ave   0171-589 4257   5–2C

*It's no longer the see-and-be-seen place it once was, but,
for many, a "beautiful" and "romantic" atmosphere lingers
at this pretty Brompton Cross Italian; the cooking "varies
enormously", though, and the hallmark "awful", "rude"
service has yet to be fully eradicated. / 11.30 pm.*

Daquise SW7 £ 19 ④❸④

20 Thurloe St   0171-589 6117   5–2C

*"A one-off", this "totally Polish" fixture, by South Kensington
tube, dishes up "good, cheap" food at "student prices" to
an "eccentric clientele" in surroundings that are "homely,
if rather gloomy". / 10.45 pm; no Amex; no smoking area; set weekday L
£7(FP).*

De Cecco SW6 £ 30 ❷④❷

189 New King's Rd   0171-736 1145   10–1B

*Those who remember the glory days, not so long ago, of this
Parson's Green trattoria say "it's lost its charm"; still, it retains
much of its "buzzy, young and fun" spirit, and "there's a good
variety of pastas and other dishes". / 10.45 pm; closed Sun.*

Deals   **£ 28**   ⑤④④
14-16 Foubert's Pl, W1   0171-287 1001   3–2C
Chelsea Harbour, SW10   0171-795 1001   5–4B
Broadway Centre, W6   0181-563 1001   7–2C
"A clown for the kids" (on a weekend visit) is the main –
some might say the only – attraction of a trip to these
would-be upmarket diners, whose food is "expensive" and
"not very good". / 11 pm, W1 & W6 – Sat & Sun 11.30 pm;
W1 closed Sun D.

Del Buongustaio SW15   **£ 31**   ❶❷❷
283 Putney Br Rd   0181-780 9361   10–2B
Nothing in the "grotty façade" hints at the "marvellous"
and "authentic" cooking served at this "friendly and
unpretentious" Putney Italian; given that it offers the "perfect
cost/quality ratio" there's no surprise that it's "sometimes too
busy". / 11.30 pm, Sun 10.30 pm; closed Sat L, Jun-Aug closed Sun L.

La Delizia   **£ 24**   ❷④❸
63-65 Chelsea Manor St, SW3   0171-376 4111   5–3C
Farmers Mkt, Sydney St, SW3   0171-351 6701   5–3C
246 Old Brompton Rd, SW5   0171-373 6085   5–2A
"Reliable" pizzas (together with a few pasta and more
substantial dishes) make this small, "trendy" Chelsea chain
a superior stand-by; the Farmer's Market branch (mainly al
fresco) is the summer spiritual home of the capital's younger
Eurotrash. / Midnight; no credit cards; no booking in summer.

dell'Ugo W1   **£ 35**   ⑤⑤④
56 Frith St   0171-734 8300   4–2A
Service has always "taken an age" at this large
Mediterranean-inspired Soho landmark; the cooking, though,
has now "gone downhill" to such an extent as to kill off any
lingering enthusiasm for what was once a fun central
stand-by. / Midnight; closed Sun.

The Depot SW14   **£ 27**   ④④❷
Mortlake High St   0181-878 9462   10–1A
"Fabulous views" make you "feel away from it all" at this
family-friendly brasserie which has a "great location" near
Barnes Bridge – "try for a table with a river view"; the
Mediterranean cooking is "nothing special". / 11 pm;
no smoking area.

Diverso W1   **£ 41**   ❷❷❸
85 Piccadilly   0171-491 2222   3–4C
This "opulently rustic" Italian, not far from the Ritz, provides
"quality" cooking, "attentive" service and "well spaced" tables
– all of which equip it well for business encounters. / 11.30 pm;
closed Sun L.

Diwana Bhel-Poori House NW1   **£14**   ❶④④
121 Drummond St   0171-387 5556   8–4C
*"Concentrate on the delicious and plentiful food, not the
décor"* at this estimable veggie Indian near Euston, in whose
'60s-canteen setting supporters find *"an uncompromising
charm of its own"; "fabulous buffet lunch".* / 11.30 pm;
no smoking area; Fri–Sun no booking; set weekday L £9(FP).

Dixie's Bar & Grill SW11   **£19**   ⑤④❸
25 Battersea Rs   0171-228 7984   10–2C
The *"local, thriving atmosphere"* is the strength of this
"casual" Cajun-style Battersea joint; the food is *"very
average".* / 11.30 pm.

Dôme   **£21**   ⑤④④
57-59 Old Compton St, W1   0171-287 0770   4–3A
32 Long Acre, WC2   0171-379 8650   4–2C
8 Charing Cross Rd, WC2   0171-240 5556   4–4B
354 King's Rd, SW3   0171-352 2828   5–3B
194-196 Earl's Court Rd, SW5   0171-835 2200   5–2A
Kensington Ct, W8   0171-937 6655   5–1A
341 Upper St, N1   0171-226 3414   8–3D
58-62 Heath St, NW3   0171-431 0399   8–1A
57-59 Charterhouse St, EC1   0171-336 6484   9–1A
4 St Paul's Churchyard, EC4   0171-489 0767   9–2B
"Poor service and very average food" let down this *"relaxed"*
and often *"buzzing"* chain; the *"fun"* décor (Rive Gauche,
circa 1935) works surprisingly well, though, and its branches
make *"good meeting-places".* / 10.30 pm-11 pm; EC1 closed Sat &
Sun; some restaurants have no smoking areas.

don Fernando's TW9   **£22**   ❸❷❷
27f The Quadrant   0181-948 6447   1–4A
Large, *"lively"* and *"consistent"* Spaniard which is one of the
best bets in Richmond (it's right by the BR station); its tapas
are *"not subtle, but tasty".* / 11 pm; no Amex.

Don Pepe NW8   **£23**   ❸❸❸
99 Frampton St   0171-262 3834   8–4A
It *"feels like Spain"*, at this *"authentic"* tapas bar (the oldest
in town) and restaurant, near Lords. / Midnight; closed Sun.

Dorchester Grill
Dorchester Hotel W1   **£64**   ❷①❷
53 Park Ln   0171-317 6336   3–3A
"Heaven" for traditionalists – this vintage Mayfair dining room
(decorated in Spanish Baronial style) *"cannot be beaten for
smoked salmon and roast beef"*, and the like, with the
"friendly, attentive and professional" service being amongst
the best in town. / 11 pm; smart casual.

Dorchester, Oriental
Dorchester Hotel W1   £66   ❷③④
53 Park Ln   0171-317 6328   3–3A
*Enthusiasm is waning a little for the capital's grandest
Chinese; it has never had much atmosphere, and those who
laud "quite simply superb" cooking are losing ground to those
who find it "vastly overpriced". / 11 pm; closed Sat L & Sun;
smart casual.*

La Dordogne W4   £35   ❷❷❷
5 Devonshire Rd   0181-747 1836   7–2A
*"Bring your passport – you're really in France" when you
visit this archetypal, "old-fashioned and comfortable"
neighbourhood restaurant, whose "reliable" cooking has
made it a Chiswick fixture for years. / 11 pm; closed Sat L & Sun L.*

Dove W6   £19   ❸④❷
19 Upper Mall   0181-748 5405   7–2B
*Thai cooking is no more at this "wonderful" Dickensian
Hammersmith pub on the river, where new management is
gently ringing the culinary changes; "you have to fight through
the crowd" to get fed. / 10 pm; no Amex; no booking.*

Dover Street W1   £40   ⑤⑤❸
8-9 Dover St   0171-629 9813   3–3C
*"It's great to eat to a band and then get up and dance",
at this Mayfair basement – one of the few places in town
offering a dine 'n' boogie package; the food "really is poor",
though, and "expensive", too. / 3 am; closed Sat L & Sun; no jeans.*

Down Mexico Way W1   £27   ⑤④❷
25 Swallow St   0171-437 9895   3–3D
*"Cocktails compensate" for the "lousy" food at this vibrant
"Latin" bar/restaurant, just off Piccadilly Circus; you don't
have to be an architecture buff to appreciate the "lovely" tiled
interior – a hangover from the '20s, when this was London's
first Spanish restaurant. / 11.45 pm, Sun 10.30 pm.*

Drones SW1   £38   ⑤④⑤
1 Pont St   0171-259 6166   2–4A
*It has "so much potential", but this smart Belgravian has
utterly lost the plot – "so bland" modern British cooking and
a "snobby" attitude conspire to produce a total "lack of
atmosphere". / 10.15 pm.*

The Eagle EC1   £22   ❷④❷
159 Farringdon Rd   0171-837 1353   9–1A
*"Excellent" Mediterranean cooking maintains the lofty
reputation of this "very good value" superpub, near The
Guardian – it's "hack city" in there; the atmosphere is always
"buzzing", but some find it too "squashed" and "smoky" to
be really enjoyable. / 10.30 pm; closed Sun; no credit cards; no booking.*

East One EC1 £25 ❸❷❷
175-179 St John St   0171-566 0088   9–1A
It's "fun watching the wok-jocks" (who "try to make
something half-decent out of your weird selection of
ingredients") at this trendily-designed Smithfield oriental –
the results tend to be above-average, too, for the type of
place. / 11 pm; closed Sat L & Sun D.

Eat £9 ❷❷❸
3 Duke Of York Street, SW1   0171-930 0960   3–3D
39 Villiers Street, WC2   0171-839 2282   4–4D
170 Fleet St, EC4   0171-583 2585   9–2A
"Better than Prêt", say converts to this "innovative" fledgling
chain of "sandwich, coffee and soup emporia"; can they keep
it up? /—

Ebury Street Wine Bar SW1 £33 ❸④④
139 Ebury St   0171-730 5447   2–4A
"Not brilliant, but straightforward" cooking has long made
this Pimlico fixture "a great neighbourhood restaurant"; it
"can have its off-days", though. / 10.30 pm.

Eco SW4 £24 ❶④❸
162 Clapham High St   0171-978 1108   10–2D
"Exceptional pizzas" – "when they eventually arrive" –
and the "fun" and "trendy" atmosphere, make it "essential to
book" at this "deafeningly noisy" Clapham phenomenon.
/ 11 pm, Sat & Sun 11.30 pm; Mon-Fri only, no smoking area.

Ed's Easy Diner £21 ❸❷❷
12 Moor St, W1   0171-439 1955   4–2A
Trocadero, W1   0171-287 1951   3–3D
362 King's Rd, SW3   0171-352 1956   5–3B
16 Hampstead High St, NW3   0171-431 1958   8–1A
"Great shakes", "good quality burgers", and "non-greasy
chips" make these "Happy Days"-style diners a popular
option for a "fast and friendly" snack. / Midnight, Fri & Sat 1 am,
W1 Sun 11 pm; no booking.

Efes Kebab House £24 ④❸❸
1) 80 Great Titchfield St, W1   0171-636 1953   2–1B
2) 175-177 Gt Portland St, W1   0171-436 0600   2–1B
For some reason, "food and service have deteriorated" at
these favourite Marylebone Turks (otherwise "unchanged
since about 1972"); "good quality grilled meat" and meze
can still be had, though, and their "cheerful" atmosphere
(with belly-dancing nightly at Efes II) continues to make them
popular party places. / 11.30 pm, Fri & Sat 3 am; I closed Sun.

1837 at Brown's Hotel W1 £72 ❸⑤❸

Albemarle Street   0171-408 1837   3–3C

*Pretentious pricing and "poor" and "obsequious" service have
marred the relaunch of this Mayfair dining room – a shame
as it offers some "imaginative" modern French cooking, and a
"stunning selection of wines by the glass". / 10.30 pm; closed Sat L
& Sun; no smoking area; set weekday L £36(FP).*

Elena's L'Etoile W1 £38 ❷❶❶

30 Charlotte St   0171-636 7189   2–1C

*This "old-fashioned", but "rather good" "Parisian"-style
bourgeois Fitzrovian has real "personality", largely thanks
to Elena Salvoni, doyenne of London's maîtresses d'. / 11 pm;
closed Sat L & Sun; smart casual.*

Elistano SW3 £26 ❷❶❶

25-27 Elystan St   0171-584 5248   5–2C

*A "fun", "loud", "lively" atmosphere, "friendly" staff and
Chelsea's best "local-Italian food" make this "easy-going"
back street spot "good all round", and "excellent value".
/ 11 pm; closed Sat L & Sun.*

Elvis Gracelands Palace SE15 £25 ④④❸

883 Old Kent Rd   0171-639 3961   1–3D

*Elvis lives! – disguised as a chef in an otherwise
ordinary-looking New Cross Chinese; as a native of Memphis,
it's perhaps no surprise that his oriental cooking skills are a
touch limited, but the King singing – nightly – is certainly
quite an experience. / 11.30 pm; D only, ex Fri & Sat, when open L & D.*

Emile's £24 ❷❶❸

144 Wandsworth Br Rd, SW6   0171-736 2418   10–1B
96-98 Felsham Rd, SW15   0181-789 3323   10–2B

*"Well executed" British food, "from a regularly changing
menu" and "at reasonable prices" makes these "very
friendly" and "mellow" establishments "good value"; their
locations in Fulham and Putney, mark the beginnings of
suburbia. / 11 pm; D only; closed Sun; no Amex.*

Enak Enak SW11 £29 ❸④❸

56 Lavender Hill   0171-924 3148   10–1C

*"Barking mad" TV chef Nancy Lam's Clapham HQ is a
small, no-frills establishment that's "not for the faint-hearted";
we're with those who think the cooking "overrated", but, still,
it's best to book. / 9 pm; D only, closed Sun-Tue; no Switch; no smoking.*

The Engineer NW1 £32 ❸⑤❷

65 Gloucester Ave   0171-722 0950   8–3B

*Especially for its "great Sunday brunch – if you can get a
table" – this Primrose Hill superpub (with a fab garden)
remains a "hang-out" of choice with trendy north Londoners;
"work is needed on the service", though – it can be
appallingly "slow". / 11 pm; no Amex.*

English Garden SW3 £ 44 ❸❷❷
10 Lincoln St   0171-584 7272   5–2D
*An "oasis" in the busiest part of Chelsea, this "lovely"
townhouse generally gets the thumbs-up, especially for its
delightful conservatory; though most praise the modern British
cooking, the odd "complete failure" is not unknown. / 11.15 pm;
set Sun L £28(FP).*

English House SW3 £ 44 ④❸❸
3 Milner St   0171-584 3002   5–2D
*Cramped and rather twee Chelsea townhouse, decorated in
the style which Americans think typically English; it retains a
small band of enthusiasts, who are prepared to tolerate the
expensive and pedestrian cooking for the "wonderfully cosy"
atmosphere. / 11.15 pm, Sun 10 pm; set weekday L £23(FP).*

Enoteca Turi SW15 £ 32 ❷❷❸
28 Putney High St   0181-785 4449   10–2B
*"Excellent" cooking at a reasonable price, and a "brilliant
choice of wine to suit an ever-changing menu" is winning
growing support for this "cramped", but "friendly" Italian,
near Putney Bridge. / 11 pm; closed Sat L & Sun; smart casual.*

The Enterprise SW3 £ 32 ❸❸❶
Walton St   0171-584 3148   5–2C
*"Great atmosphere, great people, great fun", say regulars
at this "crowded", "smart", "see-and-be-seen" Knightsbridge
boozer-conversion; by local standards, the modern British
cooking is "good value for money". / 11 pm; no Amex;
smart casual; book Mon-Fri L only.*

Esarn Kheaw W12 £ 22 ❷④④
314 Uxbridge Rd   0181-743 8930   7–1B
*"Good and spicy" northern Thai cooking still gives rise to
favourable reports on this Shepherd's Bush oriental, though
there were a few disappointments this year; service can be
"slow". / 11 pm; closed Sat L & Sun L; no Switch.*

L'Escargot W1 £ 39 ❷❷❸
48 Greek St   0171-437 2679   4–2A
*Regularly "surpassing expectations" with its very "well
presented" modern French cooking and "exceptional" service,
this former Soho classic is finally beginning to make waves
again; the brasserie setting is still perhaps a mite bland;
upstairs the pricier Picasso room has prints by the master.
/ 11.30 pm; closed Sat L & Sun.*

L'Escargot Doré W8 £ 40 ❸❷④
2 Thackeray St   0171-937 8508   5–1A
*Little-known Gallic basement, off Kensington High Street;
"good, if not cheap". / 11.30 pm; closed Sat L & Sun; smart casual; set
weekday L £26(FP).*

L'Estaminet WC2 £ 36 ❷❷❸

14 Garrick St   0171-379 1432   4–3C

Some think we are "harsh" in describing this "cosy and typically French" Covent Garden outfit as 'suburban'; whatever the style verdict, the dependable Gallic fare ("the best cheeseboard", in particular) wins praise, and the place makes a useful pre- or post-theatre stand-by. / 11 pm; closed Sun; set pre-th. £20(FP).

Euphorium N1 £ 35 ❸❷❸

203 Upper St   0171-704 6909   8–2D

"Still as good after the expansion", say fans of this decidedly "modern" Islingtonian, which is praised for its "inventive" cooking and "friendly and professional" service. / 10.30 pm; closed Sun D; no smoking area.

Fakhreldine W1 £ 37 ❸❷④

85 Piccadilly   0171-493 3424   3–4C

Large and glitzy Mayfair Lebanese, which gets into its swing as the evening wears on; it's a "favourite" for some, but it's "pricey", and disappointments are not unknown. / Midnight; smart casual.

Il Falconiere SW7 £ 26 ❸❷❸

84 Old Brompton Rd   0171-589 2401   5–2B

It may be a "bog-standard" trattoria of a certain vintage, but this "reasonably priced" South Kensington location "keeps its regulars coming" (and those in the know go for the "very good-value set menus"). / 11.45 pm; closed Sun.

La Famiglia SW10 £ 39 ❸④❷

7 Langton St   0171-351 0761   5–3B

"Cool and arrogant" service is the only real drawback at this pricey, but "reliable" World's End trattoria, which – with the help of its particularly charming garden – has long attracted a "star-studded" clientele. / 11.45 pm.

Il Faro W1 £ 35 ❸❷❸

10 Charlotte Street   0171-636 2889   2–1C

"Mildly quirky", "small, cosy and candlelit" Fitzrovia Italian which – though a newcomer – is pretty traditional in style; it's quite a good place (and "good on fish"), if a bit pricey. / 11 pm; closed Sat L.

Fashion Café W1 £ 31 ⑤⑤⑤

5-6 Coventry St   0171-287 5888   4–4A

"Disastrous" West End theme-diner; let's hope that, like all fashions, this "nightmare" – "a simply awful experience in all regards" – passes very soon. / Midnight; no smoking area; no booking on Sat.

Fat Boy's W4　　　　　　　　£ 24　　❸❸❸
10a Edensor Rd　0181-994 8089　10–1A
"Very fresh" Thai cooking means this "good, cheap" Chiswick "oasis" is "always buzzing"; it's licensed, but you can BYO. / 11 pm; closed Sat L; no credit cards.

Faulkner's E8　　　　　　　　£ 21　　❶❸⑤
424-426 Kingsland Rd　0171-254 6152　1–2D
"Worth a trip" – this "large and clean, if not exactly trendy", East Ender is a worthy contender for the title of "best fish 'n' chips in London". / 10 pm; no credit cards.

The Fence EC1　　　　　　　　£ 34　　❸❷❸
67-69 Cowcross St　0171-250 3414　9–1A
"Always busy" Farringdon bar/restaurant that is "fine if you want loud music, and good wine" and "one of the few places in the City with a nice garden"; no one pretends the grub is more than "OK". / 10 pm; closed Sat & Sun.

Feng Shang NW1　　　　　　　£ 30　　❸❷❷
Opp 15 Prince Albert Rd　0171-485 8137　8–3B
For a "special night out", this floating Chinese barge – in a "great setting" at the tip of Regent's Park – makes a good venue; the food is superior, for the type of place. / 11 pm; no Switch.

Ffiona's W8　　　　　　　　　£ 25　　❸❷❷
51 Kensington Ch St　0171-937 4152　5–1A
Ffiona makes a "very hospitable" hostess, and her Kensington bistro offers "wholesome" cooking in a "homely" atmosphere. / 11.30 pm; D only ; closed Sat L; no Amex & no Cheques.

**The Fifth Floor at
Harvey Nichols SW1**　　　　　£ 49　　④❸❷
Knightsbridge　0171-235 5250　5–1D
As ever, the modern British cooking at this "spacious, light" room atop the AbFab department store "promises much and delivers less"; still, it makes a pleasant place for a Knightsbridge lunch, with more than its fair share of "beautiful people". / 11.30 pm; closed Sun D.

**Fifth Floor at
Harvey Nichols (Café) SW1**　　£ 31　　④④❷
Knightsbridge　0171-823 1839　5–1D
The simple food is "decent, but very predictable" and, of course, rather pricey at this stylish, but "easy going" café; nonetheless, it makes a useful Knightsbridge stand-by. / 10.30 pm; closed Sun D; book eve only.

Fileric £ 9 ❷❷④
57 Old Brompton Rd, SW7 0171-584 2967 5–2C
12 Queenstown Rd, SW8 0171-720 4844 10–1C
"Fabulous pastries" (and good snacks) make it worth seeking out these "very cramped" pâtisseries in Battersea and, for maximum Gallic authenticity, South Kensington. / 8 pm; no booking.

Fina Estampa SE1 £ 27 ❷❸⑤
150 Tooley St 0171-403 1342 9–4D
The "decor is wanting", but otherwise this "great Peruvian", near Tower Bridge, is highly praised for its "generous portions" of "different" grub. / 10.30 pm; closed Sun.

La Finca £ 19 ❸④❷
96-98 Pentonville Rd, N1 0171-837 5387 8–3D
185 Kennington Ln, SE11 0171-735 1061 10–1D
"A few language problems" aside, these "loud" and "lively" bars (both occupying gastronomic wastelands) provide "reasonably priced", "tasty" tapas and "excellent atmosphere". / 11.15 pm; Fri & Sat N1 1.30 am, SE11 11.30 pm.

First Floor W11 £ 36 ⑤⑤④
186 Portobello Rd 0171-243 0072 6–1B
"A definite has-been" – this once fashionable Notting Hill joint now plumbs the depths with "pretentious", vastly "overpriced" cooking and "patronising" service. / 11.30 pm.

Fishnets SW6 £ 36 ❸❷⑤
Chelsea Village, Fulham Rd 0171-565 1430 5–4A
Quite ambitious, but monstrously misjudged new fish restaurant – part of the grimly glitzy new Stamford Bridge development; a dearth of feedback seems to confirm our view that no sane person (other than those who edit guides, of course) would ever seek it out. / 10.30 pm.

Florians N8 £ 30 ④❸❷
4 Topsfield Parade 0181-348 8348 1–1C
This "crowded" Hornsey Italian may be "a good local, especially the bar", but the cooking in the restaurant is "mediocre". / 10.45 pm; no Amex.

La Fontana SW1 £ 42 ❸❸④
101 Pimlico Rd 0171-730 6630 5–2D
This long-established, family-owned Pimlico Italian wins a corner in the hearts of its devotees with its "olde world charm" and, in season, the house speciality – "excellent truffles"; prices are "elevated", though, and some think the place is getting "frayed at the edges". / 11 pm; no Switch.

Food for Thought WC2   £ 15   ❷❸④
31 Neal St   0171-836 0239 4–2C
"Fight for a table" at this north-Covent Garden veggie
basement, whose *"consistently good and healthy"* grub comes
very *"cheap"*; shame some of the staff are so *"grim"* and
"surly". / 8.15 pm, Sun 3.45 pm; no credit cards; no smoking; no booking.

Football Football SW1   £ 25   ⑤⑤⑤
57/60 Haymarket   0171-930 9970 2–2C
Some say it has *"great atmosphere, if you're a fan"*, but,
from the majority of reporters, the message is Ref', please
call time on this *"horrific"* West End theme-diner, which
manages to achieve *"awful"* standards of everything.
/ 10 pm, Fri & Sat 11 pm, Sun 9 pm; smart casual; no smoking area.

Footstool SW1   £ 31   ⑤④❸
St John's, Smith Sq   0171-222 2779 2–4C
Recently revamped Westminster crypt where it's a
shame they didn't refurbish the *"truly dire"* standards of the
"incompetent" staff and *"outrageous"* food, both of which
continue to *"go rapidly downhill"*. / L only but buffet concert eves;
closed Sat & Sun except when eve concerts; no smoking area.

Formula Veneta SW10   £ 34   ❸❷❸
14 Hollywood Rd   0171-352 7612 5–3B
"Good pasta" is a particular attraction of this fashionable
younger-crowd Chelsea side street Italian, where the service
is *"great"* if you know the owner – *"questionable"* if not;
the *"garden in summer is wonderful"*. / 11.15 pm; closed Sun.

The Foundation SW1   £ 33   ❸④⑤
Knightsbridge   0171-201 8000 5–1D
Some are *"pleasantly surprised"* by the quality of the designer
bites at Harvey Nics' basement restaurant; the over-cool
styling creates an arctic atmosphere, though, making this a
place *"just for snacking"*. / 11 pm; closed Sun D.

Four Regions SE1   £ 29   ❸❸❸
County Hall   0171-928 0988 2–3D
"Eat outside in summer", and you can have a good
standard Chinese meal while enjoying fine views of the Palace
of Westminster; eat inside, in this former GLC banqueting
suite, and the attraction is less apparent. / 10.45 pm.

The Four Seasons W2   £ 21   ❸④❸
84 Queensway   0171-229 4320 6–2C
"Excellent roast duck, pork and chicken" are amongst the
superior dishes offered at this not particularly welcoming
Bayswater Chinese. / 11.15 pm.

Fox & Anchor EC1 £21 ❷④❷
115 Charterhouse St 0171-253 4838 9–1B
*"The greatest breakfast" ("black pudding to die for") with
"a good pint", too, can be had at this famed Smithfield
boozer.* / 11 pm; closed Sat L (but open Sat bkfast) & Sun.

The Fox Reformed N16 £22 ❸❸❸
176 Stoke Newington Ch St 0171-254 5975 1–1C
*"Relaxed, eccentric" Stoke Newington wine bar (with a "nice",
if small, garden), whose pleasant British cooking and good
wines makes it a "great local".* / 10.30 pm.

Foxtrot Oscar SW3 £28 ④④④
79 Royal Hospital Rd 0171-352 7179 5–3D
*"Everything is fairly mediocre, but the overall experience is
good" at this "relaxed, mid-priced venue" – "an old friend"
for its toffish Chelsea crowd; culinarily, the "burgers are OK,
the rest is in the realms of school dinners".* / 11.30 pm.

Francofill SW7 £24 ❸❸④
1 Old Brompton Rd 0171-584 0087 5–2C
*Some are "pleasantly surprised" by this "good value and good
fun" snackery opposite South Kensington tube, though there
are quibbles that is has "become too expensive for the cheap
bistro it's supposed to be".* / 11 pm; no smoking area.

Frederick's N1 £36 ❸❷❷
106 Camden Pas 0171-359 2888 8–3D
*This long-established Islington institution's modern British
cooking "is still good" (if by no means remarkable), but its
most notable attraction is the "beautiful" conservatory –
an ideal setting for a special occasion.* / 11.30 pm; closed Sun;
smart casual; no smoking area; set weekday L £24(FP).

French House W1 £31 ❸❷❸
49 Dean St 0171-437 2477 4–3A
*"Different" dining room, above a famous Soho pub, whose
performance is patchy, but improving; it offers "decent"
modern British cooking from a "limited" menu.* / 11.15 pm;
closed Sun.

Frocks E9 £28 ❸④❷
95 Lauriston Rd 0181-986 3161 1–2D
*"I know of no better place for brunch", say East End fans
of this English bistro – "a favourite local haunt after a walk
across Victoria Park"; when busy, the service can be "terrible".*
/ 11 pm; closed Sun D; no Sunday bookings.

Front Page SW3 £24 ❸❷❷
35 Old Church St 0171-352 2908 5–3C
*Some find it a bit "too Chelsea", but this very agreeable
backwater pub offers "interesting and good value
Euro-English fun and food".* / 10 pm; no booking.

Fryer's Delight WC1 £ 8 ❷③④
19 Theobald's Rd 0171-405 4114 2–1D
"Hundreds of cabbies can't be wrong" – this *"timeless and authentic chippy"*, behind Gray's Inn, serves up *"the best fish 'n' chips near the West End"*, and at *"knock-down prices"*, too. / 10 pm; no credit cards.

Fuego EC3 £ 25 ❸④④
1a Pudding Ln 0171-929 3366 9–3C
Despite the "dreary" setting, this basement Spaniard (by the Monument) is "a good laugh" – it *"gets very packed"* – and provides a *"more than adequate selection of tapas"*. / 9.30 pm; closed Sat & Sun; smart casual.

Fung Shing WC2 £ 33 ❶④⑤
15 Lisle St 0171-437 1539 4–3A
The *"best Chinese in town"* has long been the reputation of this Chinatown luminary and – for seafood in particular – it lives up to its billing; despite some efforts with the décor, it's still *"cramped"* and *"dingy"*, and service is erratic. / 11.30 pm.

Futures EC2 £ 24 ❸❸❸
2 Exchange Sq 0171-638 6341 9–1D
"Buzzing" veggie bar/restaurant in Broadgate, *"great for a speedy City lunch"*. / L only; closed Sat & Sun; no credit cards; no smoking except bkfast.

Futures EC3 £ 9 ❷❸–
8 Botolph Alley 0171-623 4529 9–3C
Shrewd City workers know that the veggie fare at this smart take-away near the Monument *"beats a sandwich any day"*; (and it also does *"the best breakfast in the Square Mile"*). / L only; closed Sat & Sun; no credit cards; no smoking; no booking.

Galicia W10 £ 22 ❸④❸
323 Portobello Rd 0181-969 3539 6–1A
"Simple", *"very authentic"*, *"no-nonsense"* North Kensington tapas bar serving *"OK"* food; waiters range from *"friendly"* to *"moody"*. / 11.30 pm; closed Mon; set Sun L £12(FP).

Garlic & Shots W1 £ 27 ④❸④
14 Frith St 0171-734 9505 4–2A
"Providing you don't mind garlic breath", and like your drinking-dens seedy, this quirky Soho dive (where all dishes – including the ice cream – are spiked with the pungent root) is certainly different, and can be good fun. / 11.15 pm, Fri & Sat 12.15 am; D only; no Amex; no booking.

Gastro SW4 £ 22 ④❸❶
67 Venn St 0171-627 0222 10–2D
"Lots of fun, no fuss and no frills" – this *"truly Gallic"* café/bistro, opposite the Clapham Picture House, is a classic *"Sunday morning"* sort of place (although the *"authentic country cooking"* served of a *"candlelit"* evening also has its fans). / Midnight; no credit cards; no smoking area; only groups of 15+.

The Gasworks SW6   £27   ⑤④❶
87 Waterford Rd   0171-736 3830   5–4A
*"Eat before you go" – the food's "gruesome" – "for a great
night out" at this "weird", decadent Fulham institution, whose
antique-infested room has been a "very original" party choice
for years.* / 11 pm; D only; closed Mon & Sun; no credit cards.

The Gate W6   £24   ❶❶❷
51 Queen Caroline St   0181-748 6932   7–2C
*"Brilliant", "beautifully presented" vegetarian food –
London's best, of its type – and a "lively" atmosphere make
it worthwhile ("even for non-veggies") to truffle out this
obscurely located Hammersmith spot.* / 10.45 pm; closed Sat L
& Sun L.

El Gaucho SW3   £24   ❸❸❸
Chelsea Farmers' Mkt, 125 Sydney St   0171-376 8514   5–3C
*"Still the best steaks", say supporters of this "lively" Chelsea
Argentinian, housed in a "rustic" shed in the Farmers Market
(and with great outside tables on sunny days); BYO.* / 11 pm;
no credit cards.

Gaucho Grill   £35   ❷❷❷
19-25 Swallow St, W1   0171-734 4040   3–3D
64 Heath Street, NW3   0171-431 8222   8–1A
*The "best Argentinian steaks" win strong praise for this
"funkily decorated" duo (Mayfair, and now Hampstead) of
"slickly" run South American grills.* /—

Gaudi EC1   £38   ④④④
63 Clerkenwell Rd   0171-608 3220   9–1A
*"Eclectically" decorated Spanish Clerkenwell yearling
whose standards have been erratic – some find "flavourful,
well prepared, imaginative" cooking, but others decry a
"dreadful" experience.* / 10.30 pm; closed Sat & Sun.

LE GAVROCHE W1   £94   ❷❷❸
43 Upper Brook St   0171-408 0881   3–2A
*Thanks to Michel Roux Jr's fine cooking, and the "formal,
but flawless" service, London's oldest "shrine to classic
gastronomy", in Mayfair, is still pronounced "heavenly" by
its many acolytes; heretics tend to dwell on the
"in-need-of-a-revamp" basement setting.* / 11 pm;
closed Sat & Sun; jacket & tie; set weekday L £40(FP).

Gay Hussar W1   £33   ❸❷❷
2 Greek St   0171-437 0973   4–2A
*"Comfort food and olde worlde service" make this 'old Soho'
Hungarian, rich with socialist and literary associations, a
special place; the "renaissance of high-profile guests under
the new government" has, however, had no positive impact
on the "variable" cooking.* / 10.45 pm; closed Sun; smart casual.

FSA

Geale's W8 £20 ②③④
2 Farmer St   0171-727 7969   6–2B
"Traditional" fish 'n' chips "worth waiting for" – you may
have to queue – are to be had at this half-centenarian chippy,
just off Notting Hill Gate; service – not a strong point in
recent years – seems to be on the mend. / 11 pm; closed Mon
& Sun.

Geeta NW6 £14 ②③⑤
59 Willesden Ln   0171-624 1713   1–1B
"Forget the décor" – you get "amazingly cheap" grub and a
"warm welcome" at this Indian café in Kilburn. / 10.30 pm, Fri
& Sat 11.30 pm; no Switch.

George & Vulture EC3 £29 ④③③
3 Castle Ct   0171-626 9710   9–3C
Dickensian (literally) City back-alley chop-house, where the
"standard traditional English fayre" is "always the same".
/ L only; closed Sat & Sun; no Switch; jacket & tie.

Ghillies £30 ②③③
271 New King's Rd, SW6   0171-371 0434   10–1B
20 Bellevue Rd, SW17   0181-767 1858   10–2C
"Relaxed" local diners in Wandsworth and Parson's Green,
much praised for their "varied" menus (including "great fish
'n' chips") and "friendly" service. / 10.45 pm.

Gilbert's SW7 £26 ⑤⑤⑤
2 Exhibition Rd   0171-589 8947   5–2C
"Unrecognisable", now, as what was once an excellent local,
by South Kensington tube; "dreadful" – "keep away". / 10 pm;
closed Sun.

Gladwins EC3 £50 ③②④
Minster Ct, Mark Ln   0171-444 0004   9–3D
An "inventive" modern British menu, "professional" service
and "widely spaced tables" make this bright basement one
of the more recommendable venues for a serious City lunch –
"on expenses", of course. / L only; closed Sat & Sun.

Glaisters £28 ④⑤④
4 Hollywood Rd, SW10   0171-352 0352   5–3B
8-10 Northcote Rd, SW11   0171-924 6699   10–2C
Their "pleasant atmosphere" (with, in Chelsea, a "very nice
garden") is the best point of these popular and informal
brasseries, though, for many, "boring" food and "slovenly"
service "set the scene for a disappointing evening". / 11.30 pm;
set pre-th. £18(FP).

Globe Restaurant NW3   £ 22   ④❷④

100 Avenue Road   0171-722 7200   8–2A
*"Imaginative" menus are hardly ten-a-penny in Swiss Cottage,
so it's a shame that the cooking at this "original" modern
British newcomer doesn't hit its mark more often; the "weird"
location and "dismal" colour-scheme don't help. / 11 pm;
closed Sat L; no Amex; set Sun L £13(FP).*

Golden Dragon W1   £ 23   ❸④④

28-29 Gerrard St   0171-734 2763   4–3A
*"Good dim sum", and other fare which is "ambitious by
the standards of a large Chinese" are served in "a buzzy
atmosphere" at this "mainstay" of Chinatown. / 11.30 pm,
Fri & Sat midnight.*

Goolies W8   £ 32   ❷❷❷

21 Abingdon Rd   0171-938 1122   5–1A
*"Seriously tasty and visually appealing food" wins high
praise for this small modern British bar/restaurant, just off
Kensington High Street; we're with those who say it "seems
pricey" for what it is. / 10.30 pm; closed Sat L & Sun D.*

Gopal's of Soho W1   £ 25   ❷❸④

12 Bateman St   0171-434 1621   4–2A
*It may look like a typically "dreary" curry house, but this
"excellent" Soho Indian provides "subtly spiced" cooking that
knocks the socks of most other places; service varies from
"attentive" to "off-hand". / 11.15 pm; smart casual.*

GORDON RAMSAY SW3   £ 60   ❷❷④

68-69 Royal Hospital Rd   0171-352 4441   5–3D
*Gordon Ramsay, who established Aubergine as London's most
consistent culinary success, is now installed in the Chelsea site
which until recently housed La Tante Claire; a day three visit
found variable cooking (whose heights reached top past form)
somewhat unctuously served in an expensively sterile setting –
Michelin will love it! / 11 pm; closed Sat & Sun; set weekday L £40(FP).*

Gordon's Wine Bar WC2   £ 17   ④❸❶

47 Villiers St   0171-930 1408   4–4D
*A "basement that excels" – it may be "a dump", but no one
would have this ancient, "candlelit" wine-cellar any other way;
the "great lunchtime snacks" are much better than you might
expect, and there's a 'hidden gem' terrace, by Victoria
Embankment Gardens. / 9 pm; closed Sat L & Sun; no Amex;
no booking.*

Goring Hotel SW1   £ 46   ④❶❸

15 Beeston Pl   0171-396 9000   2–4B
*"Old-fashioned", "very English" Victoria hotel dining room,
where a tinkling piano sets the tone; "average" cooking,
but "wonderful" service. / 9.45 pm; closed Sat L.*

Le Gothique SW18 £30 ❸❸❸

The Royal Victoria Patriotic Bldg, Fitzhugh Gr, Trinity Rd
0181-870 6567   10–2C
*The "stunning outdoor setting in summertime" is the highlight
at this hidden-away Gallic venture, which occupies part of a
wonderfully overblown Victorian pile in Wandsworth;
"standards can vary".* / 10.30 pm; closed Sat L & Sun.

Gourmet Pizza Company £21 ❸④❸

7-9 Swallow St, W1   0171-734 5182   3–3D
Gabriels Whf, 56 Upper Ground, SE1   0171-928 3188   9–3A
18 Mackenzie Walk, E14   0171-345 9192   1–3D
*"Exciting and different" pizzas, "well executed", make
this small chain one of the "best in town"; "be prepared to
queue" at the Gabriels Wharf branch, which has a "great
riverside setting" and brilliant view.* / 10.45 pm; W1 & E14,
no smoking area; need 8+ to book.

Gow's EC2 £38 ④④④

81/82 Old Broad St   0171-920 9645   9–2C
*Even if "Captain Birdseye could teach the chef a thing or
two", the "traditional English seafood" at this basement
near Liverpool Street is good enough to make it useful "for
entertaining less adventurous colleagues".* / L only; closed Sat
& Sun; smart casual.

Goya SW1 £32 ❸④❸

34 Lupus St   0171-976 5309   2–4C
*A "good Spanish neighbourhood spot", in Pimlico, with a
"great ground-floor tapas bar" and "pretty ordinary"
downstairs restaurant.* / 11.30 pm; no smoking area.

Granita N1 £32 ❷❷④

127 Upper St   0171-226 3222   8–2D
*The "austerity" of this popular modern British Islingtonian still
gets to some people – a shame, as the "delicious, interesting,
simple" cooking (if from a "limited" menu) is more consistent
than ever.* / 10.30 pm; closed Mon & Tue L; no Amex & no Switch.

Grano W4 £33 – – –

162 Thames Rd   0181-995 0120   1–3A
*Opening near Kew Bridge shortly after we go to press, Grano
aims to bring to the burghers of Chiswick (on the site of
Oliver's Island, RIP) the culinary standards of its stellar South
Bank sibling, Tentazioni.* /—

The Grapes E14 £31 ❷❸❸

76 Narrow St   0171-987 4396   1–2D
*A "fabulous, traditional, atmospheric pub in Limehouse",
whose first-floor restaurant, offering huge portions of well
prepared grub, is still one of the better bets in Docklands.*
/ 9.15 pm; closed Sat L & Sun D.

Great Eastern Dining Room EC2   £27   – – –
54 Great Eastern Street   0171-613 4545   9–1D
*Cicada has been a contributor to the trendification of
Clerkenwell – perhaps its new Italian sibling (to open in
late-1999) will be an equal ornament to Shoreditch.*

Great Nepalese NW1   £21   ❷❷⑤
48 Eversholt St   0171-388 6737   8–3C
*"High-quality, tasty and different" cooking makes it worth
braving the "inconvenient" location of this rather "dingy"
subcontinental, whose prospect is of the eastern side of
Euston Station. / 11.30 pm; no Switch.*

Greek Valley NW8   £20   ④❷❸
130 Boundary Rd   0171-624 3217   8–3A
*"Fun", well established St John's Wood taverna where it's
"like eating dinner at your Greek auntie's house"; "meze are
exceptional, grills are not". / Midnight; D only; closed Sun; no Amex.*

The Green Olive W9   £35   ❷❷❸
5 Warwick Pl   0171-289 2469   8–4A
*"Very welcoming and relaxed" Maida Vale Italian, just by
Clifton Nurseries, which numbers very "superior" cooking
among its attractions; it's "romantic", too, if you don't sit in
the "hopeless" basement. / 10.45 pm; D only Mon-Fri, Sat & Sun open
L & D.*

Green's SW1   £45   ❸❷❸
36 Duke St   0171-930 4566   3–3D
*"So English", "discreet and clubby" St James's hide-away
with a strongly Establishment ("fogie") following; the
"perfectly fresh fish and seafood" are the best bets from
a rather "unexciting" menu. / 11 pm.*

Greenhouse W1   £44   ❸❷❸
27a Hays Mews   0171-499 3331   3–3B
*"Still a fave, post-Gary", say the many fans of this cosily grand
Mayfair dining room, whose glory days were when Mr Rhodes
was at the stove; we're with the few who say it's "average in
everything". / 11 pm; closed Sat L; smart casual; set Sun L £30(FP).*

Grenadier SW1   £36   ④❸❷
18 Wilton Rw   0171-235 3074   2–3A
*"Still the best Bloody Mary ever" is the top gastronomic
attraction at this "quaint", "hidden" Belgravia mews pub;
we prefer a sausage at the bar to the "solid" and expensive
English food in the "cramped" restaurant. / 9.45 pm.*

FSA

Gresslin's NW3 £34 ❷❸⑤
13 Heath St   0171-794 8386   8–2A
*Thanks to its "delicious" modern British food – from a chef
with a strong classical background – the "best restaurant in
Hampstead" goes from strength to strength; pity nothing's
been done about the "stark" décor. / 10.45 pm; closed Mon L
& Sun D; no Amex; no smoking area; set weekday L £19(FP).*

Grissini SW1 £35 ❸❷④
Hyatt Carlton Tower, 2 Cadogan Place   0171-858 7171   2–4A
*"Exciting and fresh" Italian cooking – if at grand hotel prices
– make this first-floor restaurant (with its conservatory
overlooking the gardens of Cadogan Place) a useful Belgravia
stand-by. / 10.45 pm; closed Sat L & Sun; no smoking area.*

Grumbles SW1 £27 ④④❸
35 Churton St   0171-834 0149   2–4B
*"Reliable, old faithful" Pimlico English bistro which offers a
"candlelit and fun" experience; its pricey, though, for what it
is. / 11.45 pm.*

The Guinea W1 £47 ❸④④
30 Bruton Pl   0171-499 1210   3–2B
*Traditionalists take no notice of the "tourist trap reputation"
of this comfortable, old-fashioned restaurant, behind a
Mayfair mews pub, and praise "the best steak in London"
and "excellent steak and kidney pies"; (also "great sarnies"
in the front bar). / 11 pm; closed Sat L & Sun.*

Gung-Ho NW6 £26 ❷❸❸
330-332 West End Ln   0171-794 1444   1–1B
*"A thoroughly good package" – including "excellent, well
presented Chinese food" and "nice surroundings" – makes
this West Hampstead's "best kept local secret". / 11.30 pm.*

Häagen-Dazs £7 ❸④⑤
14 Leicester Sq, WC2   0171-287 9577   4–3B
Unit 6, Covent Gdn, WC2   0171-240 0436   4–3D
83 Gloucester Rd, SW7   0171-373 9988   5–2B
88 Queensway, W2   0171-229 0668   6–1C
75 Hampstead High St, NW3   0171-431 1430   8–2A
*This ice–cream parlour chain "gets worse and worse" – the
"food, service and ambience are all nothing to what they were
a few years ago". / 11.45 pm-12.45 am; no credit cards at many
branches; all but SW10 no smoking; no booking.*

Haandi NW1 £19 ❸④④
161 Drummond St   0171-383 4557   8–4C
*"Cheap & cheerful" subcontinental in Euston's Little India,
which does a great-value buffet lunch. / 11.30 pm, Fri, Sat
& Sun midnight; closed Sat L; no Switch.*

Halcyon Hotel W11 £61 ❷❸❸
129 Holland Pk Ave 0171-221 5411 6–2B
*"Superb", but "very expensive" modern British cooking
helps attract a dedicated following to the basement of this
discreet Holland Park hotel; the "intimate" and "romantic"
atmosphere, especially in the garden, is also a plus for many
– we're among those who find it curiously "dull".* / 10.30 pm, Fri
& Sat 11 pm; closed Sat L; smart casual; set weekday L £41(FP).

Halepi W2 £23 ❸❶❸
18 Leinster Ter 0171-262 1070 6–2C
*Though its regulars hold out this characterful Bayswater
taverna, decorated in dated and "OTT" style, as "the best",
it's "expensive"; "stick to the meze" is a good policy.*
/ 12.30 am.

The Halkin SW1 £64 ④❸❸
5 Halkin St 0171-333 1234 2–3A
*"Great north Italian cooking, but what a price" – for those
not on expenses only the "great set lunch menu" is really of
any interest at this Belgravia hotel, whose atmosphere is
"stunningly sophisticated" or "dead", to taste.* / 10.45 pm;
closed Sat L & Sun L; smart casual; set weekday L £37(FP).

Hamine W1 £16 ❸④④
84 Brewer St 0171-439 0785 3–2D
*"Cheap" Soho Japanese noodle bar offering "reliable-to-good,
but not outstanding" grub, late in to the night; the
atmosphere is authentic, thanks in part to a predominantly
oriental clientele.* / 2.30 am, Sat 1.30 am, Sun midnight; no credit cards;
no booking.

Harbour City W1 £26 ❸⑤⑤
46 Gerrard St 0171-439 7859 4–3B
*"The dim sum is intriguing, but evening meals are
unexceptional", at this large, "chaotic" and "typically
dismissive" Chinatown outfit.* / 11.15 pm, Fri & Sat 11.45 pm.

Hard Rock Café W1 £26 ④❸❷
150 Old Park Ln 0171-629 0382 3–4B
*The oldest and still "the best" of the theme restaurants
"keeps on trucking", and many still find the "greatest
burgers" in its "unbeatable" ("loud") all-American
environment; expect "long waits during the tourist season".*
/ 12.30 am, Fri & Sat 1 am; no Switch; no smoking area; no booking.

Hardy's W1 £33 ❷❶❸
53 Dorset St 0171-935 5929 2–1A
*"Always welcoming" service and "good and moreish" eclectic
grub, make it worth seeking out this superior Marylebone
wine bar; it has a "varied and good-value wine list".* / 10.30 pm;
closed Sat & Sun.

Havana W1 £ 25 ⑤④❸
17 Hanover Sq   0171-629 2552   3–1C
*"Loud, but fun" Mayfair basement (formerly the Chicago
Pizza Pie Factory, RIP) which is "good for what it is", even if
the "Cuban-style" cooking is no great attraction.* / 11.45 pm.

The Havelock Tavern W14 £ 24 ❷❸❷
57 Masbro Rd   0171-603 5374   7–1C
*"Consistently good", modern British food (if anything, it's
getting better) and "vastly improved service" ensure a wide
following for this "enjoyable, relaxing and informal" Olympia
gastropub.* / 10 pm, Sun 9.30 pm; no credit cards; no booking.

Heather's SE8 £ 19 ❷④❸
74 McMillan St   0181-691 6665   1–3D
*The catch is that you have to go to Bermondsey,
but otherwise, this brave venture serving an eat-as-much-
as-you-like formula of "adventurous veggie food" is a total
bargain experience, incorporating an agreeable setting and a
nice garden.* / 11 pm, 9 pm Sun; closed Mon; no credit cards; no smoking.

Helter Skelter SW9 £ 26 ❷❷④
50 Atlantic Rd   0171-274 8600   10–2D
*"Inventive" modern British cooking ("especially the vegetarian
options") "easily outweighs" the "grim location" of this
"up and coming", "dress-down" Brixtonian.* / 11 pm, Fri & Sat
11.30 pm; D only.

Hilaire SW7 £ 48 ❸❷❸
68 Old Brompton Rd   0171-584 8993   5–2B
*It may be "boring" and a touch "crowded", but this
South Kensington "neighbourhood place" offers "good"
modern French cooking and "friendly" service; an
"older clientele" predominates.* / 11.30 pm; closed Sat L & Sun;
no Amex.

Hodgson's WC2 £ 31 ❸❸❸
115 Chancery Ln   0171-242 2836   2–2D
*The "excellent value set lunch" makes this "wonderful
airy room" (an elegant building designed for a Victorian
auctioneer) well worth knowing about in the thin area round
Fleet Street; the basement wine bar makes a "handy
stand-by".* / 10 pm; closed Sat & Sun.

Home EC1 £ 26 ❷④❷
100-106 Leonard St   0171-684 8618   9–1D
*"Funky-groovy" basement in the ever more trendy area near
Old Street, which provides "a great bar for hanging around
in", and some "excellent", imaginative food in the adjoining
dining room (where you may have to share a table); staff
can seem "amazingly disinterested".* / 10 pm; closed Sat L & Sun;
no Amex.

The Honest Cabbage SE1 £27 ②④③
99 Bermondsey Street 0171-234 0080 9–4D
*"At last! – somewhere to eat in Bermondsey", this
modishly converted boozer by the antiques market offers an
"interesting and changing" modern British menu; service can
be iffy. / 10 pm; closed Sun D; no Amex.*

Hope & Sir Loin EC1 £34 ②③④
94 Cowcross St 0171-253 8525 9–1B
*"The best traditional breakfast" (washed down by "a lovely
pint of Guinness") makes "a terrific way to start the day"
at this characterful room, over a Smithfield pub; at lunch,
it provides a "steak to rely on". / L only; closed Sat & Sun.*

Hornimans SW4 £21 ③④③
69 Clapham Common S'side 0181-673 9162 10–2D
*"Good fun" Clapham Common-side bistro with few
pretensions, whose large outside area makes it a popular
local stand-by. / 11 pm; D only; no Amex.*

Hothouse Bar & Grill E1 £28 ④④④
78/80 Wapping Ln 0171-488 4797 1–3D
*Large, attractively-converted Wapping warehouse with a
"spacious", "relaxing" setting; though fans say it's "great to
have a good restaurant in the area", too many reports of
"disappointing" cooking may account for the fact that it's
"often empty". / 11 pm; closed Sat L & Sun D.*

House on Rosslyn Hill NW3 £30 ④④②
34a Rosslyn Hl 0171-435 8037 8–2A
*"Go for the party but not the food", or for the sometimes
"awful" service, to this "friendly" and "casual" (but
"cramped") hang-out, long popular with "good-looking
Hampstead youth". / Midnight; no Amex; no lunch bookings.*

Hujo's W1 £25 ③①②
11 Berwick St 0171-734 5144 3–2D
*"Relaxed" and "cosy" modern British bistro, worth seeking
out – in spite of its "seedy" Soho back street location – for
its "good" food and "brill" service. / Midnight; closed Sun; set pre-th.
£17(FP).*

Hunan SW1 £28 ①③④
51 Pimlico Rd 0171-730 5712 5–2D
*"Little known" Pimlico Chinese that may "look uninspiring",
but whose "interesting" and "spicy" cooking make it "well
worth a visit". / 11.15 pm; closed Sun; no Switch.*

Hyde Park Hotel
Park Room SW1   £18   ❸❸❷
Knightsbridge 0171-235 2000 2–3A
"What a way to start the day", with breakfast (to which the
price given relates) in this "beautiful, peaceful dining room
with a view" (of the Park); other meals attract little comment.
/ 11 pm; eve, jacket & tie.

I Thai W2   £70   ④④④
31-35 Craven Hill Gdns 0171-298 9001 6–2C
"Minimalism in all things but the bill" is a potent recipe
for dissatisfaction with the basement restaurant of
Lady Weinberg's "precious" Bayswater townhouse hotel;
the loss of the head chef (to The Birdcage) has robbed
the East-West cooking of its initial promise, putting the focus
even more on the "uncomfortable, really stark" décor. / 11 pm.

Ibla W1   £33   ❶❷❸
89 Marylebone High St 0171-224 3799 2–1A
"Fresh zingy flavours" from an "interesting", "reasonably
priced" southern Italian menu, with "unpretentious" and
"welcoming" service, make this "idiosyncratic" newcomer
a "notable" addition; as with the former occupant of the
Marylebone site, Villandry, the tables at the front are best
avoided. / 10.15 pm; closed Sun; no Amex.

Icon SW3   £40   ❸❸❷
19 Elystan St 0171-589 3718 5–2C
Simple modern British cooking is done well at this
discreet newcomer near Chelsea Green; a modernistic
(but not extreme) makeover has done nothing to shake
off the mature following the place achieved in its former
incarnation (Au Bon Accueil, RIP). / 11 pm; closed Sun;
set weekday L £23(FP).

Ikeda W1   £50   ❸❷④
30 Brook St 0171-629 2730 3–2B
"Expensive, but worth it", this long-established Mayfair
Japanese offers "first-class sushi" and other "very good,
authentic dishes". / 10.30 pm, Sat 10 pm; closed Sat L & Sun;
no Switch; smart casual.

Ikkyu   £26   ❷④④
67 Tottenham Ct Rd, W1 0171-636 9280 2–1C
7 Newport Pl, WC2 0171-439 3554 4–3B
"Reasonably priced sushi" and other "very good value"
Japanese dishes are consistently praised at these "cheap
and cheerful" orientals; the décor, and sometimes the service,
though, leave something to be desired. / 10.30 pm, WC2 Fri & Sat
11.30 pm; W1, closed Sat & Sun L; W1 no Switch, WC2 no Amex; WC2
no smoking area.

The Imperial Arms SW6   £21   ❸❷④
577 King's Rd   0171-736 8549   5–4A
*"Much better since the take-over", at least on the
atmosphere front, this Fulham boozer – minimalistically
revamped and incredibly dimly lit – offers surprisingly
competent cooking. / 9.30 pm; closed Sat D.*

Imperial City EC3   £33   ❷❷❸
Cornhill   0171-626 3437   9–2C
*"Always reliable" standards, and a setting which is
"reasonably spacious for the City" make this cellar-Chinese
(beneath the Royal Exchange) a "great business venue".
/ 9 pm; closed Sat & Sun.*

Inaho W2   £28   ❶④⑤
4 Hereford Rd   0171-221 8495   6–1B
*The "best sushi" and other "great value", "delicious and
excellently presented" Japanese fare make it worth tolerating
the "slow" service and sometimes zero ambience of this
"fabulous", "tiny" Bayswater café. / 11 pm; closed Sat L & Sun;
no Amex & no Switch; set weekday L £13(FP).*

L'Incontro SW1   £55   ④④④
87 Pimlico Rd   0171-730 6327   5–2D
*"Lunch is nearly good value", but at dinner they "coast" at
this "outrageously expensive" Pimlico Italian; though it was
a fashionable hotspot in its day, the '80s are now a distant
memory, and all that monochrome chic can just seem
"characterless". / 11.30 pm; closed Sat L & Sun L; smart casual; set
weekday L £32(FP).*

India Club WC2   £19   ④④④
143 Strand   0171-836 0650   2–2D
*"Authentic food and experience" win a loyal fan-club for this
quirky '50s legacy (on the second floor of a small hotel, by the
Aldwych); its "Formica" and "fluorescent tubes" décor makes
it "not for the precious", however, and some feel the cooking
has "taken a downward turn". / 10 pm; closed Sun; no credit cards;
need 6+ to book.*

Indian Ocean SW17   £21   ❷❷④
216 Trinity Rd   0181-672 7740   10–2C
*"A very tasty curry" is to be had at this above-average
Wandsworth subcontinental. / 11.30 pm.*

Indigo WC2   £38   ④❸④
1 Aldwych   0171-300 0400   2–2D
*The mezzanine of this trendy, new hotel offers a tranquil
haven on the fringe of Covent Garden; the pricey modern
British cooking does not excite, however, and it's difficult to
see why anyone would not prefer the basement restaurant,
Axis. / 11.15 pm.*

Interlude W1   £ 43   ❷❷❸
5 Charlotte St   0171-637 0222   2–1C
*The modern French cooking is better than ever at this
ambitious Fitzrovian, which has seen "innumerable changes"
in the kitchen over the last few years; the traditional,
bourgeois setting remains "too formal" for some tastes.*
/ 10.45 pm; closed Sat L & Sun.

Isfehan W2   £ 23   ❸❸❸
3-4 Bouverie Pl   0171-460 1030   6–1D
*"Authentic" and sometimes "noisy" Paddington Persian,
with festive décor and "live music which moves further to the
east by the hour".* / Midnight.

Ishbilia SW1   £ 28   ❸❸❸
9 William St   0171-235 7788   2–3A
*The number of ladies in yashmaks certainly helped create
an authentic atmosphere during our visit to this new
family-run Knightsbridge Lebanese; friendly service and
decent grub.* / Midnight; no Switch.

Italian Kitchen   £ 28   ❸❸④
43 New Oxford St, WC1   0171-836 1011   2–1C
17-21 Tavistock St, WC2   0171-379 9696   4–3D
*"Good food at moderate prices" makes these unpretentious
and welcoming Italians worth remembering; the WC2 branch
is to see an ambitious relaunch in late-1998, under the
name Maggiore's Classic Italian Kitchen – let's hope they
don't throw the bambino out with the bathwater.* / WC1 11 pm,
WC2 Midnight; no smoking area; WC1 Fri & Sat restricted booking.

THE IVY WC2   £ 45   ❷❶❶
1 West St   0171-836 4751   4–3B
*"Seamless" West End classic – again reporters' No 1
favourite – where "excellent everything" creates "just the
right vibes" for practically any occasion; given its star-studded
following – "darling, the Ivy IS theatre!" – the main problem
for mortals is to get a table; will it all last after the August '98
acquisition by the Belgo Group?* / Midnight; set Sun L £26(FP).

Iznik N5   £ 19   ❷❶❶
19 Highbury Pk   0171-354 5697   8–2D
*"It's well worth the schlepp" – to just north of Islington – to
seek out this "pretty" and "endearing" Ottoman, which still
provides a "good standard of cooking, despite its popularity";
day-time fry-ups are equally commended.* / 11 pm; no Amex.

Japanese Canteen £19 ④❸⑤
5 Thayer Street, W1 0171-487 5505 3–1A
305 Portobello Road, W10 0181-968 9988 6–1A
394 St John St, EC1 0171-833 3222 8–3D
There are enough people who like these "quick", Nipponese
diners to enable them to multiply, but they are too "stark",
and the food is very "so-so". / EC1 & W10 11 pm - W1 9 pm, Sat
6 pm; EC1 closed Sun L - W1 closed Sun; W1 no credit cards; no smoking
area, W1 no smoking; W1 no booking.

Jason's W9 £39 ❶②②
Opposite 60 Blomfield Rd 0171-286 6752 8–4A
"Steal away" – as many do – to this "delightful", canalside
"Maida Vale haunt", whose "absolutely delicious" Mauritian
fish dishes are some of the best in town. / 10.30 pm; closed Sun D.

Jenny Lo's Teak House SW1 £15 ❸②④
14 Eccleston St 0171-259 0399 2–4B
"Tasty, nourishing food" makes this "stylish" oriental noodle
bar a "functional" spot, worth knowing about in the grim
purlieus of Victoria Station; "some menu items are good,
some uninteresting". / 10 pm; closed Sun; no credit cards; no booking.

Jim Thompson's SW6 £27 ④⑤❶
617 King's Rd 0171-731 0999 5–4A
"Cheap, colourful and buzzy", this exotic Fulham
pub-conversion is "fun for a night out"; the oriental cooking
is "OK", and service is "good when quiet, chaotic when busy"
(which is most of the time). / 11 pm.

Jindivick N1 £31 ④④❸
201 Liverpool Rd 0171-607 7710 8–3D
"Bright and cheery" pub-conversion, whose "interesting"
modern British "menu" still appeals to "Islington trendies"
(and, at weekends, their "designer babies"); service can
be "slow", though, and the food can "disappoint". / 10.45 pm;
closed Mon L & Sun D; no Amex; no smoking area; set weekday L £20(FP).

Joe Allen WC2 £32 ④❸②
13 Exeter St 0171-836 0651 4–3D
"It's good for star-spotting, but don't go for the food" to
this long-established "lively", "later-in-the-evening" theatrical
scene, hidden away in a Covent Garden basement; as ever,
fans proclaim the burgers (not listed on the menu) as the
"best in town". / 12.45 am; no smoking area; set pre-th. £22(FP).

Joe's Brasserie SW6 £30 ④④④
130 Wandsworth Br Rd 0171-731 7835 10–1B
"Young, fun" Fulhamites still love this attractive bar/restaurant
(especially for group celebrations), but it's "let down" by very
"average" food. / 11 pm.

Joe's Café SW3 £ 40 ❸❸❸
126 Draycott Ave 0171-225 2217 5–2C
"Casually smart" modern British brasserie at Brompton Cross,
whose chic quarters usually harbour "some interesting
people". / 11 pm; closed Sun D.

Joy King Lau W1 £ 19 ❷❷❸
3 Leicester St 0171-437 1132 4–3A
"Chinese food how we used to eat it in Hong Kong"
("fresh, tasty and plentiful") is to be had at this very
superior, large establishment near Leicester Square; in
defiance of local custom, "they all smile". / 11.30 pm;
no Switch.

Julie's W11 £ 40 ④❸❶
135 Portland Rd 0171-229 8331 6–2A
"Mad, Gothic, sexy and Baroque", this "wonderfully
labyrinthine" Holland Park basement is "still going strong" –
thanks, of course, to its "seductive" ambience, not to the
expensive and very "unexceptional" modern British cooking.
/ 11.15 pm; closed Sat L.

Julie's Bar W11 £ 31 ⑤❸❶
137 Portland Rd 0171-727 7985 6–2A
"OK once in a while, but overpriced really", Julie's adjacent
bar has the same pros and cons as its parent, but on a
smaller scale; it's a top afternoon tea choice, though.
/ 10.30 pm.

Justin de Blank W1 £ 28 ④④④
120-122 Marylebone Ln 0171-486 5250 3–1A
"Unfussy" modern British cooking and a "casual" attitude
make this Marylebone venture a "great local restaurant"
for some; it's desperately inconsistent, though, attracting
complaints of "uninteresting" food, "awful" service and a
"cold" atmosphere. / 10.30 pm; closed Sun.

Kalamaras, Micro W2 £ 20 ❸④④
66 Inverness Mews 0171-727 5082 6–2C
"Tacky", but "pleasant" Greek experience, in a hidden mews
off Queensway; it's reasonably priced (aided by the BYO
policy) but has lost the following it had of yore; the nearby
Kalamaras Mega is no more. / 11 pm; D only; no Switch.

Kartouche SW10 £ 34 ④④❸
329-331 Fulham Rd 0171-823 3515 5–3B
Paradoxically, the fact that it's "not quite the fashionable
hang-out it once was" has made this "lively" ("noisy and
smoky") Chelsea-fringe venture "a more pleasant pit stop
than before"; the modern British grub is still "nothing
special", though. / Midnight; set pre-th. £11(FP).

Kaspia W1   £45   ❸❸④
18-18a Bruton Pl   0171-493 2612   3–2B
As the main choice to be made at this comfortable, if
subdued, Mayfair parlour (behind a shop) is which grade of
caviar to select, it's no great surprise that it's "expensive";
you don't have to spend the earth, here, but nor would you
have to try very hard. / 11.30 pm; closed Sun; no Switch; smart casual.

Kastoori SW17   £18   ❶❷④
188 Upper Tooting Rd   0181-767 7027   10–2C
"Fantastically inventive Indian/Kenyan vegetarian food"
has long made this "bland"-looking Tooting shop conversion
a celebrated destination; reports remain very upbeat, but
ratings for food and service slipped somewhat this year.
/ 10.30 pm; closed Mon L & Tue L; no Amex & no Switch.

Kavanagh's N1   £28   ❸④❷
26 Penton St   0171-833 1380   8–3D
"Likeable", if slightly "weirdly" decorated Islington local,
which offers "good value" modern British cooking; it has
"gone off a bit", though, with "ramshackle" service the top
complaint. / 10.30 pm; closed Mon & Sat L & Sun D; no Amex.

Kaya Korean W1   £38   ④❸④
42 Albemarle St   0171-499 0622   3–3C
The grandest Korean in town has, for the last couple of years,
inhabited rather dull premises, a brief stroll from the Ritz;
the cooking is competent, if pricey, and the staff "give good
advice". / 10.45 pm; closed Sun L.

Ken Lo's Memories SW1   £40   ❸④④
67-69 Ebury St   0171-730 7734   2–4B
"Good" Chinese food can still be found at this celebrated,
once-smart oriental, near Victoria Station, though it
increasingly feels "tired" and "impersonal". / 10.15 pm;
closed Sun L; smart casual.

Ken Lo's Memories of China W8   £37   ❸❸❸
353 Kensington High St   0171-603 6951   7–1D
Some still feel this "fancy" Chinese yearling – in the
no-man's-land between Kensington and Olympia – is "way
overpriced"; most, though, approve of its "well presented"
dishes. / 11.15 pm; closed Sun L; no smoking area.

Kensington Place W8   £40   ❸❸❷
201-205 Kensington Ch St   0171-727 3184   6–2B
The gentle "decline" of the "prototypical" modern British
brasserie continues – it's "still a reliable place with a good,
fun atmosphere", but nowadays "the food does not always
live up to its billing"; high noise levels and "bum-numbing"
seats, however, provide a reassuring link with the past.
/ 11.45 pm, Sun 10.15 pm; set Sun L £26(FP).

FSA

Kettners W1   £24   ⑤④❷
29 Romilly St   0171-734 6112   4–2A
*"Oscar Wilde would turn in his grave" at the continuing
"demise" of this magnificent remnant of old Soho,
whose "elegant setting" is now its only attraction; the
cooking (burgers, pizzas, salads) is poor, and service
increasingly "chaotic".* / Midnight; smart casual; no booking.

Khan's W2   £16   ④⑤❸
13-15 Westbourne Grove   0171-727 5420   6–1C
*Service "not for those of a nervous disposition" sets the tone
at this "chaotic" and "unbearably" noisy "institution" that's
more "Bombay" than Bayswater; it undoubtedly offers a
"fun curry", but, increasingly, the food's just "cheap",
rather than "good value".* / 11.45 pm.

Khan's of Kensington SW7   £22   ❷❸④
3 Harrington Rd   0171-581 2900   5–2B
*"Good value for money" – and just by South Kensington
station, as well – makes this oddly-proportioned
subcontinental a dependable local stand-by.* / 11.15 pm, Fri & Sat
11.45 pm; no smoking area; set weekday L £13(FP).

Khyber Pass SW7   £20   ❷❷⑤
21 Bute St   0171-589 7311   5–2B
*"Fresh spices and individual flavours" make this "tatty"
South Kensington curry house "a good dive"; it could
undoubtedly "do with a total refurb", but surely that would
spoil it?* / 11.30 pm; no Switch.

King's Brasserie SW6   £40   ❷❸⑤
Chelsea Village Hotel, Fulham Road   0171-565 1400   5–4A
*If it wasn't for the appalling lack of atmosphere (and often, it
seems, of people), we would join the few who commend the
restaurant of this hideously misjudged hotel by Stamford
Bridge for its "very good" modern British grub and "effective
service".* / 11 pm; no smoking area.

King's Road Café SW3   £19   ④❸❸
208 King's Rd   0171-351 6645   5–3C
*The "upmarket snackbar/café" of the King's Road's Habitat
shop is worth seeking out for "a good simple Italian lunch";
"you can wait for ages on Saturday".* / open shop hours only, with
L till 5 pm; L only; no Amex; no smoking area.

Krungtap SW10   £18   ④❸④
227 Old Brompton Rd   0171-259 2314   5–2A
*It's "back at last", after a 1997 fire, but to our mind the
new "less crowded" version of this Earl's Court Thai café lacks
the tacky charm of the original; the food is not as good either.*
/ 10.30 pm; D only; no Amex; no smoking area.

Kulu Kulu W1   £ 18   ❷④⑤
76 Brewer St   0171-734 7316   3–2D
*You get "reliable", "cheap" conveyor-belt sushi at this
ungimmicky Soho venture. / 10 pm; closed Sun; no Amex; no booking.*

Kundan SW1   £ 30   ❷❸④
3 Horseferry Rd   0171-834 3211   2–4C
*Vaguely horrible '70s décor is not the sole distinguishing
feature at this "quiet and comfortable" Westminster Pakistani
– fans "go back again and again" for the "super" food.
/ Midnight; closed Sun.*

Kwan Thai SE1   £ 26   ❸❷④
The Riverfront, Hay's Galleria   0171-403 7373   9–4D
*"Good quality Thai food" makes this large Hays Galleria
river-sider (with outside tables in good weather) a useful
place, a "nice walk" away from the City. / 10 pm; closed Sun;
no smoking area.*

The Ladbroke Arms W11   £ 23   ❷❸❷
54 Ladbroke Rd   0171-727 6648   6–2B
*"Filling, earthy and no-frills" fare (the "sausage and mash
is the business") ensures that this Notting Hill hostelry,
which feels like a "real country pub", is often "too crowded".
/ 9.45 pm; no Amex; book L only.*

Lahore Kebab House E1   £ 15   ❶⑤⑤
2 Umberston St   0171-488 2551   1–2D
*It's now "too well known", complain devotees of the
"excellent, very cheap" Indian grub at this celebrated
East Ender, where the "dreadful", "basic" setting and "lousy"
service are part of the charm; BYO. / 11.45 pm; no credit cards.*

The Landmark Hotel NW1   £ 51   ④❸❶
222 Marylebone Rd   0171-631 8000   8–4A
*"There is a fantastic feel-good factor" in the "great",
"elegant" palm-filled atrium of this Marylebone hotel;
the adjoining main dining room is most recommended for
business or breakfast, but you can take a "lovely tea" or light
bite in the atrium itself. / 10.45 pm; closed Sat L & Sun D; smart casual;
no smoking area; set weekday L £35(FP).*

The Lanesborough W1   £ 52   ④❷❶
Hyde Pk Corner   0171-259 5599   2–3A
*This "beautiful", if OTT, hotel dining room ("with its relaxing
waterfall which keeps conversations private") is "reliable" for
business, and often commended for its set lunches, teas and
dinner-dances; those who just want a decent dinner, however,
may complain of "very ordinary" food. / Midnight; no Switch.*

Langan's Brasserie W1   £ 37   ④❸❷
Stratton St   0171-493 6437   3–3C
*There's "still a real buzz" to this large, glamorous, "fun" and
"relaxed" British brasserie in Mayfair, though its fame attracts
a crowd that's rather "out-of-town" for some tastes.* / 11.45 pm;
closed Sat L & Sun.

Langan's Coq d'Or SW5   £ 38   ④❸④
254-260 Old Brompton Rd   0171-259 2599   5–3A
*The new 'son of Langan's' (on the Earl's Court site made
famous by Pontevecchio, and last occupied by Tusc, RIP) gives
a reasonable semblance of an authentically Gallic brasserie;
Stratton Street's mediocre culinary standards prevail, however,
and prices are silly.* / 11 pm.

Lansdowne NW1   £ 24   ④④❷
90 Gloucester Ave   0171-483 0409   8–3B
*"Always very busy", "bright and cheerful" Primrose Hill
gastropub, whose "wholesome" grub can be "excellent",
but is too often "hit and miss"; service remains weak.* / 10 pm;
closed Mon L; no Amex; book Sun L only.

La Lanterna SE1   £ 23   ❸❷❸
6–8 Mill Street   0171-252 2420   1–3D
*"Busy" Bermondsey Italian (three minutes' walk from the
Design Museum), whose local supporters enthuse about
"sassy" service and "excellent pizza and pasta"; we think
"decent" and "reasonably priced" are nearer the mark.*
/ 11 pm; closed Sat L.

Latymers W6   £ 20   ❷❸⑤
157 Hammersmith Rd   0181-741 2507   7–2C
*It looks "terrible from the outside", but it's worth braving the
interior of this "smoky" Shepherd's Bush gin palace for its
"great value for money" Thai cooking.* / 10 pm; closed Sun;
no Switch; no booking at lunch.

LAUNCESTON PLACE W8   £ 40   ❷❶❶
1a Launceston Pl   0171-937 6912   5–1B
*"Intimate, and with a nice feel on all counts", this "civilised"
and "understated" Kensington townhouse is now one of the
best all-rounders in town; the staff know that "timing is
everything, and get it right", and the "enterprising" modern
British cooking is extremely "reliable".* / 11.30 pm; closed Sat L
& Sun D; set pre-th. £27(FP).

Laurent NW2   £ 21   ❷❷⑤
428 Finchley Rd   0171-794 3603   1–1B
*"Don't be put off by the outside"; "wonderful, healthy
couscous" – "the best in town" – is to be had at this
"cheerful", if very basic, Cricklewood café.* / 11 pm;
closed Sun; no Switch.

Lavender £22 ❷❷❷

171 Lavender Hill, SW11   0171-978 5242   10–2C
24 Clapham Rd, SW9   0171-793 0770   10–1D
*"Inventive, tasty, modern cooking" is but one of the
attractions making a name for this "relaxed" and "friendly"
Battersea "haunt" (which now has a sibling in what was
Café Jeune, near Oval tube, with more planned for late '98);
prices are "so reasonable". /—*

Leadenhall Tapas Bar EC3 £21 ④④❸

27 Leadenhall Mkt   0171-623 1818   9–2D
*Even if the 'tapas' are rather "mediocre", this "cheerful" City
bar makes a "great meeting-place". / 9 pm; closed Sat & Sun; need
6+ to book.*

Leith's W11 £50 ❸❸④

92 Kensington Pk Rd   0171-229 4481   6–2B
*The curate's egg performance continues at this Notting Hill
townhouse, where praise for the cooking often has a catch –
a "too expensive luxury", "very good, but they should ease up
on the cream", and so on; the setting is "comfortable and
spacious" to some, "morgue-like" to others. / 11.30 pm;
closed Mon L, Sat L & Sun.*

Leith's Soho W1 £41 ❸❸④

41 Beak St   0171-287 2057   3–2D
*"Accomplished" modern British cooking can be had – at a
price – at Leith's new Soho offshoot; the ambience tends to
be "uninspiring", though, "and it can be loud, what with all
those media types". / 11.15 pm; closed Sat L & Sun; set pre-th. £28(FP).*

Lemonia NW1 £24 ❸❷❶

89 Regent's Pk Rd   0171-586 7454   8–3B
*"It never changes!" – this "sunny" Primrose Hill institution
with its "lovely waiters" offers "consistent" Greek cooking in a
"big", "buzzy" and "relaxed" setting. / 11.30 pm; closed Sat L
& Sun D; no Amex; set weekday L £15(FP).*

Leonardo's SW10 £32 ❸❷④

397 King's Rd   0171-352 4146   5–3B
*"Very welcoming", "informal" World's End trattoria, with a
loyal following for its "well priced and consistent" traditional
cooking. / 11.45 pm; closed Sun D; set weekday L £19(FP).*

The Lexington W1 £30 ④⑤❸

Lexington St   0171-434 3401   3–2D
*"Candles and a piano" set the tone at this quirky and
"friendly" Soho fixture; its devoted thirtysomething fans
still say it's "a must" especially for the "incredible value
early-evening menu", but both cooking and service are
increasingly erratic. / 11 pm; closed Sat L & Sun.*

F S A

Lindsay House W1   £48   ❷❸❷
21 Romilly St   0171-439 0450   4–3A
*"Quirky surroundings" help make this "stylish" Soho
townhouse yearling a top West End choice; Irish chef
Richard Corrigan's modern British cooking (with "lots of
offal") is certainly "pleasant" and "interesting", but not yet
up to his past best.* / 11 pm; closed Sat L & Sun.

Lisboa Patisserie W10   £5   ❶❸④
57 Golborne Rd   0181-968 5242   6–1A
*"There is no other place" like this "basic", but "superb"
North Kensington Portuguese pâtisserie – it's "so busy"
that some "always settle for a take-away".* / 8 pm;
no credit cards; no booking.

Little Bay   £13   ④❸❷
147 Lupus St, SW1   0171-834 9075   5–3D
228 Belsize Rd, NW6   0171-372 4699   1–2B
*"Honest food" at "unbelievably cheap" prices means you
find "great value" at these "bargain basement" choices;
"don't expect miracles", but everyone "trying hard" helps
to create a surprisingly "lovely" atmosphere.* / 11.45 pm;
no credit cards.

Little Havana WC2   £29   ❸❸④
Queens House, 1 Leicester Place   0171-287 0101   4–3B
*Up above the tourist hell of Leicester Square, it is clear the
"the cooking is not the crucial thing" at this large, "lively"
Cuban-themed joint; we were surprised to find 'real' food,
but some others have not been so lucky.* / 12.30 pm; closed Sat L.

Little Italy W1   £32   ❸❷❷
21 Frith St   0171-734 4737   4–2A
*"Really cool and chaotic" Soho Italian (it's "so noisy, you
have to be in the mood") that's particularly "great for late at
night"; the "simple" cooking has returned to form, and staff
are "charming".* / 4 am, Sun midnight.

Livebait   £39   ❷❸④
21 Wellington St, WC2   0171-836 7161   4–3D
43 The Cut, SE1   0171-928 7211   9–4A
*"Ingenious" dishes delivering "strong, fishy flavours" have so
far just about survived Groupe Chez Gérard's ownership of
this quirky fish specialist; increasingly, though, people find
"extraordinary" the contrast between such "high prices", and
the "upmarket working class café" décor (particularly at the
formulaic and, to our mind, horrible WC2 branch).* / 11.30 pm;
closed Sun; no smoking areas.

Lobster Pot SE11   £37   ❶❷❸
3 Kennington Ln   0171-582 5556   1–3C
"Expensive, but really excellent seafood", "bizarre" nautical "kitsch" décor and "amusing Breton staff" would make a pretty startling combination anywhere – in a dire location near the Elephant & Castle, they make this "genuinely French" fish restaurant "slightly surreal". / 11 pm; closed Mon & Sun; smart casual; set weekday L £24(FP).

Lola's N1   £34   ❸❷❸
359 Upper St   0171-359 1932   8–3D
Juliet Peston's successful yearling seems set finally to vanquish the ghosts of this difficult site, above Islington's Antiques Market; "classy" service, and "distinctive" 'global-eclectic' cooking" now set off the "light and airy" setting to best advantage. / 11 pm; closed Sun D.

The Lord Palmerston N19   £21   ④❷❸
33 Dartmouth Park Hill   0171-485 1578   8–1B
Popularity makes it "a pain to get in" to this Archway gastropub; its "stark and basic setting" is still "great for an informal time", but the "good pub food" isn't quite holding its own. / 10 pm; closed Mon L; no Amex; no booking.

Lou Pescadou SW5   £39   ④④④
241 Old Brompton Rd   0171-370 1057   5–3A
Patchy, but perennially "pricey" Earl's Court fish specialist; to loyalists, it's still a "friendly, low-key, dependable local", but too many decry an "overly French" establishment "living on its former glory". / Midnight; set Sun L £22(FP).

Luc's Brasserie EC3   £34   ❸❷❷
17-22 Leadenhall Mkt   0171-621 0666   9–2D
"A piece of Paris in the City", this "efficient", "fast and furious" Leadenhall Market fixture, is a great business lunch venue, offering "simple, well priced" Gallic fare; "they always recognize your time constraints", but "you never feel rushed". / L only; closed Sat & Sun; no Switch.

Luigi Malones SW7   £23   ④⑤❸
73 Old Brompton Rd   0171-584 4323   5–2B
South Kensington diner (now in the West End, too) where some (with whom we agree) find "awful" food and "take-it-or-leave-it" service; as ever, though, there are those who praise "consistent" burgers and so on "at reasonable prices". / 11 pm.

Luigi's WC2   £45   ④④④
15 Tavistock St   0171-240 1789   4–3D
There are those who still praise this grand and "comfortable" Covent Garden Italian as a paragon of "solid", "old-fashioned" values; we're with those who think it should be put out to grass. / 11.30 pm; closed Sun; smart casual; set pre-th. £23(FP).

Luigi's Delicatessen SW10 £ 12 ❶④❸

359 Fulham Rd   0171-351 7825   5–3B

*Those in search of "La Dolce Vita" – Chelsea 'Beach'-style –
throng this unpretentious-looking café, where "fantastic
hand-made pizzas" and other "very fresh" Italian fare
come very reasonably priced; there's an "especially good
atmosphere outside"; now open in the evening – BYO. / 8 pm,
Sat 6 pm; closed Sun; no credit cards; no booking.*

Luna Nuova WC2 £ 30 ④❸④

22 Short's Gdns   0171-836 4110   4–2C

*Potentially pleasant Covent Garden basement pizzeria,
which has been "nothing to write home about" for some time
now; we are told "new management has got it back on its
feet", and live, as ever, in hope. / 11.30 pm; no smoking area.*

Lunch EC1 £ 14 ❸❷④

60 Exmouth Market   0171-278 2420   9–1A

*It's "not very comfortable, but a good deal", say fans of
the interesting salads, soup, and sandwiches at this
ultra-minimalist café (with good garden) on Clerkenwell's
emerging little, trendy street; a second branch has opened in
Lincoln's Inn Fields. / 5.45 pm; L only; closed Sat & Sun; no credit cards;
no smoking 12.30–2.30pm; no booking.*

Ma Goa SW15 £ 27 ❶❷④

244 Upper Richmond Rd   0181-780 1767   10–2B

*"Authentic" family-run Putney bistro whose "outstanding
and very original" Goan cooking puts it "head and shoulders
above the local curry houses". / 11 pm; closed Mon, Tue & Sat L,
Sun D.*

Mackintosh's Brasserie W4 £ 26 ④④④

142 Chiswick High Rd   0181-994 2628   7–2B

*A "happy atmosphere" means you "often have to queue"
at this Chiswick "favourite", which serves a "good selection
of brasserie-style food"; these days, though, it has "more
off-nights than on-nights". / Midnight; no smoking area; no booking.*

Made in Italy SW3 £ 23 ❸❸❷

249 King's Rd   0171-352 1880   5–3C

*"Good for cheap 'drop-in' food" – in which Chelsea does not
abound – this "fun" diner offers "reliable" pizza and pasta
staples; incidents of "awful" service are not unknown.
/ 11.30 pm; no Amex; to book need 6+.*

Madhu's Brilliant UB1 £ 24 ❷❶④

39 South Road   0181-574 1897   1–3A

*"Exceptionally tasty grub", together with notably "attentive"
service, justifies the pilgrimage (three minutes' walk north of
the BR station) to this glitzy Southall curry parlour – the
upstart (and, to our mind, preferable) step-sibling of the
original Brilliant. / 11.30 pm; closed Tue, Sat L & Sun L; closed Sat L
& Sun L.*

Maggie Jones's W8   £31   ❸❷❶
6 Old Court Pl   0171-937 6462   5–1A
*With its "wonderful", "homely", "candlelit" atmosphere,
this Kensington "old favourite" is particularly "great for a cold
winter's evening"; at its best, the "70s retro" menu – actually,
it's always been like that – delivers "cottagey, rich and
plentiful" cooking.* / 11 pm; set Sun L £21(FP).

Magno's Brasserie WC2   £31   ⑤④⑤
65a Long Acre   0171-836 6077   4–2D
*An "adequate" pre-theatre menu is now all that commends
this old-timer, around the corner from the building site
formerly known as the Royal Opera House; since Magno's
departure, the overwhelming verdict is "incompetent service,
overcrowded, and overpriced".* / 11.30 pm; closed Sat L & Sun L; set
pre-th. £20(FP).

Maison Bertaux W1   £ 5   ❷❸❷
28 Greek St   0171-437 6007   4–2A
*"Cakes to die for and wonderfully strange staff" maintain
the appeal of this "chaotic and genuinely bohemian" Soho
institution – London's oldest pâtisserie (1871).* / 8.30 pm;
no credit cards; no smoking area.

Maison Novelli EC1   £51   ❷④④
29 Clerkenwell Gn   0171-251 6606   9–1A
*"Interesting" and "highly inventive" modern French cooking
wins praise for the more upmarket of J-C Novelli's City-fringe
restaurants; aggressive prices and "hopeless", "brusque"
service, however, head up the list of charges of those who
find a visit here "a joyless experience".* / 11 pm; closed Sat L & Sun.

Malabar W8   £24   ❶❷❷
27 Uxbridge St   0171-727 8800   6–2B
*"Outstanding" Indian cooking and a civilised setting
(more trattoria than curry house) combine to give this
well established subcontinental, off Notting Hill Gate, a
tremendously wide appeal.* / 11.15 pm; no Amex.

Malabar Junction WC1   £29   ❸❸④
107 Gt Russell St   0171-580 5230   2–1C
*"Above average" South Indian cooking and "spacious
surroundings" make this too-little-known Bloomsbury
conservatory-restaurant "worth a visit".* / 11.30 pm; no Switch;
no smoking area; set pre-th. £17(FP).

La Mancha SW15   £26   ❸❸❷
32 Putney High St   0181-780 1022   10–2B
*"Lively", "noisy" tapas bar – just over Putney Bridge –
whose "good solid" grub makes it very popular locally.*
/ Mon-Thurs 11 pm, Fri Sat & Sun 11.30 pm.

Mandalay W2 £15 **2①**④
444 Edgware Rd   0171-258 3696   8–4A
*It's the "lovely" staff who really make this "friendly",
family-run venture near Lords, although the Burmese cooking
– Indian with an oriental twist – is a real attraction in itself,
and "amazing value". / 10.30 pm; closed Sun; no smoking; set
weekday L £10(FP).*

Mandarin Kitchen W2 £30 **①**④④
14-16 Queensway   0171-727 9012   6–2C
*"No romance, no frills, no acoustics – you go to eat and then
you go – very Chinese – great", one report says it all about
this Bayswater fixture whose "very fresh" seafood is among
the best in town. / 11.30 pm.*

Mandeer WC1 £21 **3**④④
8 Bloomsbury Way   0171-242 6202   2–1D
*Unceremoniously ousted from its characterful cradle, London's
oldest veggie Indian has decamped to a Bloomsbury cellar;
some have been "disappointed" in the new home, but the
place's proud history leads us to put our faith in those who
say it's "re-establishing itself". / 10 pm; closed Sun; no smoking; set
weekday L £10(FP).*

Mandola W11 £21 **2③①**
139 Westbourne Grove   0171-229 4734   6–1B
*"Just you try and get a booking these days", to enjoy the
"really unusual, tasty food" served in the "Bohemian,
candlelit setting" of this "charming" Notting Hill Sudanese.
/ 10.30 pm; no credit cards.*

Mange 2 EC1 £38 ④**3**④
2 Cowcross St   0171-250 0035   9–1A
*It never quite seems to fulfil its aspirations, but this
"unusually decorated" modern French restaurant in Smithfield
is "fine for business lunches"; "it's cheaper and quicker in
the bar". / 10.30 pm; closed Sat & Sun.*

Mango Room NW1 £23 **3②①**
10 Kentish Town Rd   0171-482 5065   8–3B
*A total hit with Camden Town twentysomethings, this bright,
new bar/restaurant (opposite the tube) serves enjoyable
modern British dishes with an inventively Caribbean twist;
the charming staff cope remarkably well, considering. / 11 pm;
no Amex.*

Manna NW3 £24 **2**④**3**
4 Erskine Rd   0171-722 8028   8–3B
*"Yummy wholefood", say local fans of this Primrose Hill veggie
– on the site of the first ever UK restaurant to renounce the
use of meat; service is "slow and forgetful", though. / 11 pm;
D only, except Sun when L&D; no Amex; no smoking.*

Manorom WC2   £23   ❸❸④
16 Maiden Ln   0171-240 4139   4–3D
"Unless you come really early or book, you won't get in" to
this *"small and welcoming"* Covent Garden Thai which is
"excellent before the theatre". / 11 pm; closed Sat L & Sun.

Manzara W11   £17   ❸❸④
24 Pembridge Rd   0171-727 3062   6–2B
It can misfire, but this basic café just off Notting Hill Gate is
generally praised for its *"good value"* (*"after-pub"*) Turkish
cooking; the pastries *"are not to be missed"*. / 11.30 pm;
no smoking.

Manzi's WC2   £38   ❷❸❸
1 Leicester St   0171-734 0224   4–3A
"Eat-me fish" (*"best simply done, as the sauces can be
dodgy"*) ensures continuing popularity for this *"happy"* and
"reassuringly untrendy" Theatrelander, as do the antics of
the *"dotty"* staff. / 11.30 pm, Cabin Room 10.30 pm; closed Sun L;
set pre-th. £20(FP).

Mao Tai SW6   £33   ❶❷❷
58 New King's Rd   0171-731 2520   10–1B
"One of the best Chinese around"; expansion and a revamp
have done nothing to dent devotion to this eminent, slickly-run
Parson's Green oriental, which maintains an *"unfailingly high
standard"* of *"delicious tempting dishes"*. / 11.45 pm.

Marine Ices NW3   £23   ④❸❸
8 Haverstock Hl   0171-482 9003   8–2B
Not everyone is sure about the *"OK"* pizza and pasta at this
"brightly lit" Chalk Farm institution for all the family, but it's
definitely still *"the place to go for ice cream or sorbet"*.
/ 11 pm; no Amex; no smoking area.

Maroush   £33   ❷❷❸
I) 21 Edgware Rd, W2   0171-723 0773   6–1D
II) 38 Beauchamp Pl, SW3   0171-581 5434   5–1C
III) 62 Seymour St, W1   0171-724 5024   2–2A
The *"great value"* café/take-away sections (I and II only)
are *"perfect for a snack"* (especially after midnight) at these
glossy Lebaneses where *"everything is prepared from first
class ingredients"*; the grander restaurants are *"not cheap"*
(and at I, there is hefty minimum charge after 10.30 pm).
/ W2 1.30 am, SW3 4.30 am, W1 11.30 pm.

The Marquis W1   £32   ❷❶④
121a Mount St   0171-499 1256   3–3B
"Attentive and caring" service and *"good, simple"* modern(ish)
British food make this reasonably priced, revamped old-timer
in the heart of Mayfair well worth remembering; the *"stylish"*
décor strikes some as *"bleak"*, so evenings can be quiet –
"good for business or calm dining". / 10.45 pm; closed Sat L & Sun;
smart casual.

Mas Café W11   £ 28   ❸❸❷
6-8 All Saints Rd   0171-243 0969   6–1B
"Funky" and "friendly" Notting Hill hang-out, where
"four hours pass like two"; the top attraction is the "excellent
weekend brunch". / 11.30 pm; D only, except Sat & Sun, when brunch
& D; no Amex; no brunch bookings.

Masako W1   £ 55   ❸❷❸
6 St Christopher Pl   0171-935 1579   3–1A
Well established, comfortable Japanese – in a cute alley
off Oxford Street – whose "private and relaxed" ambience,
"charming" staff, and "delicate" dishes commend it to a loyal
band of followers. / 10 pm; closed Sun.

Mash W1   £ 40   ⑤⑤④
19-21 Gt Portland St   0171-637 5555   3–1C
"Bright", modernistic décor does inspire some at Oliver
('Atlantic') Peyton's wacky and impressively designed new
microbrewery-cum-restaurant, just north of Oxford Street;
the contrived modern British grub is "hopeless", though,
and service is "useless". / 11 pm.

The Mason's Arms SW8   £ 24   ❷④❷
169 Battersea Park Rd   0171-622 2007   10–1C
This "busy pub with excellent food and atmosphere"
transcends its uninspiring location, by Battersea Park
railway station; it "gets very packed". / 10 pm.

Matsuri SW1   £ 47   ❷❷④
15 Bury St   0171-839 1101   3–3D
"Wonderful" St James's teppan-yaki (there is also a sushi
bar), which provides "exceptional" food; "entertainment from
the chef" can make it "fun", even if the décor is not. / 10 pm;
closed Sun; no Switch.

Mayflower W1   £ 27   ❷④④
68-70 Shaftesbury Ave   0171-734 9207   4–3A
"As close to China as we've found" – avoid being fobbed
off with the dreary set menus, and this ordinary-looking
Theatreland joint can provide some "excellent", authentic
grub. / 3.45 am; Mon-Fri L; closed Sat L.

Medina's EC1   £ 19   ④❷❸
10 Clerkenwell Gn   0171-490 4041   9–1A
"Consistently cheerful" new City-fringe pizzeria, which is
usually "lively", in spite of its "slightly clinical" décor. / 11 pm;
closed Sun D.

Mediterranean Café W1   £ 17   ❸❷④
18 Berwick St   0171-437 0560   3–2D
"Endearingly quaint and shambolic" Soho back street bistro –
newly opened, though you'd never know it – which "surprises"
some with the quality of its cooking. / Midnight, Fri–Sat 1 am;
no Amex.

Mediterraneo W11 £ 28 ➋➋➋
37 Kensington Park Rd 0171-792 3131 6–1A
This newcomer may not yet be "as lively as Osteria Basilico" (its parent, a few feet away on Notting Hill's trendy restaurant strip), but, thanks to its "good", "fresh" Italian food it already boasts a similar "beautiful people" following. / 11.30 pm.

Mekong SW1 £ 19 ➌④④
46 Churton St 0171-630 9568 2–4B
"Nothing exceptional, but enjoyable" – this Pimlico Vietnamese local provides "reliable" fodder, although the service is "erratic". / 11.30 pm; no Amex.

Melati W1 £ 23 ➋④④
21 Great Windmill St 0171-437 2745 3–2D
"Still good after all these years", this conveniently located Malaysian, near Piccadilly Circus, is "definitely worth a visit, if only for the food"; it's "usually far too crowded". / 11.30 pm, Fri & Sat 12.30 am; no Switch.

Memories of India SW7 £ 21 ➋➋➌
18 Gloucester Rd 0171-589 6450 5–1B
"The best food at OK prices" and a civilised attitude make this South Kensington subcontinental a local favourite. / 11.15 pm.

Le Mercury N1 £ 18 ⑤⑤➌
140a Upper St 0171-354 4088 8–3D
"Cheap but nothing else", this budget Bohemian bistro (near Islington's Almeida Theatre), offers "boring" budget staples; for the staff, "out-of-sight is out-of-mind". / 1 am, Sun 11.30 pm; no Amex; no smoking area.

Mesclun N16 £ 25 ➊➊④
24 Stoke Newington Ch St 0171-249 5029 1–1C
Very "imaginative", "well prepared" modern British cooking makes this "cramped", and to some "precious", Stoke Newington venture one of the very best places in the area. / 11 pm; D only; except Sun when open all day; no Amex.

Meson don Felipe SE1 £ 23 ➌④➊
53 The Cut 0171-928 3237 9–4A
"Always fun" Waterloo bar, serving "genuine tapas in a pleasant, pubby atmosphere" – "it wouldn't be the same without the sometimes too enthusiastic guitarist!" / 11 pm; closed Sun; no Amex; book pre 7.30 pm only.

Le Metro SW3 £ 27 ➌➌➋
28 Basil St 0171-589 6286 5–1D
"A great place to meet", near Harrods, this soothing basement wine bar offers an "interesting", if limited menu, and an "extensive" wine list. / 10.30 pm; closed Sun; no booking at L.

Mezzanine SE1   **£27**   ③③④

National Theatre, South Bank   0171-452 3600   2–3D
"A great option before or after theatre on the South Bank" –
the modern British grub at the RNT's in-house restaurant is
"surprisingly good". / 11 pm; closed Sun; no smoking area.

Mezzo W1   **£46**   ⑤⑤④

100 Wardour St   0171-314 4000   3–2D
"Very mean portions" of *"conveyor-belt"* modern British
cooking at *"extortionate"* prices – not to mention *"pushy"*
and *"shoddy"* service – make Conran's huge Soho flagship
"the biggest let-down ever"; only three years old, and the
place is already *"well past its sell-by date"*. / Mon-Wed midnight,
Thu-Sat 1 am (crustacea till 3 am); closed Sat L; set Sun L £26(FP).

Mezzonine W1   **£32**   ⑤⑤④

100 Wardour St   0171-314 4000   3–2D
"Surely it must be illegal to be this bad?" – Mezzo's upstairs
doles out *"inadequate"* and overpriced oriental fodder in
cramped refectory conditions. / Mon-Thu 12.45 am, Fri-Sat 2.45 am;
closed Sun; set pre-th. £21(FP).

Mildreds W1   **£19**   ❷❸❸

58 Greek St   0171-494 1634   4–2A
"Small but very pleasant and cheap" West End café which
serves *"huge portions"* of *"vegetarian food that's actually
filling"*; given its sizeable Soho-Boho following, it can get
"hellishly squashed and noisy". / 11 pm; closed Sun; no credit cards;
no smoking; no booking.

Mimmo d'Ischia SW1   **£47**   ❸❸❷

61 Elizabeth St   0171-730 5406   2–4A
To its rather mature 'club' of devotees, this *"outrageously"*
expensive, *"long-running"* Belgravian is *"still the best
traditional Italian"*, and *"always a fun place to go"*.
/ 11.30 pm; closed Sun D; smart casual.

Mims EN4   **£31**   ❷⑤⑤

63 East Barnet Road   0181-449 2974   1–1B
A *"very imaginative chef"* has carved something of a
reputation for this uninspiring-looking South Barnet outfit;
our pilgrimage found wacky, but heavy cooking – worth a
detour, but not a special trip; *"the service is not good"*.
/ 11 pm; closed Mon & Sat L; no Amex & no Switch; no smoking area.

Min's Bar SW3   **£39**   ⑤❸❷

31 Beauchamp Place   0171-589 5080   5–1C
Knightsbridge Eurotrash have taken to this unusually
comfortable and *"elegant"* new bar/restaurant (on the site
long occupied by Bill Bentley's); the cooking is incidental
and very pricey.

Mirabelle W1   £40   ❷❷❷

56 Curzon St   0171-499 4636   3–4B
"Catch it early, prices must go up once it has found its feet" –
but initially one can't do anything but praise Marco Pierre
White's *"fine relaunch"* of this wonderfully glamorous
Mayfair site, where *"straightforward"* modern French
cooking is twinned with *"courteous and efficient"* service;
"lovely terrace". / Midnight; no smoking area; set pre-th. £27(FP).

Mitsukoshi SW1   £60   ❶❶⑤

14-16 Regent St   0171-930 0317   3–3D
"Quality Japanese", whose refined dishes (sushi in particular)
and impeccable service combine to make it, for some, the
capital's top representative of that cuisine; the basement
setting is smart, but very austere. / 9.30 pm; closed Sun.

Miyama W1   £53   ❷④⑤

38 Clarges St   0171-499 2443   3–4B
"Very fresh" dishes (including *"exceptional sushi"*) make
this Mayfair fixture one of the top Japaneses in town;
"no atmosphere, though". / 10.30 pm; closed Sat L & Sun L;
smart casual.

Momo W1   £36   ④④❶

25 Heddon St   0171-434 4040   3–2C
"Chic, but no stamina" – though the *"phenomenal"*
atmosphere of this *"vibrant"* Moroccan yearling, just off
Regent Street, parties on, the food is now often *"terrible"*,
and service *"just too in love with itself"*. / 11.15 pm;
closed Sat L & Sun; set weekday L £23(FP).

Mon Plaisir WC2   £34   ❷❷❶

21 Monmouth St   0171-836 7243   4–2B
"Nothing trendy or cutting edge" is precisely the point of
this Gallic *"favourite"* of over fifty years' standing; *"robust"*
cooking, charming service and *"excellent"* pre-theatre and
lunch menus are among the attractions. / 11.15 pm; closed Sat L
& Sun; set pre-th. £15(FP).

Mona Lisa SW10   £13   ❸❸⑤

417 King's Rd   0171-376 5447   5–3B
A *"smashing greasy spoon with pretensions"*, this World's End
café makes a *"useful neighbourhood spot"* for *"excellent"*
breakfasts and *"cheap Italian food"*. / 10.45 pm; closed Sun D;
no credit cards.

Mongolian Barbecue   £22   ⑤④④

12 Maiden Ln, WC2   0171-379 7722   4–3D
61 Gloucester Rd, SW7   0171-581 8747   5–2B
1-3 Acton Ln, W4   0181-995 0575   7–2A
88-89 Chalk Farm Rd, NW1   0171-482 6626   8–2B
"Ulan Bator is nothing like this"; *"everything ends up tasting
the same"* at these budget, *"help yourself"* wok-joints, which
some – we are told – think are *"fun"*. / 11 pm; D only.

Monkeys SW3 £33 ❷❸❷
1 Cale St   0171-352 4711   5–2C
"Good for a meaty dinner", this *"intimate"* Chelsea
traditionalist (known for *"the best game"*, and with a
"great list of clarets") serves up some *"delicious"* cooking;
service is *"attentive"* and *"knowledgeable"*. / 10.30 pm;
closed Sat & Sun; no Amex.

Monsieur Max TW12 £26 ❷❸❸
133 High St, Hampton Hill   0181-979 5546   1–4A
"Excellent food in the suburbs"; Max Renzland's very
competent venture produces some *"great French cooking"*
in the *"unlikely location"* of Hampton Hill; service can be
"slow", and the place is licensed, but invitation to BYO for a
fiver's corkage is a feature. / 10.30 pm; closed Sat L; no Amex.

Montana SW6 £36 ❷❸❸
125-129 Dawes Rd   0171-385 9500   10–1B
"Delicious", *"wonderfully different"* south west American
cooking maintains the popularity of this *"fun"* Fulhamite
(which has *"great live jazz"* most nights) – especially
"for Sunday brunch"; the *"somewhat shabby"* décor would
merit some attention. / 11 pm, Fri & Sat 11.30 pm; closed
Mon-Thu L; set weekday L £21(FP).

Montpeliano SW7 £42 ❷❷❸
13 Montpelier St   0171-589 0032   5–1C
"Not quite as bad as you say" and *"worth the cost"* are
two of the reports which have helped to boost ratings at this
long-established Knightsbridge trattoria; we're still with those
who say it's *"nothing special"*. / Midnight.

Monza SW3 £32 ❸❷❸
6 Yeoman's Rw   0171-591 0210   5–2C
"An old-style Italian" at heart – this small and *"relaxed"*
Knightsbridge side street newcomer *"aims to please"*; the
cooking is generally *"decent"*, if *"variable"*. / 11.30 pm;
closed Mon L.

Moro EC1 £30 ❷❷❷
34-36 Exmouth Mkt   0171-833 8336   9–1A
The *"tantalising explosion of north African flavours"* offered
by this modish and *"lively"* Clerkenwell yearling has put it well
and truly on London's culinary map. / 10.30 pm; closed Sat & Sun.

Moshi Moshi Sushi £18 ❷❸④
Unit 24, Liverpool St Station, EC2   0171-247 3227   9–2D
7-8 Limeburner Ln, EC4   0171-248 1808   9–2A
"Fun", *"quick"* and *"excellent value for money"* – no wonder
these *"consistent"* City conveyor-belt sushi cafés are *"very
crowded at lunch"*, particularly the original, which overlooks
the tracks at Liverpool Street station. / 9 pm; closed Sat & Sun;
no Amex or Switch; EC2 no smoking, EC4 no smoking area; no booking.

Motcomb's SW1   £41   ④②②
26 Motcomb St 0171-235 9170 2–4A
"Pleasant" and *"romantic"* Belgravia basement, whose *"chic"*
and fairly mature following enjoys *"professionally"* served, but
so-so English fare. / 11 pm; closed Sun; smart casual.

Moxon's SW4   £26   ②③④
14 Clapham Park Road 0171-627 2468 10–2D
The *"excellent, imaginative fish"* cooking, at this agreeable
neighbourhood newcomer, is well above the standard you
might expect, given its uninspiring Clapham location
(opposite Sainsbury's). / 10.30 pm; closed Mon; no Amex.

MPW E14   £33   ②③⑤
2nd Fl, Cabot Pl East 0171-513 0513 1–3D
This Marco Pierre White-branded venue is the most
ambitious place in Docklands, but has *"no ambience"* (and,
unsurprisingly, can be *"very quiet in the evening"*) some have
found the cooking *"superb"*, but it has been *"variable"* and
whether it will survive chef, Gary Holihead's departure (to
Moreton's) remains to be seen. / 9 pm; closed Sat & Sun.

Mr Chow SW1   £44   ③③②
151 Knightsbridge 0171-589 7347 5–1D
Despite its relaunch a couple of years ago, this once-famous,
deeply '60s, Knightsbridge oriental (where Italian waiters
deliver Chinese grub) still doesn't make many waves; some
do proclaim *"surprisingly good food"*. / Midnight; set Sun L £28(FP).

Mr Kong WC2   £20   ②③⑤
21 Lisle St 0171-437 7341 4–3A
"Always consistent", *"well above average"* dishes (the *"house
specials"*, in particular) ensure this *"cramped"* Chinatown
fixture remains a *"favourite"*; *"do not sit in the basement"*.
/ 2.45 am.

Mr Wing SW5   £36   ②③①
242-244 Old Brompton Rd 0171-370 4450 5–2A
"Expensive, but worth it" for its amazing *"jungle"* setting, this
Earl's Court Chinese remains a top party and trysting point –
*"if you could see your lover through the undergrowth,
it would be very romantic"*. / Midnight.

Le Muscadet W1   £37   ④④④
25 Paddington St 0171-935 2883 2–1A
"The atmosphere is not the same without François", at this
once much-loved bourgeois fixture in Marylebone; nor is the
"very French" grub as good as it used to be. / 10.45 pm, Sat
10 pm; closed Sat L & Sun; no Amex; smart casual.

Museum St Café WC1   £21   ❸②④
47 Museum St   0171-405 3211   2–1C
"Changed beyond all recognition", this "friendly" modern British café is now open all day (but not for dinner) seven days a week, and has shifted to an entirely veggie menu; with its quality, "light" cooking it's still "the best place near the British Museum". / L only; no smoking.

Mustards Brasserie EC1   £28   ④❸④
60 Long Ln   0171-796 4920   9–1B
"For a work lunch, or evening snack and drinks", this wine bar/brasserie, by Smithfield Market, has its advocates; the overall experience, however, is "eminently forgettable". / 11 pm; closed Sat & Sun.

Naked Turtle SW14   £28   ④❷❷
505 Upper Richmond Rd   0181-878 1995   10–2A
"A terrific evening out, topped off by live music" is to be had at this "cosy" and extremely popular East Sheen wine bar; the eclectic cooking is "OK, for the money". / 11 pm; no smoking area; set Sun L £17(FP).

Nam Long SW5   £33   ❸④❷
159 Old Brompton Rd   0171-373 1926   5–2B
"Classy" thirtysomethings are buoyed along by "exotic cocktails" (which "cost a fortune") at this "buzzy" South Kensington bar/restaurant; the Vietnamese cooking is "fine", but service is "very indifferent". / 11.30 pm; closed Sat L & Sun.

Nanking W6   £26   ❸❸❸
332 King St   0181-748 7604   7–2B
Unremarkable, but "good value" and civilised Chinese local, near Ravenscourt Park. / 11.30 pm; no Switch.

Nautilus NW6   £21   ❸④④
27–29 Fortune Gn Rd   0171-435 2532   1–1B
"The best local fish 'n' chips" (deliciously fried in matzo-meal) are to be had at this agreeably tacky West Hampstead parlour. / 10.15 pm; closed Sun; no credit cards; no booking.

Navajo Joe WC2   £29   ④❸❷
34 King St   0171-240 4008   4–3C
It's the "buzzy atmosphere" (it's an "out-of-towner dream place") that is the prime strength of this impressively designed, lofty new Covent Garden space; though some say the "south west American-style" cooking is "surprisingly good", more reports tend towards "grim". / Midnight; closed Sun.

Nayab SW6   £25   ❷❷④
309 New King's Rd   0171-731 6993   10–1B
"It's wasted on Fulham", say fans of this consistently "above average" Indian, near Parson's Green. / Midnight; smart casual; set pre-th. £14(FP).

Neal Street WC2 **£ 55** ④⑤④

26 Neal St 0171-836 8368 4–2C

The food is still – on occasions – "very good", but even fans dwell on the "horrendous" prices at celebrity funghiphile Antonio Carluccio's "cramped" and very "80s" Covent Garden Italian; it "now badly needs a face-lift". / 11 pm; closed Sun; smart casual; set pre-th. £35(FP).

New Culture Revolution **£ 17** ④❸④

305 King's Rd, SW3 0171-352 9281 5–3C
157-159 Notting Hill Gate, W11 tel n/a 6–2B
42 Duncan St, N1 0171-833 9083 8–3D
43 Parkway, NW1 0171-267 2700 8–3B

"Wagamama-wannabe", whose "bright and functional" outlets lag its rôle-model in pretty much every respect; the Camden Town branch is now under separate ownership from the others. / 11 pm; no Amex; no smoking area; to book need 4+.

New World W1 **£ 23** ❸❸④

Gerrard Pl 0171-734 0677 4–3A

"Nice for dim-sum, but other food is average" at this vast and "chaotic" Chinatown landmark (where they are "surprisingly good with children"). / 11.45 pm; no booking Sun L; set weekday L £14(FP).

Newton's SW4 **£ 26** ❸❸❸

33 Abbeville Rd 0181-673 0977 10–2D

"Reliable" modern British "local" popular with Claphamites; what was formerly James R in Parson's Green is now a second branch. / 11.30 pm; no smoking area.

Nico Central W1 **£ 39** ❷④④

35 Great Portland St 0171-436 8846 3–1C

"A restaurant thriving without a soul", this "bourgeois" Marylebone spot offers "dependable" but "unimaginative" Gallic fare, served "slowly and inattentively" at tables which are "too close together". / 11 pm; closed Sat L & Sun; smart casual.

Nicole's W1 **£ 43** ④❸❸

158 New Bond St 0171-499 8408 3–3C

"Light, cool, stylish", "very ladies-who-lunch" Mayfair fashion store basement, whose modern British cooking could be worse, but is "expensive" for what it is. / 10.45 pm; closed Sat D & Sun; no smoking area.

Nikita's SW10 **£ 36** ⑤④❷

65 Ifield Rd 0171-352 6326 5–3B

"Excellent, if you enjoy vodka", this cosy ("especially in winter") party-basement regularly occasions memory-loss amongst its patrons; given the "terrible", "mock-Russian" grub, this is probably no bad thing. / 11.30 pm; D only; closed Sun.

Nine Golden Square W1   £ 27   **❸❸**④

9 Golden Sq   0171-439 2424   3–2D

This "plain, soulless, uninteresting room", on the fringe of Soho (previously Gabriel, RIP), has never gathered much of a following; a shame, as the "good value" modern British cooking is its "redeeming feature". / Mon–Wed 10.30 pm, Thu–Sat 11.30 pm; closed Sat L & Sun.

No 1 Cigar Club W1   £ 37   ⑤**❷❷**

1 Percy St   0171-636 8141   2–1C

If you're going to close a classic (Fitzrovia's White Tower, RIP), it's as well to replace it with something better; this "civilised" club–cum–restaurant, however, has been dishing up food so "dreadful" that, within a year of opening, a change of format is already being contemplated. / 11 pm; closed Sat L & Sun.

NOBU W1   £ 50   **❶❸❷**

Metropolitan Hotel, Old Park Ln   0171-447 4747   3–4A

"Wow" flavours, and dishes that are "a feast for the eyes" mean you just "have to like" Matsuhisa Nobu's cooking – a wizard blend of Japanese and South American inspirations; some, though, "hate the attitude" of this mega-trendy Mayfair venue, whose prices are nothing short of "horrific". / 10.30 pm; closed Sat L & Sun; no smoking area.

Noho W1   £ 21   **❷❷❸**

32 Charlotte St   0171-636 4445   2–1C

Groovy and comfortable, new Fitzrovia noodle-parlour, whose cooking, on an early visit, was above par. / 11.30 pm.

Nontas NW1   £ 18   **❸❸**④

14 Camden High St   0171-387 4579   8–3C

The "Greek family atmosphere" – "cats" and all – makes this dated taverna, with its "honest" cooking at "time warp" prices, a "not bad" Camden Town choice. / 11.30 pm; closed Sun; no Switch.

Noor Jahan SW5   £ 25   **❷**④④

2a Bina Gdns   0171-373 6522   5–2B

"Consistent" cooking ensures that this South Kensington subcontinental is "confidently a favourite" for many; perfunctory service, though, helps to reduce the atmosphere to "functional". / 11.30 pm; no Switch.

The North Pole SE10   £ 27   **❸❷❸**

131 Greenwich High Road   0181-853 3020   1–3D

Le tout Greenwich seems to descend on the upstairs room of this new, large pub-conversion, which is kind of wacky (goldfish in the lamp fittings) and kind of not (cottage chairs and tables); the modern British menu comes off pretty well. / 10.15 pm; closed Mon.

F S A

C Notarianni & Sons SW11 £23 ❸④④
142 Battersea High St   0171-228 7133   10–1C
*"Authentic and generous toppings" help make this
long-established family-run Battersea pizzeria worth seeking
out, though "grumpy service" can detract from an otherwise
good time.* / 11 pm; closed Sat L & Sun; no Amex & no Switch.

Noto £19 ❸❷⑤
2/3 Bassishaw Highwalk, EC2   0171-256 9433   9–3B
7 Bread St, EC4   0171-329 8056   9–2C
*"High-grade Japanese noodles" – in "big bowls" at
"reasonable prices" – make these "high turnover" City
orientals worth knowing about for a "quick, tasty" lunch.*
/ EC2 10.15 pm - EC4 8.45 pm, Sat 6 pm; EC2 closed Sat & Sun – EC4
closed Sat D & Sun; EC2 no Amex – EC4 no credit cards; EC2 no smoking
at L; EC2 no booking for L - EC4 no bookings.

Novelli EC1 EC1 £40 ❸④④
30 Clerkenwell Gn   0171-251 6606   9–1A
*"Consistently good" Gallic cooking makes this prettily located
Clerkenwell Green bistro a useful stand-by on the fringe of
the City; it's cramped and crowded, though, and service
can't always cope.* / 11.15 pm; closed Sat L & Sun.

Novelli W8 W8 £39 ④⑤⑤
122 Palace Gardens Terrace   0171-229 4024   6–2B
*"Come back the Ark" – "tables far too close together" test
the patience of even the most devoted J-C Novelli fan at his
Kensington venture, where the setting is "unpleasantly hot"
and the service is "cold"; and "watch out for extras" –
the Gallic brasserie menu "looks cheaper than it is".* / 11 pm, Fri
& Sat midnight, Sun 10 pm; closed Mon L; closed Sun.

O'Conor Don W1 £30 ❸❷❷
88 Marylebone Ln   0171-935 9311   3–1A
*"Lively" Irish Marylebone tavern, with "great Guinness"
(together with oysters and so on) in the downstairs bar; the
"wholesome", "good value" cooking in the "relaxed" first-floor
restaurant is "what pub food is all about."* / 10.30 pm; closed Sat L
& Sun; smart casual.

**OAK ROOM MARCO PIERRE WHITE
HOTEL MERIDIEN W1** £102 ❸④④
Piccadilly   0171-437 0202   3–3D
*To MPW disciples, "you get what you pay for" at his
stratospherically pricey Mayfair flagship – "the best food in
town" – while to his legion of detractors "the emperor has no
clothes"; opinions unite, though, on the "horribly grand" décor
and the "cold" service (of a place which Michelin, risibly,
plugs as the UK's top 'restaurant agréable').* / 11.15 pm;
closed Sat L & Sun; set weekday L £53(FP).

Oceana W1   **£33**   ❸❸④
Jason's Ct, 76 Wigmore St   0171-224 2992   3–1A
*This obscurely located basement yearling near the Wigmore
Hall still generates mixed feedback, but the consensus is that
it is getting "more settled", with the modern British fare,
in particular, "much better". / 11.15 pm; closed Sat L & Sun.*

L'Odéon W1   **£50**   ④④④
65 Regent St   0171-287 1400   3–3D
*"Pedestrian" cooking – "shocking", say some, "considering
the prices" – makes it difficult to see why anyone would dine
at this West End Gallic mega-brasserie; the "good value lunch
menu" has its fans, though, but it can take an age to come.
/ 11.30 pm; closed Sun; no smoking area; set pre-th. £31(FP).*

Odette's NW1   **£39**   ❷❷❶
130 Regent's Pk Rd   0171-586 5486   8–3B
*"Gorgeous, narcissistic décor" (mirrors everywhere) makes
this "fine Primrose Hill landmark" a "truly romantic setting";
"skilful" eclectic cooking and a "varied choice of
excellent-value wines" also play their part in making this a
"top-class" all-rounder. / 11 pm; closed Sat L & Sun; set Sun L £20(FP).*

Odin's W1   **£35**   ❷❶❶
27 Devonshire St   0171-935 7296   2–1A
*"Excellent for a romantic dîner-à-deux" (and also a favourite
for business entertaining), this "comfortable", "old-fashioned"
establishment is sumptuously decorated with the late
Peter Langan's art collection; outstanding service combines
friendliness with discretion, and the traditional cooking is "well
prepared and presented". / 11 pm; closed Sat & Sun; smart casual.*

The Old School Thai SW11   **£24**   ❸❶❸
147 Lavender Hl   0171-228 2345   10–1C
*This Battersea yearling inspires local rave reviews for its
"authentic", "reasonably priced" Thai food; we are with those
who feel the "professional" and "caring" service is a greater
attraction. / 11 pm; closed Sun L; no smoking area; bookings only after 5pm.*

Oliveto SW1   **£29**   ❷❸❸
49 Elizabeth St   0171-730 0074   2–4A
*"Naples comes to Victoria" at this "stylish" and "innovative"
pizzeria; the "great, original pasta" is quite good, too.
/ 11.30 pm.*

Olivo SW1   **£34**   ❷❸❸
21 Eccleston St   0171-730 2505   2–4B
*"Attentive, friendly and focussed, and with no airs and
graces", this Victoria Italian offers "well prepared",
"flavoursome" dishes from an "interesting" Sardinian menu.
/ 11 pm; closed Sat L & Sun L.*

On the Rise SW11 £ 26 ④❸④

30 Battersea Rise 0171-228 0611 10–2C

The "erratic" modern British cooking – but "when it's good, it's very good" – at this "unatmospheric" Battersea yearling gives rise to a sense of promise unfulfilled. / 11 pm, Fri & Sat 11.30 pm; no Amex.

1 Lawn Terrace SE3 £ 30 ❸④❸

1 Lawn Terrace 0181-355 1110 1–4D

"West End quality in Blackheath" makes this "stylish" modern British yearling – that's "lofty and intimate at the same time" – a "welcome addition to south east London"; in September '98, it moved into the same ownership as Bank. / 10.30 pm; closed Sat L.

1 Lombard Street EC3 £ 36 ❷❸❸

Lombard Street 0171-929 6611 9–3C

Elegant, modern British newcomer, in an old banking hall by the Bank of England, where an early visit found Herbert Berger's cooking off to a flying start; siting the bar in the middle of the brasserie makes for an ambience some may find discordant, but a more contemplative (and expensive) 'fine dining' room is promised. / 10 pm, closed Sat & Sun.

192 W11 £ 35 ④④❸

192 Kensington Pk Rd 0171-229 0482 6–1A

The "expensive and average" food is "not really the point" of this "too popular" Notting Hill hang-out – it's "where trustafarians go to see and be seen"; to the rest of the world it can just seem "passé" now, and service, as ever, can be "atrocious". / 11.30 pm; set Sun L £24(FP).

One-O-One SW1 £ 60 ④❷④

Sheraton Park Tower, Knightsbridge 0171-290 7101 5–1D

Appalling Muzak ('specially selected', apparently) sets an odd tone at this would-be swanky, revamped hotel dining room (which has a panoramic view of Knightsbridge's traffic); the Gallic fish and seafood specialities are OK, but why are the prices so high?; and why are the staff dressed as fugitives from Star Trek? / 10.30 pm.

L'Oranger SW1 £ 43 ❶❶❷

5 St James's St 0171-839 3774 3–4D

The "consistent" success-story of this "discreet" and comfortable modern French establishment in St James's was interrupted in mid-1998, when the chef left in an acrimonious blaze of publicity; it's now down to former sous-chef Benamar Kamal to maintain its reputation. / 11.15 pm; closed Sat L & Sun L.

Oriel SW1   **£ 29**   ⑤④❸
50-51 Sloane Sq   0171-730 2804   5–2D
Location, location, and location make this "classic" brasserie,
on a prominent Sloane Square corner, a natural rendezvous;
it's "a must for brunch", perhaps, but food that "could be
better" and service that "fancies itself" makes this
"a place to meet, not eat". / 10.45 pm; no smoking area;
need 6+ to book; no w/e bookings.

Orrery W1   **£ 50**   ④❸❸
55 Marylebone High St   0171-616 8000   2–1A
"Stylish", but "cramped" new Conran venture – overlooking a
Marylebone churchyard – where "proficient", but unambitious
modern French cooking is served at premium prices.
/ 10.30 pm.

Orsino W11   **£ 39**   ❸④❸
119 Portland Rd   0171-221 3299   6–2A
"Elegant and sophisticated" Italian, hidden away in a quiet
Holland Park back street; its cooking has "improved" of late,
but a "cold" and "arrogant" attitude can still put people's
backs up. / 11.30 pm; no smoking area; set weekday L £23(FP).

Orso WC2   **£ 38**   ④④④
27 Wellington St   0171-240 5269   4–3D
"This used to be my favourite for all occasions, now it's
disappointing" is the overwhelming verdict on this
once-luminous Covent Garden basement Italian, whose
style has become "rushed, expensive and indifferent".
/ Midnight; no smoking area; set Sun L £24(FP).

Oslo Court NW8   **£ 37**   ❶❶❸
Prince Albert Rd   0171-722 8795   8–3A
A "happy, bubbly group of waiters" and "food which is always
super" create a fanatical following for this "old-fashioned, but
consistently excellent" International old-timer, in a Regent's
Park apartment block; "take your parents" – "the staff really
know how to look after more elderly diners". / 11 pm; closed Sun;
smart casual.

Osteria Antica Bologna SW11   **£ 27**   ❸④❸
23 Northcote Rd   0171-978 4771   10–2C
"Rustic" Italian, near Clapham Junction, long celebrated for
its "unique" menu of "wonderful, authentic" dishes; the
cooking, however, is currently "not as good as it could be".
/ 11 pm, Fri & Sat 11.30 pm.

Osteria Basilico W11   **£ 28**   ❸④❷
29 Kensington Pk Rd   0171-727 9957   6–1A
"Absurdly popular", "buzzy, buzzy, noisy" Notting Hillbilly
hangout, whose Italian cooking, though still "good", is not
up to its best past form. / 11 pm; no booking Sat L.

OXO TOWER SE1   £ 42   ④④❷

Barge House St   0171-803 3888   9–3A

*"A room with a view, but little else" – the "stunning"
panorama from this eighth-floor vantage point has made
it the most-mentioned place in our survey; it "trades on its
location", though – the modern British fare is "nothing special
for a lot of money" and service can be "abysmal"; those not
on expenses should definitely stick to the brasserie (to which
our price relates). / 11 pm; closed Sat L.*

Pacific Spice EC1   £ 30   ❸❸④

42 Northampton Rd   0171-278 9983   9–1A

*Oddly situated in a quiet Clerkenwell backstreet (overlooking
a small park), this agreeable-enough new pub-conversion –
an adjunct to the Silks & Spice chain – conjures up some
interesting Pacific rim dishes. / 11 pm; no smoking area.*

Le Palais du Jardin WC2   £ 35   ❸❸❷

136 Long Acre   0171-379 5353   4–3C

*Many still applaud "excellent food at a reasonable price" at
this large, popular and once-exemplary Gallic brasserie in
Covent Garden; "surly" service is a now recurrent problem,
however, and standards have fallen across the board. / Midnight.*

Palatino W4   £ 28   ❸❷④

6 Turnham Green Terrace   0181-994 0086   7–2A

*It's a touch "unpredictable", but on a good day you get
"very flavoursome Tuscan staples" at this "excellent local
Italian", near Turnham Green tube. / 11 pm; no smoking area.*

Palio W11   £ 31   ⑤⑤❸

175 Westbourne Grove   0171-221 6624   6–1B

*It may still be "lively and fun", but far too many think the
modern British food is a "nightmare" at this Notting Hill
bar/restaurant; it's "good for a late snack, but nothing else".
/ 11.30 pm; set weekday L £18(FP).*

Paparazzi Café SW3   £ 28   ④④❷

58 Fulham Rd   0171-589 0876   5–2C

*For a "riotous night out", this "young and fun" Chelsea
Euroscene has its attractions (though these do not include the
"weak" pizzas and sometimes "slow" and "grumpy" service);
a Mayfair sibling is promised soon. / 11 am; no Switch; smart casual;
non on Sun.*

The Papaya Tree W8   £ 27   ❸❷④

209 Kensington High Street   0171-937 2260   7–1D

*"Charming" Kensington "family outfit", offering "good"
Thai cooking in a pleasant-enough basement. / 11 pm;
closed Sun; no smoking area.*

Pasha SW7 £31 ④❸❶

1 Gloucester Rd   0171-589 7969   5–1B
*This glamorous new South Kensington Moroccan may have
a "lovely" atmosphere, but the "uninspiring" food and iffy
service bear all the hallmarks of a Mogens Tholstrop creation
– are things set to improve, we wonder, under Belgo Group,
the new owners? / 11.30 pm; closed Sun.*

Pasha N1 £23 ❸❶❶

301 Upper St   0171-226 1454   8–3D
*"Obliging service", and "outstanding-value set meals"
ensure that this is "still a favourite Turkish for Islingtonians".
/ 11.30 pm, Fri & Sat midnight; no Switch; set weekday L £14(FP).*

Pasta di Milano £20 ❸❸④

15 Greek Street, W1   0171-434 2545   4–2A
373 Kensington High Street, W8   0171-610 5552   7–1D
*"Capable pasta, and on-the-ball service" – for the majority
of early reporters, at least – makes this an "interesting"
new chain; we are in the minority who thought it "a
disappointment, especially from the PizzaExpress group".
/ Midnight; book for 7+ only.*

Patio W12 £17 ❸❷❷

5 Goldhawk Rd   0181-743 5194   7–1C
*"A real gem", this "shabby", but "cosy and fun" Shepherd's
Bush Pole is unanimously praised for its festive atmosphere,
and "friendly" and "eccentric" service; it serves an
"amazing-value set meal" (including a "free shot of vodka").
/ Midnight; closed Sat L & Sun L; no smoking area.*

Pâtisserie Valerie £20 ❸❸❷

105 Marylebone High St, W1   0171-935 6240   2–1A
44 Old Compton St, W1   0171-437 3466   4–2A
RIBA Centre, 66 Portland Pl, W1   0171-631 0467   2–1B
8 Russell St, WC2   0171-240 0064   4–3D
215 Brompton Rd, SW3   0171-823 9971   5–2C
*"Cakes to die for", "proper coffee", "the best croissants"
and "wonderful scrambled eggs" – such are the attractions
of these "cosy", "bustling" and "good value" rendezvous.
/ 6 pm-8 pm, Sun earlier; Portland Pl, closed Sun; no smoking area; no booking.*

Paulo's W6 £24 ❸❷❸

30 Greyhound Rd   0171-385 9264   7–2C
*"To feel like a guest at a Brazilian family meal", check out
the all-you-can-eat buffet at this "fun and different"
Hammersmith spot; it's popular for parties, and caters well
for veggies. / 10.30 pm; D only – Sun L only, closed Mon; no credit cards.*

The Peasant EC1 £31 ❸❷❸

240 St John St   0171-336 7726   8–3D
*"Reliable" Clerkenwell gastropub with an "unexpectedly nice
first floor dining room", which pleases with its "good value",
Mediterranean-inspired grub from "quality ingredients".
/ 11 pm; closed Sat L & Sun.*

Pelham Street SW7 £39 ④④❸

93 Pelham St   0171-584 4788   5–2C

Pace rave press reviews for this agreeably understated Brompton Cross newcomer, we found modern British cooking that was trying too hard, and service which, though amiable, was too slow. / 11 pm; closed Sun D.

The Pen SW6 £29 ❸❸❸

51 Parson's Green Ln   0171-371 8517   10–1B

Above a lively, trendified pub (opposite Parson's Green tube), this agreeable dining room offers "decent" cooking at a fair price. / 11 pm.

The People's Palace SE1 £38 ④❸④

South Bank Centre   0171-928 9999   2–3D

"Uninspired" modern British cooking and a slightly "gloomy" atmosphere make it difficult to get excited about the Festival Hall's cavernous dining room; on a sunny day, though, the "superb river views mean all is always forgiven". / 11 pm.

The Pepper Tree SW4 £17 ❷❷❸

19 Clapham Common S'side   0171-622 1758   10–2D

"Long tables and no reservations" set the scene at this "always buzzing", "brilliant", "cheap and cheerful" Clapham Thai; "there are always queues, but they move quickly". / 11 pm, Mon and Sun 10.30 pm; no Amex; no smoking area; no D bookings.

La Perla WC2 £24 ❸④❷

28 Maiden Ln   0171-240 7400   4–4D

"Raucous" Covent Garden "cantina", providing "big portions of edible, if not wholly authentic, Mexican fare"; service can be "abrupt". / 11 pm; closed Sun D.

La Perla SW3 £33 ❸❸❸

62 Fulham Rd   0171-584 8375   5–2C

"Glamorous", amiably glitzy, new Chelsea Italian (on the former site of San Frediano, RIP), which is "tempting a well-heeled crowd to pay some pretty hefty prices"; service verges on "fawning". / Midnight.

Le P'tit Normand SW18 £27 ❸❷❸

185 Merton Rd   0181-871 0233   10–2B

"A small piece of France in Southfields", this "very traditional" family-run restaurant wins special praise for its "amazing value" set lunches; à la carte, though, there is a feeling that its "good, simple" cooking is "unreasonably expensive". / 10 pm, Fri & Sat 11 pm; closed Sat L; set weekday L £17(FP).

Pharmacy W11 £ 38 ④④❸

150 Notting Hill Gate   0171-221 2442   6–2B
"After all the hype", this prominently located, Damien Hirst-designed newcomer is "not as wild as hoped"; in fact, it's "just another trendy place" where staff who are "in love with themselves" serve "very ordinary and pricey" cooking. / 10.30 pm; set weekday L £26(FP).

Phoenicia W8 £ 34 ❷①❸

11-13 Abingdon Rd   0171-937 0120   5–1A
The "fresh, direct tastes" of the meze (and other fare), together with its warm welcome, make this family-run establishment in Kensington a "favourite Lebanese". / 11.45 pm; set weekday L £18(FP).

Phoenix Bar & Grill SW15 £ 29 ❸❷❷

Pentlow St   0181-780 3131   10–1A
"Stark", but agreeable Putney sibling to Sonny's which is now getting into its stride, offering "reliable" and "varied" modern British cooking. / 11.30 pm, Sun 10 pm; closed Sat L.

Phuket SW11 £ 19 ❸❷④

246 Battersea Pk Rd   0171-223 5924   10–1C
"The food never lets you down at this "friendly" Battersea Thai" (though the same could not be said for the "rather dull" ambience). / 11.30 pm; D only.

PIED À TERRE W1 £ 55 ❷❸④

34 Charlotte St   0171-636 1178   2–1C
"Very serious" modern French cooking, offering some "rich and gorgeous flavours", wins acclaim for this "gastro-tastic" Fitzrovian; last year's improvements on the service front have reversed, however, and there are resurgent niggles that the place "lacks soul". / 10.30 pm; closed Sat L & Sun; smart casual; set weekday L £38(FP).

La Piragua N1 £ 17 ❸❷❷

176 Upper St   0171-354 2843   8–2D
"The vibes are great" at this "cheap" and "interesting" Islington Latin American, where "very good steaks" are the highlight of the menu. / Midnight; no credit cards.

Pitcher & Piano   £ 23   ④④❷
69-70 Dean St, W1   0171-434 3585   4–2A
40-42 King William IV St, WC2   0171-240 6180   4–4C
214 Fulham Rd, SW10   0171-352 9234   5–3B
316-318 King's Road, SW3   0171-352 0025   5–3C
871-873 Fulham Rd, SW6   0171-736 3910   10–1B
18-20 Chiswick High Rd, W4   0181-742 7731   7–2B
69 Upper St, N1   0171-704 9974   8–3D
94 Northcote Rd, SW11   0171-738 9781   10–2C
8 Balham Hill, SW12   0181-673 1107   10–2C
11 Bellevue Rd, SW17   0181-767 6982   10–2C
194-200 Bishopsgate, EC3   0171-929 5914   9–2D
The Arches, 9 Crutched Friars, EC3   0171-480 6818   9–3D
"Lively" twentysomething bars, "good for after-work drinks"
and weekend "lazing around"; go for the buzzing
atmosphere, rather than the sometimes "appalling"
snacks. / 10 pm - 11 pm; W1, EC3 & EC2 closed Sun.

Pizza Metro SW11   £ 23   ❶❶❸
64 Battersea Rise   0171-228 3812   10–2C
"You usually have to be Italian to get a good table" at this
"enormously popular" and "cramped" Battersea venture,
which provides "real pizza" (served by the metre), and
"blasts of warm Italian hospitality". / 11 pm; closed Mon & weekday
Lunch; no Amex.

Pizza On The Park SW1   £ 22   ④❸❷
11 Knightsbridge   0171-235 5273   2–3A
Large and airy, "souped up" PizzaExpress, just by Hyde Park
Corner, which is wearing well. / Midnight; no smoking area; no booking.

Pizza Pomodoro   £ 22   ④④❷
51 Beauchamp Pl, SW3   0171-589 1278   5–1C
7 Steward St, E1   0171-377 6186   9–1D
The "cheerful and lively" original of this small pizzeria chain
– situated in a seedy Knightsbridge basement – is famed for
its "live bands", and happening late-night atmosphere; its
offshoots are nothing special, but useful after a hard day in
the City. / SW3 1 am – E1 midnight; E1 closed Sat & Sun; E1 book only till
12.30 pm L, 7.30 pm D.

Pizza the Action SW6   £ 19   ❸❸❸
678–680 Fulham Rd   0171-736 2716   10–1B
"Good pizza" (and a wide range of other fare), served in "a
pleasant atmosphere", makes this a useful Fulham local
(which is expanding into the adjoining premises). / Midnight.

PizzaExpress £19 ❸❸❸
154 Victoria St, SW1   0171-828 1477   2–4B
10 Dean St, W1   0171-437 9595   3–1D
133 Baker St, W1   0171-486 0888   2–1A
20 Greek St, W1   0171-734 7430   4–2A
21-22 Barrett St, W1   0171-629 1001   3–1A
23 Bruton Pl, W1   0171-495 1411   3–2B
29 Wardour St, W1   0171-437 7215   4–3A
6 Upper St James Street, W1   0171-437 4550   3–2D
7-9 Charlotte St, W1   0171-580 1110   2–1C
30 Coptic St, WC1   0171-636 3232   2–1C
80-81 St Martins Lane, WC2   0171-836 8001   4–3B
9-12 Bow St, WC2   0171-240 3443   4–2D
363 Fulham Rd, SW10   0171-352 5300   5–3B
6-7 Beauchamp Pl, SW3   0171-589 2355   5–1C
Pheasantry, 150-152 King's Road, SW3   0171-351 5031   5–3C
895 Fulham Rd, SW6   0171-731 3117   10–1B
137 Notting Hl Gt, W11   0171-229 6000   6–2B
7 Rockley Rd, W14   0181-749 8582   7–1C
26 Porchester Rd, W2   0171-229 7784   6–1C
252 Chiswick High Rd, W4   0181-747 0193   7–2A
35 Earl's Ct Rd, W8   0171-937 0761   5–1A
335 Upper St, N1   0171-226 9542   8–3D
30 Highgate High Street, N6   0181-341 3434   8–1B
187 Kentish Town Road, NW1   0171-267 0101   8–2B
85-87 Parkway, NW1   0171-267 2600   8–3B
194 Haverstock Hill, NW3   0171-794 6777   8–2A
70 Heath St, NW3   0171-433 1600   8–1A
39-39a Abbey Rd, NW8   0171-624 5577   8–3A
Cardomom Bldg, Shad Thames, SE1   0171-403 8484   9–4D
Chapter Ho, Montague Cl, SE1   0171-378 6446   9–3C
230 Lavender Hill, SW11   0171-223 5677   10–2C
46 Battersea Br Rd, SW11   0171-924 2774   5–4C
305 Up Richmond Rd W, SW14   0181-878 6833   10–2A
144 Up Richmond Rd, SW15   0181-789 1948   10–2B
539 Old York Rd, SW18   0181-877 9812   10–2B
43 Abbeville Rd, SW4   0181-673 8878   10–2D
125 London Wall, EC2   0171-600 8880   9–2B
7-9 St Brides Street, EC4   0171-583 5126   9–2A
"Are the pizzas getting smaller?", at this paragon among pizza-multiples; for a huge number of people, however, it remains the "reassuringly reliable" benchmark by which other chains are to be judged. / 11 pm-Midnight - Greek St Wed-Sat 1 am - Chapter Hs 4.30 pm - St Bride's St 10 pm - London Wall Sat & Sun 8 pm; Chapter Hs, St Bride's St, Upper James Street & Bruton Pl closed Sat & Sun (Chapter Hs open Sat in summer); not all branches take bookings.

Pizzeria Castello SE1 £18 ❸❸❸
20 Walworth Rd   0171-703 2556   1–3C
This "bustling" pizzeria may not be "quite as good as it used to be", but many say it's still "worth the trek" – beware the "queues" to enter "the Elephant & Castle's greatest achievement". / 11 pm; closed Sat L & Sun; smart casual.

Pizzeria Condotti W1 £21 ❸❸❷

4 Mill St 0171-499 1308 3–2C

"A more upmarket PizzaExpress", with a *"spacious and attractive"* setting in a quiet Mayfair street. / Midnight; closed Sun.

Pizzeria Franco SW9 £19 ❶❸④

Brixton Market 0171-738 3021 10–2D

There's a permanent queue for a table at this great-value Brixton Market pizzeria – forebear to Clapham's ultra-trendy Eco. / 5 pm; L only; closed Wed & Sun; closed Sat D; no booking.

PJ's SW3 £31 ④④❸

52 Fulham Rd 0171-581 0025 5–2C

Prices are *"too high for average food and service"*, but none of the trendy Chelsea thirtysomething hanging out at this *"fun"*, and attractive American bar/diner seem to care. / 11.45 pm.

The Place Below EC2 £15 ❷⑤❸

St Mary-le-Bow, Cheapside 0171-329 0789 9–2C

"If you can bear the queues", it's worth a visit to this *"interesting"*, if *"crowded"*, City crypt which serves *"good and original"*, but *"somewhat pricey"* veggie dishes. / L only; closed Sat & Sun; no Amex; no smoking; no booking.

Planet Hollywood W1 £35 ⑤④❸

13 Coventry St 0171-287 1000 4–4A

"Tinseltown-appeal is wearing thin" at this West End mega-theme-joint; that said, it's not quite as dire as much of its competition, and some still think it *"fun"* for a *"brash night out"*. / 1 am; no smoking area; only groups of 6+.

Plummers WC2 £25 ④④⑤

33 King St 0171-240 2534 4–3C

"Not bad, but not great" British cooking still pleases the loyal following of this Covent Garden *"time-warp"*, whose *"provincial"*, and *"cramped"* setting some find *"claustrophobic"*. / 11.30 pm.

Poissonnerie de l'Avenue SW3 £47 ❷❸❸

82 Sloane Av 0171-589 2457 5–2C

"They really know how to cook their fish" at this *"old-fashioned"* (*"passé"*) Brompton Cross fixture, which provides *"expensive, but very good"* seafood in a *"comfortable"*, if *"cramped"*, setting; service *"can be a little offhand and slow"*. / 11.30 pm; closed Sun; smart casual; set weekday L £29(FP).

The Polish Club SW7 £27 ❸❸❷

55 Prince's Gt, Exhibition Rd 0171-589 4635 5–1C

"Unique" South Kensington émigrés' club dining room which provides a *"grand"*, time-warp setting (and, weather permitting, a *"fantastic outside terrace"*); the grub *"continues to improve"*. / 11 pm; smart casual; set Sun L £15(FP).

Pollo W1 £15 ④④❸
20 Old Compton St   0171-734 5917   4–2A
"If you like chaos, you will love" this Soho institution, where "stupidly cheap" Italian cooking is served to a "friendly, mixed clientele". / Midnight; no credit cards; no booking.

Polygon Bar & Grill SW4 £32 ❸❸❷
4 The Polygon, Clapham Old Town   0171-622 1199   10–2D
This "lively", "refreshingly modern" Clapham yearling offers "interesting" contemporary cooking; "it's getting expensive", though, and "not really living up to its early promise". / 11.30 pm; D only Mon-Thu.

Pomegranates SW1 £35 ④❸❷
94 Grosvenor Rd   0171-828 6560   2–4C
"Weird, was this once fashionable?" – this "enticingly dark" Pimlico basement, with its curiously illicit atmosphere, deserves a footnote in history as one of the cradles of 'modern British' cooking, though the food is nowadays "more miss than hit". / 11.15 pm; closed Sat L & Sun; no Switch.

LE PONT DE LA TOUR SE1 £56 ④④❷
36d Shad Thames   0171-403 8403   9–4D
Thanks to its "superb" location – looking across the river to Tower Bridge – Conran Restaurants' 'crown jewel' still offers a top "way to impress"; both the modern French cooking and the service are "going downhill", however, and more and more people just want to know "how do they get away with it?" / 11.30 pm; closed Sat L.

Le Pont de la Tour Bar & Grill SE1 £39 ❷❸❷
36d Shad Thames   0171-403 8403   9–4D
Sharing the "great" riverside location (not to mention the "lovely view" and "outdoor eating" possibilities) of its parent, the adjoining steaks and seafood bar is – in terms of value – a very much better bet. / 11.30 pm; no booking; set Sun L £20(FP).

Poons WC2 £20 ❸④④
4 Leicester St   0171-437 1528   4–3A
"A reliable place", this "busy", very well known Chinese, just off Leicester Square, pleases its widespread following with its "cheap", "good value" chow. / 11.30 pm.

Poons, Lisle Street WC2 £19 ❸④⑤
27 Lisle St   0171-437 4549   4–3B
The "very basic" original Poons remains a "Chinatown refuge" for its loyal fans; standards are very similar to the better-known relation (above). / 11.30 pm; no Amex; no smoking area.

Popeseye W14 £29 ❶❷❸
108 Blythe Rd 0171-610 4578 7–1C
*"Single-handedly attempting to save the British beef industry",
this unpretentious Brook Green café has a simple, but brilliant
formula – "the best steak and chips", accompanied by "great
wines at reasonable prices".* / 10.30 pm; D only; no credit cards.

La Porchetta Pizzeria N4 £17 ❷❸❷
147 Stroud Green Rd 0171-281 2892 8–1D
*"OTT Italian atmosphere", "monster pizzas", and other
"great value dishes" sum to a larger-than-life formula at
this "noisy" Finsbury Park phenomenon; no booking makes
it "hard to get in".* / Midnight; closed Sat D & Sun D.

La Porte des Indes W1 £43 ❸❸❷
32 Bryanston St 0171-224 0055 2–2A
*Some still think the Blue Elephant's Indian cousin, near
Marble Arch, "overrated", "overpriced" and "soulless"; the
"impressive" décor has many fans, though, and holding prices
static since opening has helped the Indian/French colonial fare
to find more favour.* / Midnight, Sun 10.30 pm; closed Sat L;
smart casual; no smoking area; set Sun L £25(FP).

Porters WC2 £21 ④⑤⑤
17 Henrietta St 0171-836 6466 4–3D
*"Pies, pies, pies" top the bill at this English-theme Covent
Garden establishment; standards are "lacklustre and
overpriced", and some think it just a "tourist trap".* / 11.30 pm.

Il Portico W8 £32 ❸❸❸
277 Kensington High St 0171-602 6262 7–1D
*"Bubbly", "classic" Italian – next to the Odeon Kensington;
regulars "love it" for its "friendly staff" and "pleasant,
if unexciting" menu.* / 11.15 pm; closed Sun.

La Poule au Pot SW1 £40 ❸❸❶
231 Ebury St 0171-730 7763 5–2D
*"Still the most romantic rendezvous in London", say reporters
of this Pimlico old-timer, where "liaisons abound" in the
"dark", "candle-lit" nooks; French "home-cooking", and
characterful Gallic service add to the experience.* / 11.15 pm;
set weekday L £24(FP).

Prego TW9 £37 ❸❸❸
100 Kew Rd 0181-948 8508 1–4A
*Richmond locals haven't got a bad word to say about this
"lively", "friendly", "relaxed" Italian, and wax lyrical on the
subject of its "interesting", "delightful" cooking; whether it
really deserves a wider audience is questionable, however.*
/ 11 pm, Fri & Sat 11.30 pm; no smoking area; set Sun L £24(FP).

Pret A Manger   £ 9   ❸❶④
12 Kingsgate Pd, Victoria St, SW1   0171-828 1559   2–4B
75b Victoria St, SW1   0171-222 1020   2–4C
120 Baker St, W1   0171-486 2264   2–1A
163 Piccadilly, W1   0171-629 5044   3–3C
173 Wardour St, W1   0171-434 0373   3–1D
18 Hanover St, W1   0171-491 7701   3–2C
298 Regents St, W1   0171-637 3836   4–1A
54-56 Oxford St, W1   0171-636 5750   3–1C
63 Tottenham Court Rd, W1   0171-636 6904   2–1C
7 Marylebone High St, W1   0171-935 0474   2–1A
122 High Holborn, WC1   0171-430 2090   2–1D
240-241 High Holborn, WC1   0171-404 2055   2–1D
77/78 St Martins Ln, WC2   0171-379 5335   4–3B
80 King's Rd, SW3   0171-225 0770   5–2D
8-10 King St, W6   0181-563 1985   7–2C
Kensington Arcade, W8   0171-938 1110   5–1A
27 Islington High St, N1   0171-713 1371   8–3D
157 Camden High St, NW1   0171-284 2240   8–3B
10 Leather Ln, EC1   0171-831 7219   9–2A
140 Bishopsgate, EC2   0171-377 9595   9–2D
17 Eldon St, EC2   0171-628 9011   9–2C
28 Fleet St, EC4   0171-353 2332   9–2A
*This chain of steel-clad café/take-aways "still really does
deliver the goods" – "delicious snacks and the best
sandwiches", and exemplary "quick" and friendly service;
we've listed only the sit-in branches.* / 3.30 pm-11 pm; closed Sun
except some more central branches; no credit cards; no smoking area;
no booking.

The Prince Bonaparte W2   £ 23   ❷④❸
80 Chepstow Rd   0171-229 5912   6–1B
*"Fresh, simple and hearty" modern British food makes this
Bayswater boozer a "relaxed" (if sometimes "loud") venue for
a meal "of almost restaurant-type quality"; it's "very busy"
(and "understaffed").* / 10.20 pm; closed Tue L; no credit cards;
no booking.

Pucci Pizza SW3   £ 19   ❷④❶
205 King's Rd   0171-352 2134   5–3C
*"Unbeatable prices" and "great party atmosphere" make this
"sociable" pizza-joint a perennial hit with Chelsea's young
guns.* / 12.30 am; closed Sun; no credit cards.

Purple Sage W1   £ 32   ❷❷❷
90-92 Wigmore St   0171-486 1912   3–1A
*"Top class food" ("delicious pizza", plus salads, risotti and so
on) at "extremely reasonable prices" mean that – like its
Maida Vale' sibling, the Red Pepper – this bright and buzzy
Italian north of Oxford street really "hits the spot".* / 10.30 pm;
closed Sun.

Putney Bridge SW15   **£40**   ⑤⑤④
Embankment   0181-780 1811   10–1B
"The setting is good, but nothing works" at this architecturally
stunning modern British yearling, where, for many, the
combination of *"terrible"* cooking and service *"that's just
as bad"* make the venture *"an overpriced disgrace"*. / 11 pm.

QUAGLINO'S W1   **£38**   ④④❸
16 Bury St   0171-930 6767   3–3D
Conran's *"see-and-be-seen"* St James's behemoth provokes
the usual complaints – *"bland"* and *"overpriced"* brasserie
cooking and *"slow"* and *"unfriendly"* service; a certain
"glamour" remains, but, even on this front, its star is
waning. / Midnight, Fri & Sat 1 am, Sun 11 pm.

The Quality Chop House EC1   **£31**   ❸❸❸
94 Farringdon Rd   0171-837 5093   9–1A
This restored Clerkenwell 'Working Class Caterer' may
recently have been expanded with an adjoining 'Quality Fish
House', but *"the benches do not get any softer"*; its many
fans say *"simple food is served well"* – we're with those who
say it's *"much too plain, for the money"*. / 11.30 pm; closed Sat L;
no Amex; no smoking area.

The Queen's NW1   **£28**   ④④④
49 Regents Park Road   0171-586 0408   8–3B
Though locals praise the *"great pub grub"* served in the
"slightly cramped" first-floor room of this trendified
Primrose Hill landmark, others (ourselves included) feel
it *"lacks punch"*. / 9.45 pm; no Amex; no booking.

Quincy's NW2   **£32**   ❶❶❸
675 Finchley Rd   0171-794 8499   1–1B
"The most brilliant local in town", say north London fans of
the *"great"* Anglo-French food and *"amazing"* service at this
"cramped", *"friendly"* bistro, on the way to Golder's Green.
/ 11 pm; D only.

Quo Vadis W1   **£38**   ④④④
26-29 Dean St   0171-437 4809   4–2A
"Hugely overpriced and over-hyped", this Gallic brasserie
in Soho includes Marco Pierre White and *"oh-so-witty"*
artist Damien Hirst among its backers, so *"it's full of wealthy
tourists seeking Cool Britannia"* – how sad that they are likely
to take home an experience which is *"nothing special"* in
any department. / 11 pm; closed Sat L & Sun L.

Ragam W1   **£21**   ❸④⑤
57 Cleveland St   0171-636 9098   2–1B
"Go for the food, not for the surroundings" to this long
established Indian veggie, near the Telecom Tower, where
"reliable" grub is served in *"basic"* conditions. / 11.30 pm;
no Switch.

Rain W10 £34 ④④❸

303 Portobello Road   0181-968 2001   6–1A
*Exotic North Kensington newcomer (on the site of Jimmy
Beez, RIP), where an ex-Vong chef creates potentially
intriguing – but, on our visit, bland – East-meets-West dishes;
the quantity of lavishly upholstered furniture in the small rear
dining room makes it overstuffed in every sense of the word.*
/ 10.30 pm; closed Mon.

The Rainforest Café W1 £28 ⑤⑤❸

20 Shaftesbury Avenue   0171-434 3111   3–3D
*With its animated jungle setting, this impressive West End
theme-diner is "wonderful for kids"; no matter how much
you "suspend belief", though, the food is a "rip-off".*
/ 10.45 pm, Fri & Sat 11.45 pm; no smoking; only groups of 6+.

Randall & Aubin W1 £28 ❷❸❷

16 Brewer St   0171-287 4447   3–2D
*Somehow, the "casual" service "adds to the charm" of this
"simple but convenient" grills-and-shellfish deli-diner, where
"good-life" Soho-Bohos can spectate on the to-ing and fro-ing
at neighbouring sex shops.* / 11 pm.

Rani £24 ❸❷❸

7 Long Ln, N3   0181-349 4386   1–1B
3 Hill St, Richmond, TW9   0181-332 2322   1–4A
*They "may not be the cheapest", but these "alternative"
Indians – with their wide choice of reliable veggie dishes –
are useful options in thin areas; some find the settings
"slightly harsh".* / TW9 10.45 pm, N3 10.30 pm; TW9 closed
Mon all day & Tue L; N3 closed Mon-Sat L; TW9 smoking at bar only;
N3 Sat no smoking area, no smoking at weekends.

Ranoush W2 £17 ❶④④

43 Edgware Rd   0171-723 5929   6–1D
*For a "fresh, fast, healthy" snack (especially in the wee hours)
seek out this fab Bayswater Lebanese café, with the "best
kebabs", and "great fruit drinks".* / 3 am; no credit cards or cheques.

Ransome's Dock SW11 £38 ❷❷❷

35 Parkgate Rd   0171-223 1611   5–4C
*"Reliable, fun and good value for money", this "intimate"
Battersea riversider (no view) justifies a trip across the
Thames for its "wonderful, well priced wine list" and very
"enjoyable" modern British cooking.* / 11 pm; closed Sun D;
smart casual.

Raoul's Café W9 £26 ❸❸❸

13 Clifton Rd   0171-289 7313   8–4A
*Very popular, "Eurotrashy" Maida Vale snackerie, praised as
a breakfast/brunch venue, but also for its "delicious range of
beautiful pastries".* / 10.30 pm; no Amex; no smoking area; book eve only.

Rapscallion SW4   **£ 26**   ❸❸④
75 Venn St   0171-787 6555   10–2D
"Exotic (if "not always successful") food combinations" have
helped launch this *"loud"* Clapham newcomer (near the
cinema), to the acclaim of younger locals; conditions are
"cramped", but expansion is planned. / 11 pm.

Rasa   **£ 28**   ❶❷❸
6 Dering Street, W1   0171-629 1346   3–2B
55 Stoke Newington Ch St, N16   0171-249 0344   1–1C
"Heaven for vegetarians" – the Stoke Newington original of
what is now a duo is a *"class act"* providing *"wonderful"* and
"very different" Indian dishes; the new, larger offshoot, near
Hanover Square, is glossier but, of course, not such excellent
value. / 11 pm; closed Sun-Thu L; no smoking.

Rebato's SW8   **£ 22**   ❸❶❷
169 South Lambeth Rd   0171-735 6388   10–1D
It's *"worth the venture to Vauxhall"* for the *"first-class,
authentic tapas"*, *"cheery welcome"* and sunny atmosphere of
this long-established Hispanic; there is a tackily festive rear
restaurant. / 10.30 pm; closed Sat L & Sun.

Red Fort W1   **£ 36**   ④④⑤
77 Dean St   0171-437 2525   4–2A
Though it has its supporters, we are with those who reckon
this large, well-known Soho Indian *"no more than ordinary in
all senses"*; at last, refurbishment is planned – let's hope it's
not limited to the décor. / 11.30 pm; no smoking area.

The Red Pepper W9   **£ 28**   ❷④❸
8 Formosa St   0171-266 2708   8–4A
"Excellent", *"light"* pizzas (and other *"good value"*
Mediterranean fare) have created a reputation which
belies the size of this *"great little Italian"* in Maida Vale;
it's *"cramped"* and *"noisy"*, though, and service could be
better. / 10.45 pm; no Amex.

Redmond's SW14   **£ 33**   ❸❷❸
170 Upper R'mond Rd West   0181-878 1922   10–1A
A *"solid neighbourhood spot"*, say devotees of this Sheen
yearling, who praise *"above-average"* modern British cooking;
"why do people rave?", ask others, who gripe of *"insipid
flavouring"* and dismiss this as a dull, *"middle-aged"* place.
/ 10.30 pm; closed Sat L & Sun D; no Amex.

Restaurant 190 SW7   **£ 46**   ❸❷❸
190 Queen's Gt   0171-581 5666   5–1B
The relaunch of this South Kensington basement – with its
"rich, louche décor and big fireplaces" – has caused few
ripples; that's a shame as the (mainly fish) cooking is good
(if rather *"expensive"*) and service *"charming"* (if *"slow"*).
/ 11 pm; closed Sat L & Sun D.

Restaurant du Marche SW11   £20   ❸❸④
78 Northcote Road   0171-350 2385   10–2C
*Little known, authentic, family-run Battersea bistro, which
offers good value set dinners. / 11 pm; closed Mon L & Sun; no Amex
& no Switch.*

Reubens W1   £40   ❸❸④
79 Baker St   0171-486 0035   2–1A
*"Hearty kosher fare" is again to be found at this Marylebone
deli-diner (resurrected, after several years' absence, in
expensively featureless new premises); gentiles may find
service "a mite perfunctory", and the "NY deli"-style
ground floor (with its "terrific salt beef sandwiches") is often
preferred to the basement restaurant. / 10 pm; Fri D & Sat.*

Reynier Wine Library EC3   £15   ④❸❷
43 Trinity Sq   0171-481 0415   9–3D
*"The value of the wine is key" to the success of these
merchant's cellars near Tower Hill – a "buffs' paradise";
"choose your bottle off the shelf" – "there are hundreds of
'em!" – and quaff it (after paying £2 corkage) with a pâté
and cheese buffet; book ahead. / L only; closed Sat & Sun.*

Rib Room
Hyatt Carlton Tower Hotel SW1   £54   ❷❶❷
2 Cadogan Pl   0171-858 7053   2–4A
*With its "consistent", if "pricey", fare ("prime rib and
wonderful fresh horseradish") and "discreet" and "spacious"
conditions, this comfortable Belgravia grill room is "perfect
for a business lunch". / 11.15 pm; no Switch; smart casual.*

Riccardo's SW3   £25   ❷④❷
126 Fulham Rd   0171-370 6656   5–3B
*"Chelsea girls eat in droves", at this "relaxed" Italian
"favourite" whose "good food with reasonable prices" comes
"in starter sizes only". / Midnight.*

Ristorante Italiano W1   £28   ❸❸④
54 Curzon St   0171-629 2742   3–3B
*This welcoming Mayfair stalwart is a "good buy", delivering
reliable Italian grub "efficiently" at reasonable prices.
/ 11.15 pm; closed Sat L & Sun; no smoking area.*

The Ritz W1   £65   ④❷❶
150 Piccadilly   0171-493 8181   3–4C
*You "can't beat the setting" of this "priceless", "lofty and
romantic" Louis XVI room, where, fortunately, the indifferent
Gallic cooking is "almost beside the point". / 11 pm; jacket & tie;
set Sun L £44(FP).*

Riva SW13 £ 35 ❷❸④
169 Church Rd, Barnes   0181-748 0434   10–1A
*"Top class" Italian food that's "different, too" makes this
smart, but "cramped" Barnes eminence a shrine of foodie
pilgrimage; a vocal minority, though, finds it "uninspiring in
every department".* / 11 pm, Fri & Sat 11.30 pm, Sun 9.30 pm;
closed Sat L; smart casual.

THE RIVER CAFÉ W6 £ 48 ❷❸❷
Thames Whf, Rainville Rd   0171-381 8824   7–2C
*Those "baffled by the fuss" about this stylish, but notoriously
difficult-to-find Hammersmith Italian are no longer a cranky
minority; even those who say it's "fabulous" fear it's "far too
expensive", and increasingly the feeling is that the cooking is
"good, but not THAT good".* / 9.30 pm; closed Sun D.

RK Stanleys W1 £ 27 ④❸❸
6 Little Portland St   0171-462 0099   3–1C
*An "imaginative upmarket café image", "fun service",
and a "fantastic beer selection" have made this new,
retro-look diner, just north of Oxford Street, a useful addition
to the area; the sausages (the house speciality) are "not quite
as delicious as you'd hope", but are not aggressively priced.*
/ 11.30 pm; closed Sun; no smoking area.

Rodizio Rico W11 £ 23 ⑤④④
111 Westbourne Grove   0171-792 4035   6–1B
*The early promise of this "different" Bayswater Brazilian
newcomer (with its all-you-can-eat buffet) has been betrayed
by too much "astonishingly bad and poorly prepared" food,
and "lousy" live bands.* / 11 pm; closed Mon–Fri L; no Amex.

Rôtisserie £ 26 ④❸⑤
56 Uxbridge Rd, W12   0181-743 3028   7–1C
134 Upper St, N1   0171-226 0122   8–3D
*The "super-value set menus" are the reason to visit this
(excessively) unpretentious small rôtisserie/grill chain, where
the "good simple nosh" is generally "well done".* / 11 pm; W12
closed Sat L & Sun – N1 closed Mon & Tue L.

Rôtisserie Jules £ 19 ❸❸⑤
338 King's Rd, SW3   0171-351 0041   5–3C
6-8 Bute St, SW7   0171-584 0600   5–2B
133 Notting Hill Gate, W11   0171-221 3331   6–2B
*"Great chicken, but nothing else" (to be strictly accurate,
you can order lamb for a party if you call in advance) is the
formula at these "swift", Gallic-inspired diners.* / 11 pm.

Roussillon SW1   £45   – – –

16 St Barnabas St   0171-730 5550   5–2D

Under the name Marabels (too close to Mirabelle for comfort) this rather obscure Pimlico newcomer was deservedly making waves with the quality of its modern Franco-Italian cooking; after a major re-fit, it's being relaunched in late-1998, and should be one to watch. / 10.30 pm; closed Sun; no Amex.

Rowley's SW1   £45   ⑤④④

113 Jermyn St   0171-930 2707   3–3D

Though this traditional St James's spot has some fans (who say it's "good for pre-theatre"), the prevailing view is that it's a "stuffy time warp" with "snotty" service and cooking which is too "expensive" for what is basically "mediocre steak and chips". / 11.30 pm; smart casual.

Royal China   £29   ❶❸❸

40 Baker St, W1   0171-487 4688   2–1A
13 Queensway, W2   0171-221 2535   6–2C

"The best dim sum in London" is widely acknowledged to be served at this "tacky" duo, decked out like '70s nightclubs; "they get very busy", and staff can be "shirty". / 11 pm, 11.30 pm Fri & Sat.

Royal China SW15   £29   ❷❸❸

3 Chelverton Rd   0181-788 0907   10–2B

It has for some years been separately owned and managed, but the Putney Royal China offers a very good all round experience not dissimilar to its brilliant cousins in Bayswater and Baker Street. / 10.45 pm; only Amex & Diners; no bookings for Sun L.

RSJ SE1   £30   ❷❸❸

13a Coin St   0171-928 4554   9–4A

The "unbeatable, idiosyncratic list of Loire wines" is the star attraction at this "always reliable" modern British fixture, convenient to the South Bank; most find the setting "relaxing" – to a few it's "cold". / 11 pm; closed Sat L & Sun.

Rudland & Stubbs EC1   £32   ❷❸❸

35-37 Greenhill Rents, Cowcross St   0171-253 0148   9–1A

"Fish as it ought to be served" is the majority verdict on this tiled Smithfield fish parlour, though we are with those who say it "never really makes the grade". / 10.45 pm; closed Sat L & Sun.

La Rueda   £25   ④④❷

102 Wigmore St, W1   0171-486 1718   3–1A
642 King's Rd, SW6   0171-384 2684   5–4A
66-68 Clapham High St, SW4   0171-627 2173   10–2D

"Muy bien", cry fans of the Clapham original – a "perfect" choice "for large drinking and dancing groups" on account of the "great staff" and "brilliant" atmosphere (and the tapas are fine, too); the other branches don't match up. / 11.30 pm.

F S A

Rules WC2 £42 ❸❷❶

35 Maiden Ln   0171-836 5314   4–3D
*"The best traditional English restaurant" – and also London's
oldest (1798) – this "beautiful" and "convivial" Covent
Garden institution provides "solid" cooking of "good" quality;
it's emphatically not the tourist trap which some assume it to
be. / 11.30 pm.*

Rupee Room EC2 £26 ❸❸④

10 Copthall Ave   0171-628 1555   9–2C
*A "great curry", "well served", makes this "dingy",
"seriously expensive" basement near London Wall popular
with some City reporters. / 10 pm; closed Sat & Sun; no smoking area.*

S&P £29 ❷❷④

181 Fulham Rd, SW3   0171-351 5692   5–2C
9 Beauchamp Pl, SW3   0171-581 8820   5–1C
*You "can't go wrong" at this duo of "reliable",
"neighbourhood" Thais, whose "original" and "well prepared"
cooking is "good value"; the tables are "too packed", though,
and the décor lacklustre. / 10.30 pm; no smoking areas.*

Sabai Sabai W6 £23 ❷❷④

270-272 King St   0181-748 7363   7–2B
*"Friendly staff", and food that's "consistently good" make it
worth braving this "no-atmosphere" Hammersmith Thai.
/ 11.30 pm; closed Sun L.*

Sabatino W8 £35 ❸❷④

1 Palace Gt   0171-589 9992   5–1B
*"Oh dear, it's circa 1975!" – this would-be upmarket
Kensington Italian yearling may offer "attentive service and
acceptable food", but it "feels like a tourist hotel". / 10.45 pm;
closed Sun.*

Le Sacré-Coeur N1 £21 ❶❷❶

18 Theberton St   0171-354 2618   8–3D
*"Some say cosy, others cramped", but this "lovely" and
"very Gallic" Islington bistro gets rave reviews from regulars
for its "amazing selection" of "very rich" dishes and its
"unbelievably good value". / 11 pm; set weekday L £13(FP).*

Saffron SW10 £25 ❸④❸

306B Fulham Rd   0171-565 8183   5–3B
*"Small", bright, new Chelsea-fringe Indian whose cooking is
"unusual and plentiful", but also a touch erratic; service can
be slow and "obsequious". / Midnight; closed Mon; D only Tue-Fri.*

Saigon Times EC3 £30 ❸❸❸

Leadenhall Market   0171-621 0022   9–2D
*"An interesting mix of French and Vietnamese cuisine" has
made this "great newcomer" a useful rendezvous for
informal, reasonably priced City lunching, or an evening snack.
/ 9.30 pm; closed Sat & Sun.*

Saint WC2 £32 ❸④❷
8 Great Newport St   0171-240 1551   4–3B
This "lovely, trendy" central venue attracts a "great, young crowd" thanks to its "brilliant combination of bar and food", and its "amazingly good" fusion cooking; "not every customer", though "can survive on their 'model' portions"; ('non-members' face a £5 entrance fee at weekends). / 11 pm; D only; closed Sat L & Sun.

St John EC1 £33 ❸❷❸
26 St John St   0171-251 0848   9–1B
"Offal heaven" – this "weird", "Spartan" Smithfield smokehouse-conversion rejoices in a menu is which is "sometimes too extreme, even for carnivores"; still, it's an "honest" and "imaginative" approach, and one which found a more appreciative audience this year. / 11.30 pm; closed Sun.

St Moritz W1 £30 ❸❷❸
161 Wardour St   0171-734 3324   3–1D
"Good for a group party, even if there's no snow", this "cosy Swiss chalet", unaccountably lost in Soho, offers "excellent fondues" ("not cheap, but plentiful") and other simple cooking using "the best ingredients". / 11.30 pm; closed Sat L & Sun.

Sale e Pepe SW1 £37 ❸❷❶
9-15 Pavilion Rd   0171-235 0098   2–3A
Who cares if it's "too, too crowded"? – it's the "great atmosphere" which draws people to this "loud and hectic" Knightsbridge trattoria, whose waiters double as "part-time entertainers". / 11.30 pm; closed Sun.

Salloos SW1 £47 ❶❸④
62-64 Kinnerton St   0171-235 4444   2–3A
Luxurious, long-established Belgravian that "has to be given a go if you like Indian", thanks to the quality of its "great", "authentic" Pakistani (as it is, in fact) cooking; "it is expensive", though. / 11.15 pm; closed Sun; smart casual; set weekday L £26(FP).

Sambuca SW3 £33 ❸❶❸
6 Symons St   0171-730 6571   5–2D
"Amiable" and "attentive" service combined with "consistently good fish and pasta" make it worth tolerating the "very cramped" conditions at this "old-fashioned" Italian, just off Sloane Square. / 11.30 pm; closed Sun.

San Carlo N6 £34 ④④❸
2 Highgate High St   0181-340 5823   8–1B
Swanky Highgate trattoria that's "too expensive for a local restaurant", especially given the unevenness of feedback on both food and service. / 11 pm; closed Mon; no jeans; no smoking area.

San Daniele del Friuli N5   £ 23   ❸❸④
72 Highbury Park   0171-359 0341   8–1D
*Locals proclaim this Italian (a short walk from the home of
the 'Gunners') as "stylish" and "above-average" – by the
standards of the area, this is undoubtedly true.* / 11 pm;
closed Mon L; closed Sun; no Amex; set weekday L £14(FP).

San Lorenzo SW3   £ 50   ④④❷
22 Beauchamp Pl   0171-584 1074   5–1C
*"Making the customer feel small" seems to be something of
a hobby for staff at this infamously "overpriced" Knightsbridge
trattoria, that is "overfilled with people to spot, and those
wishing to join the spotted".* / 11.30 pm; closed Sun; no credit cards;
smart casual.

San Martino SW3   £ 41   ④❸❸
101-105 Walton St   0171-589 3833   5–2C
*Long-established Chelsea Italian, liked by some for its
"quality" cooking and "friendly" service; it's a shame that
"ridiculous" prices cause some to dismiss it as a "very
average trattoria trading on its location".* / 11.30 pm;
no smoking area; set weekday L £13(FP).

Sandrini SW3   £ 37   ❸❷④
260 Brompton Rd   0171-584 1724   5–2C
*Now eclipsed by all the surrounding trendy new places,
this once-fashionable Brompton Cross Italian remains an
"attentive and polite" stand-by.* / 11.30 pm.

Santini SW1   £ 55   ⑤④⑤
29 Ebury St   0171-730 4094   2–4B
*Swanky, but "seriously overpriced" Belgravia Italian, where
the "quality of the food is in inverse relation to the cost".*
/ 11.30 pm; closed Sat L & Sun L; smart casual; set weekday L £33(FP).

Sarastro WC2   £ 26   ⑤④❶
126 Drury Ln   0171-836 0101   2–2D
*"One of the most amusing and interesting restaurants in
London, though the food is simply horrible" sums up this
"wacky dining experience", whose "bordello-operatic" Covent
Garden setting "never fails to delight first-timers".* / 11.30 pm.

Sarcan N1   £ 15   ❷❸❸
4 Theberton St   0171-226 5489   8–3D
*"Fresh and simple" Turkish fare is found at this "good value"
Islington side street café, which is "usually crowded".* / Midnight.

Sartoria W1   £ 52   ④④❸
20 Savile Row   0171-534 7000   3–2C
*"Actually a good Conran!", say those surprised to have found
"exciting" Italian food and "elegant" décor at this "very
grown-up", tailoring-themed Mayfair newcomer; to too many
others, though, it's just "a bit of a yawn".* / 11.15 pm; closed Sun D.

Sash £20 ⑤④❸

825 Fulham Rd, SW6   0171-736 9429   10–1B
32 Abbeville Rd, SW4   0181-673 9300   10–2D
*Sadly, since expansion, these "cosy and fun" Oriental tapas
bars "have gone downhill very fast", and any praise for the
"interesting and fairly cheap food" is drowned by criticism
of "measly portions" of "terrible" grub. /—*

Satsuma W1 £23 ❸❷❷

56 Wardour St   0171-437 8338   3–2D
*If you're a bit scared of going Japanese, try this stylish Soho
newcomer – an unintimidating menu offers a good range of
tasty dishes, agreeably served. / 11 pm; no smoking; no booking.*

Les Saveurs W1 £50 ④④⑤

37a Curzon St   0171-491 8919   3–4B
*Many feel "let down badly" by J-C Novelli's relaunch of
this grand, but "dull" Mayfair basement; "fussy" cooking,
"amateur" service and a "pathetic" wine list would be bad
enough – but, to add insult to injury, "the bill invariably
mounts to twice what you'd expect". / 11 pm; closed Mon L;
closed Sat L & Sun; jacket & tie.*

Savoy Grill WC2 £65 ❸❷❷

Strand   0171-836 4343   4–3D
*The "pomp and circumstance" of this elegantly "subdued",
panelled room maintain it, for traditionalists, as "the ultimate
power lunch venue"; after a rocky patch, the safe, but never
exciting English cooking has regained its dependable form.
/ 11.15 pm; closed Sat L & Sun; jacket & tie; set pre-th. £43(FP).*

Savoy River Restaurant WC2 £65 ④❷❷

Strand   0171-420 2699   4–3D
*A "whiff of the '50s" still adheres to this "classy" riverside
"classic", which benefits from great river views – "book early
for a window table"; even some fans admit that the
Anglo-French cooking is now thoroughly "mediocre".
/ 11.30 pm; jacket & tie; set Sun L £38(FP).*

Scalini SW3 £41 ④❷❷

1-3 Walton St   0171-225 2301   5–2C
*"Mad" Knightsbridge Italian with "great atmosphere and
buzz" and "friendly service"; the cooking's "so-so", though,
and "very overpriced". / 11.30 pm; smart casual.*

The Scarsdale W8 £20 ④❸❷

23a Edwardes Sq   0171-937 1811   7–1D
*The "lovely setting" – especially the tiny garden, overlooking
Kensington's oldest square – makes this venerable boozer,
"a good place to meet" (arrive early for a seat); "predictable"
pub grub. / 9.45 pm; smart casual.*

Scoffers SW11 £24 ❷❷❷
6 Battersea Rs   0171-978 5542   10–2C
*"Still popular and still very good" (but this "cheap
and cheerful" modern British Battersea bistro is "not
recommended for over-30s"); it's "impossible to get a table
at short notice". / 11 pm.*

Scott's W1 £46 ❸❸❷
20 Mount St   0171-629 5248   3–3A
*Many praise the "beautiful", "light and airy" ambience at
this relaunched Mayfair institution (now owned by Groupe
Chez Gérard); we think "pretentious, but fun" is probably a
better summary, but the fish and seafood are certainly very
"acceptable". / 11 pm; smart casual.*

Seafresh SW1 £19 ❷❸④
80-81 Wilton Rd   0171-828 0747   2–4B
*Long-established, superior Pimlico chippy that's still a
"reliable" choice. / 10.30 pm; closed Sun.*

Searcy's Brasserie EC2 £37 ❸④④
Level II, Barbican Centre   0171-588 3008   9–1B
*"Dependable" (if rather pricey) modern British cooking
makes this a useful option at the Barbican, although many
think it "totally devoid of atmosphere". / 10.30 pm; closed Sat L
& Sun D; no smoking area.*

Seashell NW1 £23 ❷❸④
49 Lisson Grove   0171-723 8703   8–4A
*For its fans "stunning fish 'n' chips compensate for the
manifold flaws" (in particular the grotty décor) of this
pre-eminent Marylebone chippy; quite a lot of gripes this year,
though, about "cardboard" offerings. / 10.30 pm; closed Sun D;
no smoking area; no booking.*

Seattle Coffee £ 9 ❷❸❸
137 Victoria St, SW1   0171-233 5170   2–4B
14 James St, W1   0171-495 6680   3–1A
27 Berkeley St, W1   0171-629 5779   3–3C
3 Grosvenor St, W1   0171-495 5534   3–2B
34 Gt Marlborough St, W1   0171-434 0778   3–2C
357-359 The Strand, WC2   0171-836 5166   2–2D
51-54 Long Acre, WC2   0171-836 2100   4–2D
25a Kensington High Street, W8   0171-937 5446   5–1A
*The "best, most consistent coffee in London" – "it should be,
at the price" – is served at this pre-eminent caffeine chain
(together with "reliable" cookies and sandwiches); by
mid-1999, all branches will be rebranded under the name
of new owners Starbucks, the leading US chain. / 6 pm – 11 pm;
some branches closed Sat and/or Sun; no Amex; no smoking indoors;
no booking.*

The Secret Garden SE5   £18   ❸❸❷

161 Camberwell Rd   0171-703 8089   1–3C
*Recherché Camberwell site – there's no sign, you just go into
Franklin's Antiques Market and go downstairs – where simple,
pleasing, but pricey grub (brunch being the top attraction) is
served in a romantically overgrown junk-yard (if you have to
eat inside, don't bother); early-1999 may see a move to a
new, but similar location, opposite.* / 10 pm; D only ex Sat & Sun,
when open L & D; no credit cards.

755 SW6   £35   ❷❷④

755 Fulham Rd   0171-371 0755   10–1B
*"Unexpectedly delicious" modern British cooking (and a
"great value lunch") wins an enthusiastic Fulham following
for this "fancy local"; it's "cosy and intimate" to some, but to
others it "lacks atmosphere".* / 11 pm; closed Sun D & Mon.

Shampers W1   £27   ❸❷❷

4 Kingly St   0171-437 1692   3–2D
*"Surprisingly good food" distinguishes this "friendly" and
"unpretentious" '70s Soho wine bar; the "extensive
selection of wines" and the "great atmosphere" are among
the attractions which can make it "packed" and "noisy".*
/ 11 pm; closed Sun (Aug also Sat).

Shanghai E8   £23   ❷❷❸

41 Kingsland High Street   0171-254 2878   1–1C
*"Really good and healthy" Chinese food – including top dim
sum – justifies venturing to this "interesting" tiled parlour
(near Dalston Kingsland BR), formerly the East End's most
famous pie 'n' eel shop.* / 11 pm; no Amex.

Sheekey's WC2   £47   – – –

28-32 St Martins Ct   0171-240 2565   4–3B
*This venerable Theatreland fish and seafood parlour – long in
decline – is to re-open in late '98; given that the new owners
are the people who run The Ivy (reporters' no 1 favourite),
and Le Caprice (no 2), there are some grounds for optimism
about this, their third venture.* / 11.30 pm; closed Sun.

Sheekey's EC4   £40   – – –

11 Queen Victoria St   0171-489 8067   9–3C
*Large, previously execrable City basement, recently
part-relaunched (though with little in the way of visible
changes) under new owners, the Ivy/Caprice group; with that
business itself under the Belgo Group umbrella from August
1998, continue to watch this space.* / L only; closed Sat & Sun;
smart casual.

Shepherd's SW1   £24   ❸❷❷

Marsham Ct, Marsham St   0171-834 9552   2–4C
*Not far from Westminster, this "discreet", and "intimate"
panelled politicos' haunt provides a "reliable", "reassuringly
traditional" British menu.* / 11 pm; closed Sat & Sun.

The Ship SW18 £ 23 ③④❷
41 Jews Row   0181-870 9667   10–2B
*A "brilliant atmosphere and a great summer barbecue"
guarantees that, on a sunny day, this Wandsworth riverside
pub (with no great view, though) will be heaving. / 10.30 pm;
no booking for Sun L.*

Shoeless Joe's SW6 £ 30 ⑤④❷
555 King's Rd   0171-384 2333   5–4B
*"Unbeaten for a boozy sports event, otherwise, forget it" –
the food in the restaurant of this Chelsea sports
bar-cum-restaurant is "bad, and it costs too much". / 11 pm;
closed Sun D.*

Shogun W1 £ 50 ❷④④
Adam's Rw   0171-493 1255   3–3A
*The "best sushi", a "friendly" welcome and a setting which is
pretty swinging by Japanese standards makes this "first class"
Mayfair basement the most convivial top-class Nipponese in
town. / 11 pm; D only; closed Mon; no Switch.*

Le Shop SW3 £ 22 ❸❸❷
329 King's Rd   0171-352 3891   5–3C
*Superior Chelsea snackery, popular for its "great-tasting
crêpes" and (loud) "classical music". / Midnight; no Switch; set
weekday L £12(FP).*

Shree Krishna SW17 £ 18 ❶❸④
192-194 Tooting High St   0181-672 4250   10–2D
*"The best masala dosas on earth" – and other "beautifully
cooked", largely vegetarian South Indian nosh – justifies the
trek to this "very cheap" Tooting subcontinental; the service,
though still "erratic", seems to be improving. / Mon-Thu 10.45 pm,
Fri & Sat 11.45 pm; no Switch.*

Signor Sassi SW1 £ 44 ❸❶❷
14 Knightsbridge Gn   0171-584 2277   5–1D
*"High on atmosphere" – it's the "amusing" and "noisy"
style of this "slick" Knightsbridge Italian which makes it a
"favourite" for many, and justifies the premium prices.
/ 11.30 pm; closed Sun; smart casual.*

Silks & Spice £ 23 ❸④❸
23 Foley St, W1   0171-636 2718   2–1B
95 Chiswick High Rd, W4   0181-995 7991   7–2B
28 Chalk Farm Road, NW1   0171-267 5751   8–2B
103 Boundary Road, NW8   0171-624 1485   8–3A
*"Consistently good, for a chain", these Thai/Malaysian
restaurants offer "an interesting menu, well presented and
served". / 11 pm; W1 closed Sat L & Sun L; no smoking areas.*

Simply Nico £ 37 ❸❸④
48a Rochester Rw, SW1 0171-630 8061 2–4C
7 Park Wk, SW10 0171-349 8866 5–3B
*"Traditional" and "reliable" French bistro food is the
proposition from star-chef Nico Ladenis's 'diffusion' brand;
it "definitely feels like a chain".* / 11 pm; SW10 closed Mon L.

Simpson's of Cornhill EC3 £ 21 ❸❸❷
38 1/2 Cornhill 0171-626 9985 9–2C
*"An experience all of its own" – this back alley chop-house's
"well cooked school food" and "idiosyncratic service" secure
it a steady City following; should the markets crash, it makes a
great place "to get drunk".* / L only; closed Sat & Sun; no booking.

Simpsons-in-the-Strand WC2 £ 44 ⑤④❸
100 Strand 0171-836 9112 4–3D
*"Cruising on past glories", these potentially "wonderful"
Edwardian English dining rooms are now thoroughly "third
rate", thanks to their "dated", "best forgotten" cooking, and
"surly" and "pompous" service; "hearty" breakfasts are the
only cause for any enthusiasm.* / 11 pm, Sun 9 pm; smart casual; set
pre-th. £31(FP).

Singapore Garden NW6 £ 29 ❸④④
83-83a Fairfax Rd 0171-328 5314 8–2A
*Tacky Swiss Cottage fixture which, at its best, produces
"delicious" south east Asian food; it's become rather
"variable", though.* / 10.45 pm, Fri & Sat 11.15 pm; set weekday L
£17(FP).

Singapura £ 34 ❸❸④
78/79 Leadenhall St, EC3 0171-929 0089 9–2D
1-2 Limeburner Ln, EC4 0171-329 1133 9–2A
*"Good for time-restricted business lunches", this small
South East Asian chain "never seems to change its standards"
of "good food"; the stark premises "lack atmosphere",
though.* / 9.30 pm; closed Sat & Sun; smart casual.

606 Club SW10 £ 35 ④④❷
90 Lots Rd 0171-352 5953 5–4B
*Cool Chelsea Harbour music club – hidden away down a
flight of stairs, opposite the Lot's Road power station – where
even those who knock the cooking think it's "great all the
same, thanks to the jazz"; basic dishes are best.* / Mon-Thu
1.30 am, Fri & Sat 2 am, Sun 11.30 pm; D only; no Amex.

Sixty Two SE1 £ 22 ❸④④
Southwark Playhouse, 62 Southwark Bridge Road
0171-620 3494 9–4B
*"Unprepossessing, if cheerfully decorated", Southwark
newcomer which sometimes "surprises" with the "high
quality" of its modern British cooking; service can be
overstretched.* / 10.30 pm; closed Sat L & Sun; no smoking area.

Smokey Joe's SW18   £18   ❷❷❸
131 Wandsworth High St   0181-871 1785   10–2B
A "tiny, fun place to eat" – this "authentic Caribbean" diner,
in Wandsworth, offers "excellent barbecue and jerk dishes",
"eccentrically" served, in cramped surroundings; BYO. / 10 pm;
closed Sun L; no credit cards; no booking.

Smollensky's W1   £29   ④❸❸
1 Dover St   0171-491 1199   3–3C
Long-established Mayfair bar/restaurant newly kitted out
with "very swish" Star Trek-style décor; "oh dear!", though,
"if that's American food, I'm staying at home". / Midnight;
closed Sun D.

Smollensky's on the Strand WC2   £29   ④④❸
105 The Strand   0171-497 2101   4–3D
Large and impressively furnished American-style diner, which,
though the "best for children's brunch on a weekend by far",
is otherwise undistinguished. / Midnight, Thu - Sat 12.30 am, Sun
10.30 pm.

Snows by the Pond SW13   £33   ⑤⑤⑤
14-15 Barnes High St   0181-876 1471   10–1A
"Uninspired" modern British cooking, lacklustre décor and
"snail's pace" service have not made the best beginning for
this Barnes newcomer; it is actually some distance from the
Pond. / 11 pm; closed Mon & Sun D; set weekday L £19(FP).

Snows on the Green W6   £31   ④④④
166 Shepherd's Bush Rd   0171-603 2142   7–1C
A reputation for "inventive" Mediterranean cooking draws
a more-than-local following to this "blandly decorated"
Brook Green neighbourhood restaurant, but the feeling
that the food here is "overrated" grew stronger this year.
/ 11 pm; closed Sat L & Sun D.

Sofra   £27   ❸④④
1 St Christopher's Pl, W1   0171-224 4080   3–1A
18 Shepherd Mkt, W1   0171-499 4099   3–4B
18 Shepherd St, W1   0171-493 3320   3–4B
17 Charing Cross Rd, WC2   0171-930 6090   4–4B
36 Tavistock St, WC2   0171-240 3773   4–3D
This ever-expanding chain of unadorned Turkish bistros offers
"plain but reliable" food, "with a wide range of healthy
options"; the formula is "good value for money", but it's
"becoming a little impersonal", and service can be
"non-existent". / Midnight.

Soho Brewing Company WC2   £25   ❸❸④
41 Earlham St   0171-240 0606   4–2C
Surprisingly, it's the "unrelaxing" setting which is found to be
the weak point of this minimalist new microbrewery basement
in north-Covent Garden – staff are "welcoming", there is
some "good beer", and the simple grub is better than you
might expect. / 11 pm; set Sun L £10(FP).

Soho Soho (Rôtisserie) W1   £28   ④④❸
11-13 Frith St   0171-494 3491   4–2A
The "lively" and "very noisy" downstairs rôtisserie of this Soho
fixture incites more enthusiasm than the middle-brow modern
British restaurant above; "ordinary and boring" cooking is a
feature throughout, however, and service can be "woeful".
/ 12.45 am, Sun 10.30 pm; no smoking area L only.

Soho Spice W1   £25   ❸❸❸
124-126 Wardour St   0171-434 0808   3–1D
"Vibrant" Soho Indian yearling which combines "colourful food
and décor" with "friendly, attentive" service and "reasonable
prices"; the basement bar hums into the early hours.
/ 11.30 pm; 3 am Fri & Sat; no smoking area; need 4+ at L, 6+ at D to book.

Solly's Exclusive NW11   £29   ❸④❸
148 Golders Green Rd   0181-455 0004   1–1B
The schlep to this Israeli restaurant in Golder's Green is
rewarded with OK nosh and "inconsistent" service; opinions
vary as to whether you are better off in the ground floor
snack bar or the tackily festive upstairs restaurant. / 11.30 pm;
closed Fri D & Sat; no smoking area.

Sonny's SW13   £34   ❷❷❷
94 Church Rd   0181-748 0393   10–1A
It may be slightly "overhyped by south-of-the-river types",
but this large, long-established Barnes "local" deserves
plaudits for its "consistently good", modern British cooking
and "charming" service; there was a major refurb in
mid-1998. / 11 pm; closed Sun D.

Sotheby's Café W1   £31   ❸❷❸
34 New Bond St   0171-408 5077   3–2C
"A safe haven for a light lunch with chums", this "handy"
and civilised room (off the foyer of the Mayfair auction house)
offers a good-quality modern British menu of enjoyable,
"simple" fare. / L only; closed Sat & Sun, but May-Jul and Sep-Dec open
Sun L; no smoking.

Le Soufflé
Inter-Continental Hotel W1   £58   ❸❷⑤
1 Hamilton Pl   0171-409 3131   3–4A
Peter Kromberg's "beautifully presented" cooking is "always
of a high standard", and "unpretentious" Gallic service "adds
flavour" to a meal in this Mayfair hotel dining room; shame
the lacklustre setting puts off the following the place might
otherwise attract. / 10.30 pm, Sat 11.15 pm; closed Mon, Sat L & Sun D;
jacket; no smoking area.

Soulard N1   £26   ❷❷❷
113 Mortimer Rd   0171-254 1314   1–1C
"Philippe keeps trying hard", and the set menu "must be the
best value in town", say Islington and Hackney supporters of
this "cramped", but "relaxed" Gallic bistro. / 10.30 pm; D only,
closed Sun & Mon; no Switch.

Sound Republic WC2   £ 26   ④④④
Leicester Square   0171-287 1010   4–4A
New West End 'theme'-diner – a sort of quieter and more
'MOR' Hard Rock Café, minus the memorabilia; it's an
admirably spacious place, but we can't quite work out any
positive reason for going there. / I am; no jeans.

Southeast W9   £ 23   ❷④④
239 Elgin Avenue   0171-328 8883   1–2B
"Amateurish service and bland decor belie the great-tasting
food" at this minimalist Maida Vale oriental café. / I I pm;
no smoking area.

Spago SW7   £ 21   ❸④④
6 Glendower Pl   0171-225 2407   5–2B
"Great, thin crispy pizza" makes this small "authentic"
South Kensington Italian a good "cheap and cheerful" choice.
/ 12.30 am; D only; no credit cards.

La Spiga W1   £ 29   ❸❸❸
84-86 Wardour Street   0171-734 3444   3–2D
Most find this "buzzy" and "smartly styled" Italian joint in
trendiest Soho (above the wickedly fashionable K Bar) offers
generally "good value" (if sometimes erratic) fare – "especially
mile-wide pizzas and some well thought-out salads". / I I pm;
Midnight Thu-Sat; no smoking.

La Spighetta W1   £ 29   ❸④④
43 Blandford St   0171-486 7340   2–1A
The "pizzas may be good value" at this Marylebone yearling,
but the "echoey acoustics" of its slightly "bleak" basement
setting incite little affection. / 10.30 pm; no smoking area.

Sporting Page SW10   £ 23   ❸❷❷
6 Camera Pl   0171-376 3694   5–3B
It isn't just the "surprisingly good pub grub" which makes this
smart, modern Chelsea boozer stand out – it claims to be the
country's third largest vendor of Bollinger. / 10 pm; no booking.

Springbok Café W4   £ 30   ❷❶❸
42 Devonshire Rd   0181-742 3149   7–2A
A "great South African experience for the tastebuds", say
supporters of the "interesting food at competitive prices"
offered by this "fun" Chiswick venture; "friendly and
knowledgeable" service is particularly praised. / 10.30 pm;
closed Sun D; no Amex.

THE SQUARE W1   £ 59   ❷❸❸
6-10 Bruton St   0171-495 7100   3–2C
Philip Howard's "brilliant" modern French cooking is propelling
this "professional, slick" Mayfair establishment ever further
up the capital's gastronomic premier league; some find the
"grand", contemporary setting "rather formal". / 10.45 pm;
closed Sat L & Sun L; smart casual.

Sri India EC2   £ 24   ④❸❸

7-8 Bishopsgate Place   0171-628 7888   9–2D
*"Exceptionally ordinary", "badly thought out", cooking makes
it difficult to get excited about this new City Indian, whose
(listed) subterranean premises deserve better. / 9 pm; closed Sat
& Sun.*

Sri Siam W1   £ 27   ❷❸❸

16 Old Compton St   0171-434 3544   4–2A
*An "excellent Thai" – this slickly-run Soho establishment is
"always crowded", "noisy" and "fun" – no wonder, given its
consistent and "interesting" cooking. / 11.15 pm; closed Sun L.*

Sri Siam City EC2   £ 30   ❷❸④

85 London Wall   0171-628 5772   9–2C
*"Very busy" City oriental, whose continuing popularity is
founded upon its "reliable" and "attractive" Thai cooking;
the "noisy" basement setting is "a bit of a barn", though.
/ 8.45 pm; closed Sat & Sun.*

Sri Thai EC4   £ 30   ❸❸④

3 Queen Victoria St   0171-827 0202   9–3C
*Sibling to the Sri Siam twins, and a source of similar – but
not equal – levels of satisfaction for its "snappy", "light" Thai
cooking; the impressive City basement setting can be noisy.
/ 9 pm; closed Sat & Sun.*

The Stable SW13   £ 27   ❸④❸

39 Barnes High St   0181-876 1855   10–1A
*"Good home-cooked food" in the characterful rear dining
annex is a "useful adjunct to the jazz" at Barnes's Bull's
Head, and an attraction in its own right. / 11 pm; D only, closed
Sun-Wed.*

Standard Tandoori W2   £ 20   ❸❸④

21-23 Westbourne Grove   0171-229 0600   6–1C
*"Standard sums it up" – this Bayswater curry-house is the
"classic, no-frills Indian", and, foodwise, "much better than
Khan's, next door". / 11.45 pm; no smoking area.*

Star Café W1   £ 17   ❸④❸

22 Gt Chapel St   0171-437 8778   3–1D
*Soho caff (just south of Oxford Street), tipped by local
media-types for its restorative greasy breakfasts, and decent
caffeine shots. / 4 pm; closed Sat & Sun; no credit cards; no smoking area.*

Star of India SW5   £ 36   ❷④❸

154 Old Brompton Rd   0171-373 2901   5–2B
*"Entertaining" South Kensington "classic", where the
"unusually imaginative" subcontinental cooking outshines
even the camp-extravaganza muralled décor; "service wise,
it's resting on its laurels". / 11.45 pm.*

Stargazer W1 £ 25 ④❷④
11 Rathbone St 0171-636 1057 2–1C
This bright modern British newcomer would no doubt be a
'wow' in the suburbs; in Fitzrovia, however, we can't quite see
its point. / 11 pm; closed Sat L & Sun.

Stephen Bull W1 £ 38 ❷❸④
5-7 Blandford St 0171-486 9696 2–1A
Despite a "light and airy" setting that many think rather
"harsh", the "very solid" imaginative modern British cooking
ensures a continuing fan club for S Bull's original restaurant,
in Marylebone. / 10.30 pm; closed Sat L & Sun.

Stephen Bull WC2 £ 38 ❷❸④
12 Upper St Martin's Ln 0171-379 7811 4–3B
"Creative food, knowledgeable staff and interesting wines"
make an appealing package at this quality Theatreland
yearling; they have tried hard with the conversion of an
awkwardly proportioned room, but still many find it "dull
and sterile". / 11.30 pm; closed Sat L & Sun.

Stephen Bull EC1 £ 32 ④❸⑤
71 St John St 0171-490 1750 9–1A
Despite being "too austere and crammed in", this stark
Smithfield establishment is tipped as a "good business
restaurant"; the modern British cooking has always been
rather "variable", but it's "gone downhill" over the past year.
/ 10.30 pm; closed Sat L & Sun; no smoking area.

The Stepping Stone SW8 £ 33 ❷①❸
123 Queenstown Rd 0171-622 0555 10–1C
"A great effort, for Battersea" and "really good value",
this "informal", but stylish venture continues to set the
local standards for "consistently well done" and "interesting"
modern British cooking, and "charming" and "knowledgeable"
service. / 11 pm, Mon 10.30 pm; closed Sat L & Sun D; no smoking area.

Sticky Fingers W8 £ 24 ④❸❸
1a Phillimore Gdns 0171-938 5338 5–1A
Rolling Stone Bill Wyman's American diner in Kensington
"still has its place after all these years", with the "happy
ambience" (that's "great with kids") the top-of-the-bill
attraction; many continue to applaud the burgers, but the
food has had a poor press of late. / 11.30 pm; book L only.

Stock Pot   **£ 12**   ④❸④
40 Panton St, SW1   0171-839 5142   4–4A
18 Old Compton St, W1   0171-287 1066   4–2B
50 James St, W1   0171-486 9185   3–1A
273 King's Rd, SW3   0171-823 3175   5–3C
6 Basil St, SW3   0171-589 8627   5–1D
*"Filling and cheap food" (which no one pretends is art), and
service that's "always cheerful, even if it's a bit rushed" helps
fuel continuing enthusiasm for this seminal budget bistro
chain.* / 11 pm-Midnight; no credit cards; some branches have
no smoking areas; booking restricted at some times.

Stone Mason's Arms W6   **£ 22**   ❸④❸
54 Cambridge Grove   0181-748 1397   7–2C
*"Uncomfortably located" on a much-trafficked highway, this
Hammersmith gastropub is "busy, and with good reason" –
it offers "varied" fare, that's a "touch more refined than
most", in a "spacious" setting.* / 10.15 pm.

Stratford's W8   **£ 37**   ❸❷④
7 Stratford Rd   0171-937 6388   5–2A
*"Fresh fish prepared to your liking at a reasonable price"
makes this hidden-away spot "good value for money"; its
Kensington back street premises "lack atmosphere", though.*
/ 11 pm; set pre-th. £21(FP).

Suan-Neo EC2   **£ 40**   ④⑤⑤
31 Broadgate Circle   0171-256 5045   9–2D
*"Irritating – it should do better"; the "clean, sharp" new
Broadgate flagship of the Singapura chain may be "good for
business", but it is so excessively "overpriced" that it really is
very difficult to drum up any enthusiasm for it.* / 9.30 pm;
closed Sat & Sun.

The Sugar Club W1   **£ 44**   ❷④❷
21 Warwick St   0171-437 7776   3–2D
*Peter Gordon's "bold combinations" of "exotic ingredients"
have transplanted well to his new Soho premises, where the
stylishly minimalist setting is a considerable improvement on
North Kensington; service is "friendly", once you have
succeeded in attracting its attention.* / 11 pm; no smoking area.

The Sun & Doves SE5   **£ 25**   ❷❷❷
61 Coldharbour Ln   0171-733 1525   1–4C
*This groovy, art-filled Camberwell gastropub is not just the
best bet locally, but also worth a trip, thanks to its very
competent cooking, and willing service; there is a large rear
garden.* / 10.30 pm; closed Sat L; no Amex.

Suntory SW1   £72   ③③④
72 St James's St   0171-409 0201   3–4D
You do get "exceptional food and service", but it's "very, very expensive" at this grand, dated St James's fixture, which continues to offer its "international" and business clientele some of "the best Japanese cuisine in town". / 10 pm; closed Sun L; smart casual; set weekday L £40(FP).

Le Suquet SW3   £41   ②③③
104 Draycott Av   0171-581 1785   5–2C
The "plâteau de fruits-de-mer is a classic" at this Côte d'Azur "seaside" restaurant, long resident on the fringe of Chelsea; service has improved this year, but "having a French-speaker still helps". / 11.30 pm; set weekday L £21(FP).

Sushi Wong W8   £27   ③①⑤
38c Kensington Church St   0171-937 5007   5–1A
Kensington locals patronise this Nipponese yearling for its "simple but fresh" dishes, though many feel that it is not as good as when it opened; "friendly" staff help to compensate for the lacklustre setting. / 10.30 pm; closed Sun L.

Sushi-Say NW2   £29   ②②④
33b Walm Ln   0181-459 7512   1–1A
You don't get a wild time at this small Japanese, in the depths of north London (near Willesden Green tube), nor is it cheap; but you do get food of real quality and a charming welcome. / 10.30 pm; D only; closed Mon; no Amex.

Sweetings EC4   £31   ②③②
39 Queen Victoria St   0171-248 3062   9–3B
"Quality fish" in a "basic, but nostalgic" setting makes this "singular" seafood parlour an "enjoyable" lunching stand-by, relished by City traditionalists. / L only; closed Sat & Sun; no credit cards; no booking.

t'su SW3   £25   ③③③
118 Draycott Ave   0171-584 5522   5–2C
A "fun place" say fans of this Brompton Cross sushi-on-a-conveyor belt yearling and its "clean, minimalist" setting; it's "overpriced, even for the area", though, and purists gripe of "far-fetched", "would-be" sushi. / 11 pm; no smoking; no booking.

Taberna Etrusca EC4   £34   ④⑤④
9 Bow Churchyard   0171-248 5552   9–2C
An "excellent outdoor terrace" is a prime reason why you "must book" for lunch at this City Italian; "abysmal" service can take the edge off the experience, though, and the cooking is "overpriced" and "bland". / L only; closed Sat & Sun; no Switch.

Tamarind W1 £ 36 ❷❷❷
20 Queen St   0171-629 3561   3–3B
*"Fabulous" cooking – if at "sky-high prices" – continues to
bolster the reputation of this "great", "upmarket Indian",
in a groovily decorated Mayfair basement; "caring" service
is also praised.* / 11.30 pm; closed Sat L; set Sun L £23(FP).

Tandoori Lane SW6 £ 23 ❷❶❸
131a Munster Rd   0171-371 0440   10–1B
*"A class above the usual local Indian", this darkly-decorated
subcontinental in distant Fulham attracts a more-than-local
following thanks to its "superior" cooking, "very attentive"
service and "inviting" décor.* / 11 pm; no Amex.

Tandoori of Chelsea SW3 £ 37 ❸❷④
153 Fulham Rd   0171-589 7749   5–2C
*Perhaps the "décor could do with an update", but this
grand and comfortable curry house is "not expensive",
given its ever-trendier Brompton Cross location, and it provides
"consistent" food and "very kind" service.* / Midnight; set weekday L
£21(FP).

LA TANTE CLAIRE
BERKELEY HOTEL SW1 £ 75 – – –
Wilton Pl   0171-493 5699   2–3A
*Pierre Koffmann's "perfectly executed haute cuisine" has won
him deserved accolades as one of London's foremost chefs;
late-1998 sees him re-open his restaurant within a swanky
Knightsbridge hotel – let's hope the new premises provide the
charm which proved so elusive in Chelsea.* / 11 pm; closed Sat
& Sun; dinner, jacket; set weekday L £36(FP).

Tao EC4 £ 32 ④④❸
11 Bow Ln   0171-248 5833   9–2C
*"Tasty" is more often used to describe the waitresses than
the food at this flash City oriental bar/restaurant, whose
"buzzing" atmosphere is its best feature.* / 10 pm; closed Sat
& Sun; smart casual.

Tate Gallery SW1 £ 38 ④❸❷
Millbank   0171-887 8877   2–4C
*"The best-value wines in London" and "beautiful" Whistler
murals are two prime reasons to visit this Pimlico dining room;
some would number "waitresses who mother you" as a third
attraction, but few would cite the "ordinary" modern British
fare.* / L only; no smoking area.

TATSUSO EC2 £ 65 ❶❸④
32 Broadgate Circle   0171-638 5863   9–2D
*"For when others are paying", this "clinical", but excellent
City oriental offers "Japanese food at its best"; upstairs,
there's a flashy teppan-yaki, while in the low-key basement a
wider menu is served – "both are very good and equally
expensive".* / 9.45 pm; closed Sat & Sun; smart casual.

Tawana W2   £ 22   ❷④④
3 Westbourne Grove   0171-229 3785   6–1C
*"It's a great local restaurant", say regulars at this little-known
spot, a few paces from Queensway, with "delicious Thai food";
take your own atmosphere, though.* / 11 pm.

Teatro W1   £ 44   ❸❸④
93-107 Shaftesbury Ave   0171-494 3040   4–3A
*Launch-hype linking star-chef Gordon Ramsay with this
Theatreland newcomer has left many wondering "what is all
the fuss about?" – a shame, as the modern British cooking
is "good", it's just "no better than at twenty other places";
the "cool design" does not overcome the fact that it's an
"awkwardly shaped" space.* / 11.45 pm; closed Sat L & Sun;
set pre-th. £29(FP).

Teca W1   £ 42   ❷④④
54 Brooks Mews   0171-495 4774   3–2B
*New modern Mayfair mews Italian, which has made a mixed
start; we – like others – found "fresh, light and uplifting" fare,
but the menu is greedily priced, portions are small, and the
welcome-to-Milano minimalism is harsh and cold.* / Midnight;
closed Sun.

10 EC2   £ 40   ❸④④
10 Cutlers Garden Arcade   0171-283 7888   9–2D
*"Better under new management", this spacious City
basement offers "meaty" and "different" modern British
cooking, superior to that of its previous incarnation (Le
Champenois); service is "fitful", however, and prices "huge".*
/ 9.30 pm; closed Sat & Sun.

Tentazioni SE1   £ 30   ❶❶④
2 Mill St   0171-237 1100   1–3D
*"Passionately" prepared cooking "packing rustic punch" has
made this tiny Italian near Tower Bridge one of the year's
most interesting newcomers; the service is notably "warm",
but the setting is "sterile" – perhaps its new Chiswick s
ibling, Grano, will get it right across the board.* / 11 pm;
closed Sat L & Sun.

The Tenth W8   £ 42   ❸❷❸
Royal Garden Hotel, Ken' High St   0171-361 1910   5–1A
*"They know how to treat diners" at this tenth-floor eyrie,
overlooking Kensington Gardens which – given that it enjoys
the "most spectacular views" – provides "surprisingly good"
grub; there is "still too much of a hotel feel, which is a
shame".* / 11.30 pm; closed Sat L & Sun; no smoking area.

The Terrace W8   £ 35   ❷❷❸
33c Holland St   0171-937 3224   5–1A
*A "small" and "intimate" gem, this hidden-away Kensington
newcomer combines "lovely", "high quality" modern British
cooking with "winsome" service; "on a warm evening",
the quiet terrace is a major plus.* / 10.30 pm; closed Sun D.

Terraza-Est EC4   £ 25   ❸❸④
109 Fleet St   0171-353 2680   9–2A
"Operatic arias, performed live" spice up dinner at this
festive, comfortable, old-style Italian; it's "good for a business
lunch", too. / 11 pm; closed Sat & Sun.

Texas Embassy Cantina WC2   £ 28   ⑤④④
1 Cockspur St   0171-925 0077   2–2C
"Overpriced slop" really turns off reporters on this "dire"
Tex/Mex, just off Trafalgar Square; perhaps it was inevitable,
given the location, that it would abandon its initial promise to
become a "noisy" touristfest. / 11 pm, Fri & Sat midnight.

Texas Lone Star SW7   £ 22   ⑤❸❸
154 Gloucester Rd   0171-370 5625   5–2B
"Amiable atmosphere" remains the key strength of this
elderly Tex/Mex by Gloucester Road tube, especially for those
who like their live music "far too loud"; as long as you can
stomach the grub, you "never leave hungry". / Sun-Wed 11.30 pm,
Thu-Sat 12.30 am; no booking.

TGI Friday's   £ 30   ⑤❸❸
25-29 Coventry St, W1   0171-839 6262   4–4A
6 Bedford St, WC2   0171-379 0585   4–4C
96-98 Bishops Bridge Rd, W2   0171-229 8600   6–1C
"Good for the under-12s!", they may be, but these "lively"
("overcrowded") American family-restaurants, which are
famed for their "OTT" service, are way too "expensive",
and some think they're just "plain nasty". / Midnight, W2
11.30 pm; smart casual; no smoking area; W1 & WC2, no booking Fri D-
Sat L.

Thai Bistro W4   £ 21   ❷❷④
99 Chiswick High Rd   0181-995 5774   7–2B
Chiswick "local Thai caff", offering "consistent" and
"interesting" cooking in a "speedy" and "unrelaxing"
atmosphere. / 11 pm; closed Tue L & Thu L; no Amex & no Switch;
no smoking.

Thai Break W8   £ 24   ❷❸④
30 Uxbridge St   0171-229 4332   6–2B
A "good new local Thai", just off Notting Hill Gate (on the
site of La Paesana, RIP), which belies its bog-standard
appearance, delivering some really tasty and reasonably
priced cooking. / 11 pm; closed Sun L.

Thai on the River SW10   £ 30   ④❸❷
15 Lots Rd   0171-351 1151   5–4B
This "airy" Chelsea Thai has a "nice view of the Thames"
(if you get the right seat) but is "otherwise rather average".
/ 11 pm, Fri & Sat 11.30 pm; closed Sat L & Mon L; set weekday L £19(FP).

Thai Pot £24 ❸④④
1 Bedfordbury, WC2   0171-379 4580   4–4C
148 Strand, WC2   0171-497 0904   2–2D
"Sensible prices" are the watchword at this Thai duo, who
combine "reasonably well accomplished" grub, with
"variable" service; the handy location of the original, behind
the Coliseum, makes it "good for group get-togethers", while
the 'Express' branch is a useful pit stop in a thin area. I—

Thailand SE14 £30 ❷❷❸
15 Lewisham Way   0181-691 4040   1–3D
People travel from all over south east London to sample the
"wonderful", "delicately flavoured" food, served "always with
a smile", at this "small and cosy" ("very cramped") Lewisham
Thai. I 10.30 pm; D only; closed Mon & Sun; no Amex; no smoking.

Thierry's SW3 £30 ④❸④
342 King's Rd   0171-352 3365   5–3C
A mid-year refit spruced up this "old-style" Gallic bistro in
Chelsea, which was getting rather "beyond its sell-by date";
post-refurb, it remains "amiable, but somewhat overpriced".
I 11 pm.

33 SW1 £48 ❸❸④
33 St James's St   0171-930 4272   3–4C
As ever, Derek Johns's quirky, perhaps "pretentious",
St James's establishment divides opinion between those
who say this Masterchef-winner is a culinary "genius",
and those who find his modern British cooking rather
"average". I 11.30 pm; closed Sat L & Sun; smart casual.

Thomas Goode Restaurant W1 £45 ④❸❷
19 South Audley St   0171-409 7242   3–3A
"Ladies-who-lunch" spot, par excellence – a dining room
adjoining a grandiose Mayfair emporium, where light,
ridiculously pricey dishes are served on "delightful crockery,
cutlery and crystal"; "service can be over-familiar".
I L & tea only; closed Sat & Sun; no jeans.

Tibetan Restaurant WC2 £19 ❸❷❸
17 Irving St   0171-839 2090   4–4B
Up a steep flight of stairs, off Leicester Square, what claims
to be the only Tibetan restaurant in the UK is a tiny "quirky"
room, where "friendly advice" is available on choosing the
"interesting" and very cheap scoff. I 10.30 pm; closed Wed L;
closed Sun; no Amex & no Switch.

F S A

Tiger Lil's £ 23 ④④❸

500 King's Rd, SW3 0171-376 5003 5–3B
270 Upper St, N1 0171-226 1118 8–2D
15a Clapham Common S'side, SW4 0171-720 5433 10–2D
*Especially for a large party, some like these stylish,
oriental-inspired joints (where you select the ingredients –
they wok 'em up); "you can end up eating bowlfuls of muck",
though. / 11.30 pm, Fri & Sat Midnight; SW10 closed Mon-Fri L, SW4 closed
Mon-Thur L; no Amex; no smoking areas; SW10 & SW4 max 30; N1 max 40.*

Toff's N10 £ 26 ❶❸⑤

38 Muswell Hl Broadway 0181-883 8656 1–1B
*"Go and get stuffed", say fans of the "massive portions" of
"unbeatable fish 'n' chips" at this Muswell Hill institution,
which – despite the odd unsatisfactory report – seems to
have emerged relatively unscathed from its change of
ownership. / 10 pm; closed Mon & Sun; no booking; set weekday L £15(FP).*

Tokyo Diner WC2 £ 15 ❸❷❸

2 Newport Pl 0171-287 8777 4–3B
*"Cheap" bento boxes of "fairly good" grub, make this
"very friendly and efficient" café – "handily located" on the
fringe of Chinatown – a useful "cheap and cheerful" stand-by.
/ Midnight; no Amex; no smoking area; Fri & Sat no booking.*

Tom's W10 £ 15 ❷❷❷

226 Westbourne Grove 0171-221 8818 6–1B
*"It's worth the queue" at Tom Conran's deli-diner, one of
the places the "beautiful people" of Notting Hill go for
"an excellent brunch"; "nice garden". / 5 pm; L only; no Amex;
no smoking; no booking.*

Tootsies £ 21 ④④④

177 New King's Rd, SW6 0171-736 4023 10–1B
107 Old Brompton Rd, SW7 0171-581 8942 5–2B
120 Holland Pk Ave, W11 0171-229 8567 6–2A
148 Chiswick High Rd, W4 0181-747 1869 7–2A
198 Haverstock Hill, NW3 0171-431 7609 8–2A
147 Church Rd, SW13 0181-748 3630 10–1A
*"My daughter, aged 6, rates it" – and that's the important
thing for many family visitors to this smart diner chain;
among the grown-ups, the "respectable" burgers have a
following. / 11 pm - 11.30 pm, Fri & Sat Midnight; no smoking areas
at W11 & W4; no booking.*

Topsy-Tasty W4 £ 20 ❷❷④

5 Station Parade 0181-995 3407 1–3A
*With its "extremely good value" Thai cooking, and "excellent
service", the lesser-known sibling to Chiswick's Bedlington
Café is "keeping up standards" rather better; it's "slightly
smarter", too. / 10.30 pm; D only; closed Sun; no credit cards.*

Toto's SW1 £ 41 ❸❷❸

Lennox Gardens Mews   0171-589 0075   5–2D
*It's "not exactly cutting-edge" – that's part of its appeal –
but this "delightful" Italian "all-rounder", just behind Harrods,
can be "great fun", and is often thought "romantic".*
/ 11.30 pm; smart casual.

Townhouse Brasserie WC1 £ 25 ❸❸❸

24 Coptic St   0171-636 2731   2–1C
*"Discreet", little-known yearling, near the British Museum,
which makes an inexpensive and useful stand-by.* / 11.30 pm;
no smoking area; set Sun L £16(FP).

Troika NW1 £ 19 ④④❸

101 Regents Pk Rd   0171-483 3765   8–2B
*All-day Eastern café/diner in Primrose Hill, whose pros
are being "cheap" and having a "cheerful" atmosphere
(especially on music nights), and whose cons include a
propensity to "dull" cooking and so-so service.* / 10.30 pm;
no Amex; no smoking area.

Troubadour SW5 £ 15 ④⑤❶

265 Old Brompton Rd   no tel   5–3A
*"Take a book and relax" at this "eclectic" and "eccentric"
coffee house – Earl's Court's answer to St Germain;
"in such an atmospheric place, the variable service is only to
be expected".* / 10.30 pm; no credit cards; no booking.

Tui SW7 £ 29 ❷④⑤

19 Exhibition Rd   0171-584 8359   5–2C
*"The best food – the worst décor" has long been the verdict
on this grim South Kensington Thai; service, too, could now do
with some help, and, worst of all, some feel the cooking "has
lost its snap".* / 10.45 pm; smart casual.

Tuk Tuk N1 £ 23 ④❸⑤

330 Upper St   0171-226 0837   8–3D
*"No-frills" Islington stand-by, generally (but by no means
unanimously) hailed for its "decent, cheap Thai food".* / 11 pm;
closed Sat L & Sun L.

Turner's SW3 £ 55 ❷❸❸

87-89 Walton St   0171-584 6711   5–2C
*"A bit twee", pricey and "outdated", perhaps, but celeb-chef
Brian Turner's Knightsbridge "stalwart" continues to win
praise for its "reliable, well honed" French cooking –
particularly the "bargain" lunch menu.* / 11 pm, Sun 8.30 pm;
closed Sat L; smart casual; set Sun L £34(FP).

Two Brothers N3 £ 22 ❶❷④

297/303 Regent's Pk Rd   0181-346 0469   1–1B
*A "North Finchley haven", whose "outstanding fish 'n' chips"
and "friendly" service secure a dedicated local following.*
/ 10.15 pm; closed Mon & Sun; no smoking area; book L only.

The Union Café W1   £35   ❸❸⑤
96 Marylebone Ln   0171-486 4860   3–1A
*"Fresh and well prepared" modern British food can make
this Marylebone venture "an all-round good place to eat"
(particularly at lunch); it's "a little overpriced", though,
especially given the "basic" and Spartan setting. / 10.30 pm;
closed Sun; no Amex; no smoking area.*

Uno SW1   £28   ❷❸④
1 Denbigh St   0171-834 1001   2–4B
*Dwellers in the culinary wasteland which is Pimlico are very
excited about this "new-wave Italian"; they laud its "excellent
food" (not least "great pizza") and its "helpful and friendly"
service; the setting is "cramped", though, and noisy. / 11.15 pm;
closed Sun; no credit cards.*

Upper Street Fish Shop N1   £19   ❷❸④
324 Upper St   0171-359 1401   8–2D
*"Reliably good fish" – not just chippy staples – and its
"easy-going and unpretentious" charm have made this
Islington bistro a more than local institution; BYO. / 10.15 pm;
closed Mon L & Sun; no credit cards; no booking.*

Vama SW10   £35   ❷④❸
438 King's Rd   0171-351 4118   5–3B
*"Surprisingly good" Indian cuisine ("expensive, but worth it")
wins high praise for this chichi and tightly packed World's End
yearling; it remains relatively undiscovered. / 10 pm; set weekday L
£17(FP).*

Vasco & Piero's Pavilion W1   £32   ❸❶❸
15 Poland St   0171-437 8774   3–1D
*"Delightful", "diligent" service and "classy and unusual"
cooking (especially from the "excellent value" set menus) win
a devoted following for this "secret" old-Soho Italian; some
find "something slightly dull about the atmosphere". / 11 pm;
closed Sat & Sun (open one Sat D monthly); no Switch; smart casual.*

Veeraswamy W1   £33   ❸❸❸
Victory House, 101 Regent St   0171-734 1401   3–3D
*Opinions differ starkly on the modernistic relaunch of
London's oldest Indian (near Piccadilly Circus); some love the
"beautiful", "light and colourful" décor and the "delicious,
innovative" cooking – for others, "that joy of an Indian meal"
has been taken away. / 11.30 pm; Sun 10 pm; closed Sun; set Sun L
£15(FP).*

The Vegetarian Cottage NW3   £16   ❸❸❸
91 Haverstock Hl   0171-586 1257   8–2B
*"Something different" – a veggie Chinese local (in Belsize
Park) – whose competent cooking comes at a "reasonable
price". / 11.15 pm; D only ex Sun open L & D; no Amex.*

Vegia Zena NW1   £29   ❷❸④
17 Princess Rd   0171-483 0192 8–3B
*For some, this family-run Primrose Hill Italian is still a
"hidden treasure"; "you must know what to choose", though,
and those who remember the past exceptional standards may
leave somewhat disappointed; the setting is "a bit tatty" –
"don't sit in the basement". / 11 pm; set weekday L £7(FP).*

Vendôme W1   £38   ④❸❸
20 Dover St   0171-629 5417 3–3C
*The "good bar" and "fabulous", "romantic" décor –
"like being inside a chocolate box" – are the highlights of this
louche Mayfair rendezvous; the food is "unremarkable".
/ 11 pm; closed Sat & Sun.*

Veronica's W2   £32   ④❷❷
3 Hereford Rd   0171-229 5079 6–1B
*As ever, "interesting olde English recipes" maintains this
Bayswater fixture's loyal fan club, though the cooking can be
"very heavy"; supporters also say the candlelit setting is
"romantic", though others find it boring. / 11.30 pm; closed Sat L
& Sun.*

Le Versailles SW9   £30   ❸❸④
20 Trinity Gdns   0171-326 0521 10–2D
*"Locals swoon at this small French bistro in Brixton"; the set
menus (especially dinner, Mon-Thu) undoubtedly offer good
value, but we agree with those who say that, à la carte, it's
"not cheap". / 10.30 pm, Fri & Sat 11 pm; closed Mon; no Amex;
no smoking area.*

Vic Naylors EC1   £25   ④④❷
38 & 40 St John St   0171-608 2181 9–1B
*"A place to go with friends, not gourmets", this Smithfield
wine bar/restaurant offers "cheap and cheerful" City lunching,
and "a great relaxing environment after work". / 11 pm;
closed Sat & Sun.*

Il Vicolo SW1   £30   ❸❷④
3-4 Crown Passage   0171-839 3960 3–4D
*"Busy at lunch with many regulars, and quieter in the
evenings" – this unremarkable-looking trattoria is well known
to the denizens of St James's as a bastion of "good value",
and "well flavoured" cooking. / 10 pm; closed Sat & Sun.*

Vijay NW6   £19   ❷❸④
49 Willesden Ln   0171-328 1087 1–1B
*"Incredibly cheap, lovely food" (much of it vegetarian) and
"unusually friendly service" secure a dedicated following for
this obscure Kilburn Indian. / 10.45 pm, Fri & Sat 11.45 pm; no Amex.*

Villa Bianca NW3 £ 36 ④❸❷

1 Perrins Ct 0171-435 3131 8–2A

The "lovely setting" – in a very 'Hampstead' cobbled lane – is the reason to visit this chichi trattoria, much of whose cooking is "indifferent". / 11.30 pm.

Village Bistro N6 £ 33 ❸④❸

38 Highgate High St 0181-340 5165 8–1B

"Cramped" and "romantic" Highgate "local" offering enjoyable Gallic fare; the staff, though, can be "unwelcoming". / 11 pm.

Villandry Dining Rooms W1 £ 33 ❸⑤④

170 Gt Portland St 0171-631 3131 2–1B

"Not as good as in the old premises", this relocated Fitzrovia 'deli/restaurant' has made a fitful start in its grand new home, east of Portland Place; the "exceptional, when on form" Gallic "provincial fare" is "variable", and service can be desperately "slow". / 10 pm; closed Sun; no smoking.

Vincent's SW15 £ 23 ❸❷❸

147 Upper Richmond Rd 0181-780 3553 10–2B

"Cosy" Putney "neighbourhood" place, which pleases most with its "unpretentious, well prepared" modern British provisions, and its "warm" and "polite" service. / 10.30 pm; closed Sat L & Sun, open Sun L in winter; no smoking area.

The Vine NW5 £ 29 ❷④❷

86 Highgate Rd 0171-209 0038 8–1B

An "excellent pub restaurant with a nice garden" – this Kentish Town gastropub is "worth the trek", thanks to its "easy-going atmosphere" and its "fair-sized" portions of "tasty" modern British cooking. / 10 pm; closed Mon L; no smoking area.

Vingt-Quatre SW10 £ 24 ④❷❸

325 Fulham Rd 0171-376 7224 5–3B

"Wholesome food any time of night and day"; "it is staggering there aren't more places" like this "cheerful" Chelsea in-crowd diner, which is "stylish in a downbeat sort of way", and – though the cooking is nothing special – offers "fine value". / open 24 hours; no booking.

Vong SW1 £ 43 ❶❷❸

Wilton Pl 0171-235 1010 5–1D

"Highly original", "imaginatively spiced" French/Thai cooking wins plaudits for this glamorous Belgravian, though a small but vocal minority continue to gripe about an "overpriced and unenjoyable poseurs' paradise". / 10.30 pm; closed Sun L; no smoking area.

Vrisaki N22 £ 24 ❷❷❸

73 Myddleton Rd 0181-889 8760 1–1C

The "portions are huge", to the delight of addicts of the "delicious" and amazing value meze-special at this "packed" Bounds Green Greek. / Midnight; closed Sun; no Amex.

Wagamama £ 16 ❸❸❸

101 Wigmore Street, W1 0171-409 0111 3–1A
10a Lexington St, W1 0171-292 0990 3–2D
4a Streatham St, WC1 0171-323 9223 2–1C

Thanks to their "delicious ramen dishes at competitive prices", the instigators of the "no-frills" noodle-refectory revolution are still "hard to beat; "go early to avoid the queues". / 11 pm; no smoking; no booking.

Wakaba NW3 £ 40 ❸❸④

122a Finchley Rd 0171-586 7960 8–2A

"Good (but overpriced) sushi" is the speciality at this ultra-minimalist Japanese, opposite Finchley Road tube; its design is a delight to architecture-anoraks, but not everyone else. / 10.45 pm; D only; closed Sun.

The Waldorf Meridien WC2 £ 53 ④❷❷

Aldwych 0171-836 2400 2–2D

The "very reasonably priced buffet breakfast", and the famous tea dances (to which the price shown relates) provide reasons to visit this Covent Garden-fringe hotel; an MPW-badged relaunch is expected some time in 1999. / 11.15 pm; for tea dance, jacket & tie; no smoking; set pre-th. £34(FP).

The Waterloo Fire Station SE1 £ 26 ④④④

150 Waterloo Rd 0171-401 3267 9–4A

"Hit-and-miss" cooking is now the norm at this "once very good-value" bar-refectory, opposite the Old Vic; it's still hugely popular with a younger crowd, but the setting – "noisy", smoky and "brashly lit"– leads fogies to find the atmosphere "rather rough". / 11 pm; closed Sun D.

Weng Wah House NW3 £ 22 ❸❷❸

240 Haverstock Hl 0171-794 5123 8–2A

"Competent in all respects", this "calming" Chinese "local" is a Belsize Park fixture. / 11.30 pm; no Amex.

The Westbourne W2 £ 23 ④⑤❶

101 Westbourne Park Villas 0171-221 1332 6–1B

"Worth it if you can get a seat", this favourite boho boozer of Notting Hill's "trendy young things" (actually located in Bayswater) is "especially lovely" on the terrace in summer; the modern British food varies from good to mediocre, but you'll probably be beyond caring by the time it shows up. / 10 pm; closed Mon L; no Amex.

White Cross Hotel TW9 £19 ③④❷
Water Ln   0181-940 6844   1–4A
Come winter (roaring fires), or summer (beer garden overlooking the river), this fine Young's pub near Richmond Bridge makes an excellent weekend destination, complete with superior pub-grub and a child-friendly attitude. / L only; no Amex; no booking.

The White Onion N1 £32 ❶❶❸
297 Upper St   0171-359 3533   8–3D
"Unusual combinations" of "good, fresh ingredients" make this "unpretentious", well oiled modern British yearling Islington's top culinary hotspot; those who find the setting "austere" tip upstairs as "airier and more pleasant" than below. / 11 pm; closed Mon L.

Whittington's EC4 £39 ④❸④
21 College HI   0171-248 5855   9–3B
The cellar of Dick's old home, not far from St Paul's, is now a wine bar and (rather cramped) restaurant; the "pricey" food is nevertheless quite "interesting" by City standards, and service is "attentive". / L only; closed Sat & Sun.

Wilson's W14 £32 ❸❷④
236 Blythe Rd   0171-603 7267   7–1C
"Quirky" Caledonian-themed Shepherd's Bush local, where the kilted patron's bagpipes are an ever-present hazard; the fare is "reliable". / 10 pm; closed Sat L & Sun D; no Amex; set Sun L £22(FP).

Wiltons SW1 £54 ❷❷❸
55 Jermyn St   0171-629 9955   3–3C
"Prices so surreally absurd they almost cheer you up" ensure there are "no riffraff" at this "agonisingly stuffy" English restaurant in St James's; "wonderful oysters" and "excellent seafood" console those for whom money is no object. / 10.30 pm; closed Sat; jacket & tie; set Sun L £32(FP).

Windows on the World
Park Lane Hilton Hotel W1 £59 ⑤④❷
22 Park Ln   0171-208 4021   3–4A
"They probably think they could get away with murder because of the view" – presumably that's why the pricey French cooking at this 28th floor Mayfair eyrie is ridiculously "ordinary" and "uninspired"; on Sundays, though, there's "the best champagne brunch ever". / Mon-Thu 10.30 pm, Fri & Sat 11.30 pm; closed Sat L & Sun D; dinner, jacket & tie; set weekday L £40(FP).

Windsor Castle W8 £18 ④❸❶
114 Campden HI Rd   0171-727 8491   6–2B
The "great beer garden" ("in summer, get there early") is but one of the factors which makes this Kensington hostelry a "winner" – it has a "quaint" and intriguing interior and "honest", if by no means exceptional, grub. / 10.30 pm; no smoking area (L only); no booking.

Wine Gallery SW10 £20 ④❸❷

49 Hollywood Rd   0171-352 7572   5–3B
*"Very cheap wine" (house is a fiver a bottle), has rejuvenated
the appeal of this long-serving Chelsea diner (which has a
"cool garden"); the "hearty" and inexpensive cooking has no
pretensions to art. / 11.45 pm; no Amex.*

Wiz W11 £20 – – –

123a Clarendon Rd   0171-229 1500   6–2A
*On the attractive but obscure Holland Park site that was
W11, AWT's new sibling to Woz is to be opened just after we
go to press; the gimmick this time is to be tapas-style dishes
of diverse inspiration, with the bar a key attraction.*

Wódka W8 £34 ④④❸

12 St Alban's Grove   0171-937 6513   5–1B
*"Quirky and charming" Pole – in a Kensington backwater –
where the "good selection of vodkas" is a more reliable
attraction than the "solid" cooking, which varies from
"yummy" to "way off the mark". / 11.15 pm; closed Sat L &
Sun L; smart casual; set weekday L £21(FP).*

Wok Wok £25 ④④④

10 Frith St, W1   0171-437 7080   4–2A
140 Fulham Rd, SW10   0171-370 5355   5–3B
67 Upper Street, N1   0171-288 0333   8–3D
51-53 Northcote Road, SW11   0171-978 7181   10–2C
*"Slightly less attractive alternatives to Wagamamas",
these proliferating noodle-bars offer a similarly useful, but
less distinguished package of "cheap" grub in "clinical,
but efficient" surroundings. / W1 Mon-Wed 11 pm, Thu-Sat midnight,
Sun 10.30 pm – SW10 11 pm, Fri midnight - SW11 & N1 11 pm; W1 closed
Sat & Sun L; SW10 Sat & Sun no booking, Mon-Fri L only - W1 party bookings
(8+) only for D.*

Wolfe's WC2 £27 ❸❸④

30 Gt Queen St   0171-831 4442   4–1D
*"Still great hamburgers", say addicts of this "always reliable"
family diner in Covent Garden; some still "mourn the passing
of the Basil Street branch". / 11.30 pm; closed Sun.*

Wong Kei W1 £14 ❸⑤④

41-43 Wardour St   0171-437 8408   4–3A
*"The main reason for coming is the staff insults" – this
infamously insolent Chinatown behemoth maintains its
unique approach to customer relations; the food is
"scrummy", though, especially given the minimal cost.
/ 11.30 pm; no credit cards; no booking.*

Woodlands £23 ❸④④

37 Panton St, SW1   0171-839 7258   4–4A
77 Marylebone Ln, W1   0171-486 3862   3–1A
*They aren't much to look at – Marylebone is the smarter of
the two – but this long-established veggie Indian duo offer
"good value for central London", especially at lunch. / 10.30 pm.*

Woz W10 £31 ❸❷❷

46 Golborne Rd   0181-968 2200   6–1A
*Fans of TV chef 'Wozza' Thompson's grimly located North
Kensington yearling gush about the "fantastic concept" of a
no-choice five-course meal – "like throwing a dinner party
without having to cook"; we're with those who find the
cooking "very average".* / 11.30 pm; closed Mon L & Sun D.

Yas W14 £23 ④❸❸

7 Hammersmith Rd   0171-603 9148   7–1D
*We're among those who have found "dull" cooking (main
courses in particular) at this Persian, opposite Olympia; on
the plus side, the appetisers are "great", you can BYO (£2
corkage), and they are open until it's so late, it's early.* / 5 am;
no Amex.

Yo! Sushi W1 £23 ④❷❷

52-53 Poland St   0171-287 0443   3–1D
*"Funky and fantastic", "fun and frantic" – these "unrelaxing"
hi-tech eateries (delivering sushi by conveyor belt and drinks
by robot) are an amusing gimmick (the Soho original in
particular), to which you should probably go once; the food,
though, is "average".* / Midnight; no smoking; no booking.

Yoahan Plaza food court NW9 £15 ❸④⑤

399 Edgware Rd   0181-200 9856   1–1A
*Though some argue that "you have to be desperate" to brave
the noisy, basic food mall of this intriguing Japanese shopping
Mall (ten minutes from Colindale tube), there are those who
find "splendour" in the variety, chaos and budget prices.*
/ 11 pm; no Amex.

Yoshino W1 £27 ❷❸④

3 Piccadilly Pl   0171-287 6622   3–3D
*"Just like Tokyo," says a Japanese reporter in praise of this
small sushi-bar, off Piccadilly; it offers "excellent value"
and some of the "best food of its type in London", but the
atmosphere can be "awkward" (especially for those thwarted
by the absence, at lunch, of menus in English).* / 9 pm; closed Sun;
no smoking area.

Yum Yum N16 £23 ❷❷❸

30 Stoke Newington Ch St   0171-254 6751   1–1C
*"Authentic cooking" and "very reasonable prices" make
this "busy" (it can be "too crowded"), but "attentive"
Stoke Newington Thai one of the best bets in the area.*
/ 10.45 pm, Fri & Sat 11.15 pm.

ZAFFERANO SW1 £39 ❶❶❷

16 Lowndes St   0171-235 5800   2–4A
*"Fabulous", "authentic" cooking has now secured this
"sophisticated" Belgravian the title as 'London's top Italian' –
"it's worth booking a month in advance"; "lunch is cheaper
than dinner, but the food's just as excellent".* / 11 pm; closed Sun.

Zamoyski NW3 £ 20 ④④❸
85 Fleet Rd   0171-794 4792   8–2A
*"Quirky, but distinctive" south Hampstead Pole; "forget the
grub" – although the meze option is very cheap – "and enjoy
the amazing vodka selection". / 11 pm; D only ex Sun, when open all
day; no Amex & no Switch; smart casual.*

Zed SW2 £ 20 ❸❷❸
30 Acre Ln   0171-501 9001   10–2D
*The young staff may be "inexperienced", but they are "very
keen" at this "fun", large Brixton bar/restaurant, which
charges "good prices" for "decent pizza" (and less good
pasta); great terrace. / 11 pm; closed Mon.*

Zen SW3 £ 44 ❷❸④
Chelsea Cloisters, Sloane Av   0171-589 1781   5–2C
*"Expensive, but good" Chelsea Chinese of long standing,
whose only significant drawback in some people's book, is
that it is "too conservative". / 11.15 pm; no Amex; smart casual.*

Zen Central W1 £ 52 ❸❷⑤
20-22 Queen St   0171-629 8089   3–3B
*The cooking at this once market-leading, minimalist Mayfair
oriental continues to slip; it has always had a "chilly"
atmosphere, but those who find the food "delicious, if
somewhat expensive", are losing ground to those who
complain that it's "below par". / 11.30 pm; no Amex; smart casual.*

Zen Garden W1 £ 47 ❸❷❸
15-16 Berkeley St   0171-493 1381   3–3C
*"Calm", "ordered" and "well spaced" Mayfair Chinese – one
of the most comfortable of its type – whose "good dim sum"
and "quick lunchtime service" make it a useful venue,
especially for business. / 11 pm; smart casual; set weekday L £24(FP).*

ZeNW3 NW3 £ 34 ❸❷❸
83 Hampstead High St   0171-794 7863   8–2A
*"Well executed" cooking – though "small portions" are a
gripe again this year – and "elegant", "clean" design makes
this prominent Chinese one of Hampstead's best places.
/ 11.30 pm; smart casual.*

Ziani SW3 £ 34 ❸❷❶
45-47 Radnor Wk   0171-352 2698   5–3C
*"Great", happy" and "loud" family-run Italian, in a quiet
Chelsea side street, whose sizeable and well-heeled following
seems surprisingly unperturbed by the lack of any personal
space. / 11.30 pm.*

Zilli Fish W1 £ 42 ③④❸
36-40 Brewer St   0171-734 8649   3–2D
*"Delicious" Italian fish cooking has put Signor Zilli's
Soho-corner yearling on the map; even fans say it's
"expensive", though, and service is "indifferent".* / 11.45 pm;
closed Sun.

Zinc W1 £ 31 ⑤④④
21 Heddon St   0171-255 8899   3–2C
*"Another Conran failure" – nothing really works at this
"very clinical", "cramped" and "completely forgettable"
brasserie, near Regent Street, least of all the "decidedly
under-flavoured" and "uninspired" cooking.* / 11.30 pm;
closed Sun D.

Zoe W1 £ 35 ④④④
3-5 Barrett St   0171-224 1122   3–1A
*Perennially "dreadful" service and sometimes "lousy"
modern British cooking have made this bright-and-breezy
café-restaurant, just off St Christopher's Place, a byword for
mediocrity; perhaps the recent "badly needed" revamp,
will lift more than the décor.* / 11.30 pm; closed Sun; smart casual;
no smoking area.

Zucca W11 £ 32 ④❸④
188 Westbourne Grove   0171-727 0060   6–1B
*"Friendly service" helps to endear this trendy Italian yearling,
which "buzzes in the best Notting Hill style" to some;
the "uninspiring" pizzas and more menu, however,
wins limited support.* / 11 pm; no Amex; no sat lunch.

Zujuma's SW19 £ 29 ④❸④
58a Wimbledon Hill Rd   0181-879 0916   10–2B
*Traumas, including the withdrawal of Whitbread from
part-ownership, have made it a very mixed year at this
promising Wimbledon subcontinental; let's hope as a
stand-alone it will recover its "tasty", "quite different slant
on Indian food".* / 11 pm.

INDEXES

INDEXES

Big group bookings
(more expensive establishments which will contemplate large bookings in the main dining room - see also private rooms)

Suntory *(50)*
Santini *(35)*
Dordogne *(50)*
Wiltons *(30)*
MPW *(30)*
Canteen *(30)*
Elena's L'Etoile *(30)*
Mon Plaisir *(28)*
English House *(26)*
Kensington Place *(26)*
Conrad Hotel *(25)*
Soufflé *(25)*
Villandry *(20)*
Vendôme *(20)*
Poule au Pot *(20)*
Escargot *(20)*
Claridges *(20)*
City Brasserie *(20)*
Scalini *(18)*
Quo Vadis *(16)*
Dakota *(16)*
Boyd's *(15)*
Stephen Bull *(15)*
Famiglia *(14)*
Blue Print Café *(14)*
Bank *(14)*
Dorchester Oriental *(16)*

Breakfast
(with opening times)

Central
Atrium *(8)*
Aurora *(8)*
Balans: *all branches (8)*
Bank *(7.30)*
Bar Italia *(7)*
Café Bohème *(8)*
Café Flo: *WC2 (10); SW1, 103 Wardour Street W1 (9); 13 Thayer St W1 (9, Sat & Sun 10)*
Café Pasta: *all central branches (9.30)*
Café Rouge: *all central branches (10)*
Café Sofra: *all branches (7)*
Chez Gérard: *119 Chancery Ln WC2 (8, not Sat & Sun)*
Claridges Restaurant *(7)*
Connaught *(7.30)*
Cranks: *8 Marshall St W1, 9-11 Tottenham St W1 (8); 23 Barrett St W1, Unit 11, 8 Adelaide St WC2 (8, Sat 9); 17-19 Great Newport St WC2 (9)*
Dôme: *W1 (10); both WC2, (8)*
Dorchester Grill *(7, Sun 7.30)*
1837 at Brown's Hotel *(7)*
Fifth Floor (Café) *(10)*

Food for Thought *(9.30)*
Goring Hotel *(7)*
Grissini *(7)*
Häagen-Dazs: *all central branches (10)*
The Halkin *(7)*
Hyde Park Hotel Park Room *(7)*
Indigo *(6.30)*
Italian Kitchen: *WC2 (10)*
The Lanesborough *(7)*
Maison Bertaux *(9)*
Mash *(8, Sat & Sun 11)*
Mediterranean Café *(9)*
Museum St Café *(8)*
Nicole's *(10)*
L'Odéon *(Mon-Fri 8)*
Oriel *(8.30, Sun 9)*
Pâtisserie Valerie: *44 Old Compton St W1 (7.30, Sun 9); RIBA Centre, 66 Portland Pl W1 (8); 105 Marylebone High St W1 (8, Sun 9); WC2 (9.30, Sun 9)*
Pizza On The Park *(8.30)*
Pret A Manger: *63 Tottenham Court Rd W1 (7.15); 75b Victoria St SW1, 7 Marylebone High St W1, 240-241 High Holborn WC1 (7.30); 120 Baker St W1 (7.45); 12 Kingsgate Pd, Victoria St SW1, 298 Regents St W1, 54-56 Oxford St W1, 173 Wardour St W1, 18 Hanover St W1, 163 Piccadilly W1, 122 High Holborn WC1, WC2 (8)*
The Ritz *(7)*
Savoy River Restaurant *(7)*
Simpsons-in-the-Strand *(Mon-Fri 7)*
Sotheby's Café *(9)*
Star Café *(7.30)*
Stock Pot: *SW1 (7); 50 James St W1 (8)*
The Union Café *(Mon-Fri 9.30)*
Villandry *(8.30)*
The Waldorf Meridien *(Mon-Fri 7, w/e 7.30)*
Windows on the World *(7)*

West
Balans West: *all branches (8)*
Basil St Hotel *(7)*
Bedlington Café *(8)*
Beirut Express *(9.30)*
La Belle Epoque *(8)*
Bistrot 190 *(7)*
Blakes Hotel *(7.30)*
La Bouchée *(9.30)*
Brass. du Marché *(10, Sun 11)*
La Brasserie *(8, Sun 9)*
Café 206 *(8)*
Café Flo: *all west branches (9)*
Café Grove *(9.30)*
Café Laville *(10)*
Café Montpeliano *(8)*
Café Pasta: *W4 (9); W8 (9.30)*

INDEXES

Oriel
La Perla
Scott's
Smollensky's
Windows on the World
Zinc

West
Anonimato
Balans West: *all branches*
Beach Blanket Babylon
La Belle Epoque
Bistrot 190
Bluebird
La Brasserie
Cactus Blue
Café Grove
Café Laville
Chelsea Bun Diner
Coins
Conrad Hotel
Coyote Café
The Crescent
The Cross Keys
Dakota
Joe's Brasserie
Joe's Café
Kartouche
Langan's Coq d'Or
Mas Café
Montana
PJ's
Raoul's Café
Stone Mason's Arms
Tom's
Tootsies: *all branches*
Vingt-Quatre
Woz

North
Banners
La Brocca
Café Delancey
Café Mozart
Camden Brasserie
Centuria
The Engineer
House on Rosslyn Hill
Jindivick
The Landmark Hotel
Lola's
Tootsies: *all branches*
The Vine
The White Onion

South
Belair House
Bistrot 2 Riverside
Boiled Egg
The Circle

The Honest Cabbage
Hornimans
Ost. Antica Bologna
Le Pont de la Tour
Ransome's Dock
The Secret Garden
The Stepping Stone
Tootsies: *all branches*

East
Al's
Frocks

Business

Central
Atrium
The Avenue
Bentley's
Beotys
Café Royal Grill
Le Caprice
Cave
Cecconi's
Che
Chez Nico
Christopher's
Claridges Restaurant
Connaught
The Criterion
Diverso
Dorchester Grill
Dorchester, Oriental
1837 at Brown's Hotel
Elena's L'Etoile
L'Escargot
Le Gavroche
Goring Hotel
Green's
Greenhouse
Grissini
The Guinea
The Halkin
Hodgson's
L'Incontro
Interlude
The Ivy
Ken Lo's Memories
Langan's Brasserie
Leith's Soho
Malabar Junction
The Marquis
Mitsukoshi
Miyama
Mon Plaisir
Neal Street
Nico Central
O'Conor Don
Oak Room MPW
L'Odéon

INDEXES

Upper St Fish Shop

South
The Cook House
Monsieur Max
Pizzeria Franco
The Secret Garden

East
Lahore Kebab House

Children

(h – high or special chairs
m – children's menu
p – children's portions
e – weekend entertainments
o – other facilities)

Central
Al Bustan *(hp)*
Al Sultan *(h)*
Alastair Little *(hm)*
Alfred *(hp)*
Ask! Pizza: *all branches (hp)*
Au Jardin des Gourmets *(p)*
Axis *(m)*
Back to Basics *(p)*
Balans: *W1 (p)*
Bank *(hp)*
Belgo Centraal: *WC2 (hp)*
Benihana: *all branches (hm)*
Bice *(h)*
Blues *(o)*
Boudin Blanc *(h)*
Browns: *W1 (h); WC2 (hm)*
Café Emm *(h)*
Café Flo: *all branches (h)*
Café Pacifico *(hm)*
Café Pasta: *all branches (hpo)*
Café Rouge: *15 Frith St W1 (hm)*
Caffè Uno: *all branches (hm)*
Capital Radio Restaurant *(hm)*
China City *(h)*
Chor Bizarre *(h)*
Chuen Cheng Ku *(h)*
Claridges Restaurant *(h)*
Como Lario *(h)*
Cranks: *all branches (h)*
The Criterion *(h)*
Deals: *W1 (h)*
Diverso *(h)*
Dorchester Grill *(hm)*
Dorchester, Oriental *(h)*
Down Mexico Way *(h)*
Ed's Easy Diner: *Trocadero W1 (hm); 12 Moor St W1 (m)*
Efes Kebab House: *1) 80 Great Titchfield St W1 (h); 2) 175-177 Gt Portland St W1 (hp)*
1837 at Brown's Hotel *(p)*
L'Escargot *(h)*

Fakhreldine *(hp)*
Fashion Café *(h)*
Football Football *(hmo)*
Fung Shing *(h)*
The Gaucho Grill: *W1 (h)*
Golden Dragon *(h)*
Goring Hotel *(h)*
Gourmet Pizza Co.: *all branches (hm)*
The Guinea *(p)*
Häagen-Dazs: *all central branches (h)*
Hamine *(p)*
Harbour City *(h)*
Hard Rock Café *(hmpo)*
Hardy's *(h)*
Hyde Park Hotel Park Room *(h)*
Indigo *(hp)*
Italian Kitchen: *all branches (mo)*
The Ivy *(hp)*
Japanese Canteen: *W1 (hp)*
Joy King Lau *(h)*
Kettners *(h)*
Kundan *(h)*
The Lanesborough *(hm)*
Little Havana *(e)*
Luna Nuova *(h)*
Maroush: *all branches (p)*
Mash *(h)*
Matsuri *(m)*
Mayflower *(h)*
Mediterranean Café *(hp)*
Melati *(h)*
Mezzo *(h)*
Navajo Joe *(m)*
New World *(h)*
Nobu *(h)*
Oak Room MPW *(h)*
L'Odéon *(hm)*
Orrery *(h)*
Pasta di Milano: *all branches (h)*
Pizza On The Park *(h)*
PizzaExpress: *all central branches (h)*
Pizzeria Condotti *(h)*
Planet Hollywood *(hm)*
Poons *(h)*
La Porte des Indes *(h)*
Porters *(hmo)*
The Rainforest Café *(hmeo)*
Rib Room *(h)*
The Ritz *(h)*
RK Stanleys *(hp)*
Rowley's *(h)*
Royal China: *all branches (hm)*
Rueda: *all branches (hp)*
Rules *(h)*
Sartoria *(h)*
Satsuma *(h)*
Savoy Grill *(h)*
Savoy River Restaurant *(h)*

East

Entertainment
(Check times before you go)

Central

INDEXES

Café de Paris
(DJ & dancing, nightly)
Café Latino
(music, Tue, Fri & Sat)
Calabash
(African band, Fri or Sat)
Capital Radio Restaurant
(resident DJ)
Claridges Restaurant
(dinner dance, Fri & Sat)
Cy
(music, Wed-Sat)
Deals: W1
(music, Fri & Sat)
Dover Street
(band, DJ & dancing, nightly)
Down Mexico Way
(DJ & dancing, nightly)
Efes Kebab House: 2) 175-177 Gt
Portland St W1
(belly dancer, nightly)
Il Faro
(jazz, Fri eves)
Fashion Café
(regular fashion shows and late-night music)
Fifth Floor (Café)
(jazz, nightly)
Football Football
(sports screens)
The Foundation
(jazz, Fri)
Garlic & Shots
(troubador, Fri & Sat)
Grissini
(music, nightly)
The Halkin
(music, nightly)
Hamine
(karaoke, Mon-Sat)
Havana
(DJ, nightly)
Ishbilia
(music, Sat & Sun)
Kettners
(pianist evenings and lunch Wed-Sun)
The Lanesborough
(supper dances, Fri - Sat; jazz Sun brunch)
Langan's Brasserie
(jazz, nightly)
The Lexington
(pianist, Tue-Fri)
Little Havana
(DJ & dancing, nightly)
Mezzo
(music, Wed-Sat)
Nicole's
(jazz, Tue & Thu)
L'Odéon
(jazz, nightly)
Pizza On The Park
(jazz, nightly)
PizzaExpress: 10 Dean St W1
*(jazz, nightly); 20 Greek St W1
(jazz, Thu-Sat)*
La Porte des Indes
(folk dancing, Sun brunch)
Quaglino's
(bar-jazz, nightly)

The Ritz
(band, Fri & Sat)
Rueda: W1
(Spanish music & dancing, Fri & Sat)
Saint
(DJ, nightly)
Savoy River Restaurant
(dinner dance, nightly ex Sun)
Smollensky's, Strand
(music, nightly; dancing, Thu-Sat)
Sofra: both WC2,
(music, Mon-Sat)
Le Soufflé
(string trio, Sun L)
Stargazer
(jazz, Wed)
The Waldorf Meridien
(jazz, Sun L)
Windows on the World
(dinner dance, Fri & Sat)

West
All Bar One: W4
(jazz, Sun pm)
Big Easy
(band, nightly)
Bombay Brasserie
(piano & singer nightly and wkend D)
Café Lazeez
(music, Wed, Fri & Sat)
Café O
(Greek music, Thu-Sat)
Café Rouge: W8
(jazz, Mon)
Cambio de Tercio
(guitarist, Wed)
Chicago Rib Shack
(music, Wed, Thu & Fri)
Chutney Mary
(jazz, Sun L)
Conrad Hotel
(singer & pianist, nightly)
Da Mario
(disco, nightly ex Sun)
Isfehan
(music, nightly)
Maroush: W2
(music & dancing, nightly)
Mas Café
(bands & party nights)
Montana
(jazz, Wed-Sun)
Mr Wing
(jazz Thu-Sat)
Nikita's
(Russian music, weekends)
Palio
(jazz, Thu eves)
Paparazzi Café
(music, nightly)
Patio
(gypsy music, nightly)
Pizza Pomodoro: all branches
(music, nightly)
PizzaExpress: W8
*(jazz, Fri & Sat); W14
(jazz, Sat); 6-7 Beauchamp Pl SW3
(jazz, Sat & Sun)*
Rodizio Rico
(music, Tue,Thu,Sun L)

Shoeless Joe's
(video screens)
606 Club
(jazz, nightly)
Star of India
(music, Thu & Fri)
The Tenth
(pianist nightly; band nights)
Texas Lone Star
(music, 3 nights a week)
Wilson's
(bagpipes most evenings)

North

Les Associés
(accordion 1st Fri of month)
Café Rouge: NW3
(jazz, Wed)
China Blues
(jazz, nightly)
Cuba Libre
(dancing, Fri & Sat)
Don Pepe
(singing & organist, nightly)
La Finca: N1
(rhumba & flamenco, Wed; salsa some Fri)
The Fox Reformed
(regular wine tasting and backgammon tournaments; book club)
Greek Valley
(bouzouki music, Fri)
House on Rosslyn Hill
(karaoke, Mon; Winter – music, Fri & Sat)
The Landmark Hotel
(harpist Mon-Fri; jazz, Sun L; band & dancing Sat D)
Lola's
(jazz, Sun L)
PizzaExpress: 187 Kentish Town Road NW1; (jazz, Tue & Thu eves)
Troika
(Russian music, Fri & Sat)
Villa Bianca
(guitar, twice weekly)
Weng Wah House
(karoke, nightly)
Zamoyski
(Russian music, Fri & Sat)

South

Archduke Wine Bar
(jazz, nightly)
Batt. Barge Bistro
(guitarist, Thu-Sat)
Café Rouge: SW11
(pianist, Thur; clown, Sun)
Côte à Côte
(music, Fri & Sat)
Elvis Gracelands Palace
(Chinese Elvis, nightly)
Fina Estampa
(music, Fri & Sat)
La Finca: SE11
(Latin music, Sat)
Heather's
(jazz, first Tue of mo)
The Honest Cabbage
(pianist and singer)

Hornimans
(jazz, Sun; DJs Mon)
La Mancha
(guitar, nightly)
Meson don Felipe
(flamenco guitar, nightly)
Naked Turtle
(jazz, nightly & Sun L)
1 Lawn Terrace
(jazz, Sun pm)
Oxo Tower
(jazz, nightly)
PizzaExpress: SW18
(large sports TV)
Pizzeria Castello
(guitarist, nightly)
Le Pont de la Tour Bar & Grill
(jazz, nightly)
Putney Bridge
(jazz, Sun)
Rebato's
(music, Wed-Sat)
La Rueda: SW4
(disco, Fri & Sat)
Zed
(jazz, Fri & Sat eves)

East

Al's
(DJ, Thu-Sat)
Babe Ruth's
(basketball; games area)
Barcelona Tapas: EC3
(magician, regularly; occasional flamenco)
Café du Marché
(music, nightly)
Dôme: EC1
(jazz, Fridays)
The Fence
(music, Thu)
Fuego
(disco, Tue-Fri)
Hothouse Bar & Grill
(jazz & blues, Fri - Sat)
Pizza Pomodoro: all branches
(music, nightly)
Sri Siam City
(music, Thu)
Sri Thai
(music, Wed)
Terraza-Est
(opera singers, nightly)

Late
(open till midnight or later as shown; may be earlier Sunday)

Central
a.k.a. (1 am, 11.30 pm Wed-Sat)
Atlantic Bar & Grill (bar food until 2.30 am)
The Avenue
Balans: W1 (Mon-Sat 3 am, Sun 1 am)
Bar Italia (4 am, Fri & Sat 24 hours)
Beiteddine
Benihana: all branches (Fri & Sat only)

INDEXES

Novelli W8 *(Fri & Sat only)*
Paparazzi Café *(1 am)*
Pasta di Milano: *all branches*
Patio
La Perla
Pizza Pomodoro: *SW3 (1 am)*
Pizza the Action
PizzaExpress: *SW10, both SW3, W11, W14, W2, W4, W8*
Pucci Pizza *(12.30 am)*
Ranoush *(3 am)*
Riccardo's
Saffron
Le Shop
606 Club *(Mon-Thu 1.30 am, Fri & Sat 2 am)*
Spago *(12.30 am)*
Tandoori of Chelsea
Texas Lone Star *(Thu-Sat 12.30 am)*
Tiger Lil's: *all branches (Fri & Sat only)*
Tootsies: *all branches (Fri & Sat)*
Wok Wok: *SW10 (Fri only)*
Yas *(5 am)*

North
Ali Baba
Anglo Asian Tandoori *(Fri & Sat 12.15 am)*
Banners *(Fri & Sat only)*
Bar Gansa
Benihana: *all branches (Fri & Sat only)*
Caffè Uno: *all branches*
Calzone: *all north branches*
Cuba Libre *(Fri & Sat only)*
Don Pepe
Ed's Easy Diner: *NW3*
La Finca: *N1 (1.30 am, Fri & Sat)*
Greek Valley
Haandi *(Fri, Sat & Sun only)*
House on Rosslyn Hill
The Little Bay: *all branches*
Le Mercury *(1 am, ex Sun)*
Pasha *(Fri & Sat)*
La Piragua
PizzaExpress: *all north branches*
La Porchetta Pizzeria
Rasa: *N16 (Fri & Sat only)*
Sarcan
Tiger Lil's: *all branches (Fri & Sat only)*
Tootsies: *all branches (Fri & Sat)*
Vrisaki

South
Buona Sera
Caffè Uno: *all branches*
Gastro
PizzaExpress: *230 Lavender Hill SW11, SW14, SW15, SW18; Cardomom Bldg, Shad Thames SE1 (not Sun)*
Tiger Lil's: *all branches (Fri & Sat only)*
Tootsies: *all branches (Fri & Sat)*

East
Al's *(midnight, Wed-Sat 2am (bar 2am))*
Babe Ruth's
Brick Lane Beigel Bake *(24 hr)*
Cantaloupe
Pizza Pomodoro: *E1*

No-smoking areas
(* completely no smoking)

Central
Atrium
Au Jardin des Gourmets
Beotys
Bertorelli's: *all branches*
The Birdcage*
Café Fish (Restaurant)
Café Pacifico
Café Sofra: *all branches*
Caldesi
Capital Radio Restaurant
Caravan Serai
Cecconi's
Chez Gérard: *all central branches*
China City
Chor Bizarre
Chuen Cheng Ku
Connaught*
Cork & Bottle
Cranks: *all branches**
1837 at Brown's Hotel
Fashion Café
Food for Thought*
Football Football
Footstool
Gourmet Pizza Co.
Goya
Grissini
Häagen-Dazs: *all branches**
Hard Rock Café
Ibla
Ikkyu: *WC2*
Joe Allen
Livebait
Luna Nuova
Maison Bertaux
Malabar Junction
Mandeer*
Mildreds*
Mirabelle
Museum St Café*
Neal's Yard Dining Rooms*
Nicole's
Nobu
L'Odéon
Oriel
Orso
Pizza On The Park
Planet Hollywood

INDEXES

Naked Turtle
Newton's
The Old School Thai
The Pepper Tree
Prego
Rani: *all branches*
Sixty Two
The Stepping Stone
Thailand*
Tiger Lil's: *all branches*
Le Versailles
Vincent's

East

Babe Ruth's
Café Sofra: *all branches*
Cantaloupe
Chez Gérard: *EC2*
Cicada
Futures*
Gourmet Pizza Co.
Japanese Canteen
Lunch*
Moshi Moshi Sushi: *EC2**
Pacific Spice
The Place Below*
Pret A Manger: *EC4**; *EC1, both EC2,*
The Quality Chop House
Rupee Room
Searcy's Brasserie
Stephen Bull

Outside tables
(* particularly recommended)

Central

Al Bustan
Al Hamra*
Alfred
All Bar One: *48 Leicester Sq WC2**; *3-4 Hanover St W1, 289-293 Regent St W1*
Andrew Edmunds
L'Arte
L'Artiste Musclé*
Ask! Pizza: *48 Grafton Way W1*
Aurora*
Back to Basics
Bar Italia
Bertorelli's: *W1*
The Birdcage
Boisdale
Boudin Blanc*
Boulevard
Café Bohème
Café Coq
Café des Amis du Vin*
Café du Jardin
Café Emm
Café Flo: *13 Thayer St W1*

Café Latino
Café Pasta: *all branches*
Café Rouge: *all central branches*
Café Sofra: *10 Shepherd Mkt W1**; *63 Wigmore St W1, both WC2,*
Caffè Uno: *28 Binney St W1, 24 Charing Cross Rd WC2*
Caldesi
Capital Radio Restaurant
Caraffini
Caravan Serai
Chez Gérard: *31 Dover St W1, 45 East Ter, Covent Gdn WC2**; *8 Charlotte St W1, 119 Chancery Ln WC2*
Cork & Bottle
Cranks: *all in W1, 17-19 Great Newport St WC2*
Cy
Deals
dell'Ugo
Ed's Easy Diner: *12 Moor St W1*
Efes Kebab House: *80 Great Titchfield St W1*
Elena's L'Etoile
Il Faro
Fifth Floor (Café)
Garlic & Shots
Gordon's Wine Bar*
Goya
Grumbles
Häagen-Dazs: *all branches*
Hard Rock Café
Hardy's
Hunan
Ishbilia
Italian Kitchen: *all branches*
Jenny Lo's
Justin de Blank
Little Bay*
Little Havana
Little Italy
Maison Bertaux
Mediterranean Café
Mekong
Mildreds
Mirabelle*
Momo
Mongolian Barbecue
Motcomb's
Museum St Café
Nine Golden Square
No 1 Cigar Club
Noho
Oriel
Le Palais du Jardin
Pâtisserie Valerie: *RIBA Centre, 66 Portland Pl W1**; *105 Marylebone High St W1, WC2*
Pizza On The Park
PizzaExpress: *133 Baker St W1, 7-9 Charlotte St W1, 21-22 Barrett St W1, WC1*

INDEXES

Pret A Manger: *EC1*
Singapura: *EC4*
Sri India
Taberna Etrusca*
Tao*

Private rooms

**(for the most comprehensive
listing of venues for functions –
from palaces to pubs – see
Harden's London Party Guide,
available in all good bookshops)
* particularly recommended**

Central

a.k.a. *(12)*
Al Bustan *(10)*
Alastair Little *(25)*
Alfred *(16)*
L'Artiste Musclé *(26)*
Atlantic Bar & Grill *(60)**
Atrium *(12,24)*
Au Jardin des Gourmets *(80)*
Aurora *(20)*
Axis *(30)**
Back to Basics *(40)*
Belgo Centraal *(25,30)*
Benihana *(10)*
Bentley's *(16)**
Beotys *(6-60)*
Bertorelli's: *W1 (18,38)*
Bice *(22)*
Blue Jade *(40)*
Blues *(40)*
Boisdale *(20)*
Boudin Blanc *(35)*
Boulevard *(40)*
Browns: *WC2 (120,80,50);*
  W1 (16,8,8,4)
Café des Amis du Vin *(65)*
Café du Jardin *(55)*
Café Flo: *WC2 (20); 13 Thayer St*
  W1 (30)
Café Latino *(20,40,16)*
Café Sofra: *33 Old Compton St W1,*
  63 Wigmore St W1 (20)
Caldesi *(22)*
La Capannina *(12-30)*
Capital Radio Restaurant *(60)*
Caravan Serai *(15)*
Chez Gérard: *31 Dover St W1 (30);*
  119 Chancery Ln WC2 (35)
Chez Nico *(20)**
Chiang Mai *(25)*
China City *(20,30,50)*
Chor Bizarre *(30)*
Christopher's *(50)*
Chuen Cheng Ku *(20-300)*
Circus *(16)*
Claridges Restaurant *(14)*
Como Lario *(14)*

Connaught *(22)**
Cy *(100)*
dell'Ugo *(16,8)*
Dorchester, Oriental *(6,10,16)**
Dover Street *(24)*
Drones *(60)*
Efes Kebab House: *W1 (1) 80*
  Great Titchfield St W1 (45)
Elena's L'Etoile *(6-28)*
L'Escargot *(24,60)**
L'Estaminet *(22)*
Il Faro *(6)*
Fashion Café *(130)*
Football Football *(50)*
French House *(30)*
Fung Shing *(25)*
Garlic & Shots *(25)*
Le Gavroche *(20)**
Gay Hussar *(12,24)**
Golden Dragon *(40)*
Goring Hotel *(8,12,30,55)*
Green's *(34)*
Grissini *(50)*
Grumbles *(12)*
The Guinea *(10-30)*
The Halkin *(26)*
Harbour City *(40,60,70)*
Hardy's *(15,80)*
Hodgson's *(20)*
Hunan *(20)*
Hyde Park Hotel
  Park Room *(22)*
Ibla *(25)*
Ikeda *(8)*
Ikkyu *W1 (10)*
L'Incontro *(35)*
Indigo *(40)*
Interlude *(20)*
Ishbilia *(25)*
The Ivy *(20-60)**
Jenny Lo's *(20)*
Joy King Lau *(60)*
Justin de Blank *(40)*
Kaspia *(12)*
Kaya Korean *(12,8)*
Ken Lo's Memories *(20)*
Kettners *(12-70)*
The Lanesborough *(100)*
Leith's Soho *(18)*
Lindsay House *(18)*
Little Havana *(150/60/40)*
Little Italy *(35)*
Luigi's *(35)*
Malabar Junction *(40)*
The Marquis *(25,30)**
Masako *(16)*
Matsuri *(18)*
Mediterranean Café *(4)*
Mekong *(14,24)*
Mezzo *(46)*

INDEXES

INDEXES

South
Alma (70)
The Apprentice (55)
Archduke Wine Bar (50)
Batt. Barge Bistro (16)
Belair House (14)
Bellinis (35)
Beyoglu (35)
Bombay Bicycle Club (22)
Le Bouchon Bordelais (40)
Buchan's (50-60)
Chez Bruce (20)
Côte à Côte (50,70)
Emile's (45,30)
Enoteca Turi (30)
Fina Estampa (20-60)
Four Regions (120)
Ghillies: (25)
Glaisters: (36)
Kwan Thai (50)
La Lanterna (56)
Lobster Pot (12)
Mezzanine (12)
Monsieur Max (10,20)
Naked Turtle (36)
The North Pole (30)
1 Lawn Terrace (24–30)
Le P'tit Normand (20)
Phoenix (30)
Pitcher & Piano: SW17 (60)
PizzaExpress: SW15 (30); Chapter Ho, Montague Cl SE1 (80)
Le Pont de la Tour (20)*
Prego (14)
Restaurant du Marche (16)
RSJ (40)
Scoffers (12)
The Ship (14-20)
Shree Krishna (80)
Sonny's (22)
The Waterloo Fire Station (90)
Zed (60)

East
1 Lombard Street (60)
Al's (60 downstairs)
Alba (30)
Aquarium (130)
Arkansas Café (50)
Ashtons (12)
Aykoku-Kaku (8,4)
Babe Ruth's (100-120)
Beauchamp's (20,30)
The Bow Wine Vaults (70)
Bubb's (4,10,15,25)
Café du Marché (60)
Café Flo (30)
Café Spice Namaste (35)
Chez Gérard: EC2 (12)

City Miyama (10,8,4)
City Rhodes (12)
Dôme: EC1 (100,175)
Fox & Anchor (8,7,24)
Frocks (26)
Fuego (60)
Gaudi (45)
George & Vulture (16)
Gow's (100)
Hope & Sir Loin (30,25)
Imperial City (16)*
Leadenhall Tapas Bar (80)
Lunch (20)
Maison Novelli (40)
Mange 2 (20)
Medina's (25)
MPW (30)
Novelli EC1 (80)
Pacific Spice (60)
Pitcher & Piano: The Arches, 9 Crutched Friars EC3 (100); 194-200 Bishopsgate EC3 (8-200)
PizzaExpress: EC2 (200)
Saigon Times (20)
St John (18)
Shanghai (60, 40)
Singapura: EC3 (12); EC4 (30)
Sri India (20)
Suan-Neo (20)
Taberna Etrusca (40)
Tao (16)
Tatsuso (6,8)

Romantic

Central
Al Bustan
Andrew Edmunds
Bentley's
The Birdcage
Boudin Blanc
Café de Paris
Café Royal Grill
Le Caprice
Christopher's
Claridges Restaurant
Connaught
The Criterion
Dover Street
La Fontana
French House
Le Gavroche
Gay Hussar
Greenhouse
The Guinea
Hodgson's
Ibla
L'Incontro
The Ivy
Joe Allen

The Depot
Four Regions
Gourmet Pizza Co.
Oxo Tower
The People's Palace
Le Pont de la Tour
Le Pont de la Tour Bar & Grill
Putney Bridge

East
Aquarium
Brasserie 24
Coq d'Argent
Searcy's Brasserie

Vegetarian

Central
Chiang Mai *(W1)**
Cranks *(W1, WC2)*
Dorchester Grill *(W1)**
Food for Thought *(WC2)**
India Club *(WC2)*
The Lanesborough *(W1)*
Malabar Junction *(WC1)*
Mandeer *(WC1)*
Mildreds *(W1)**
Museum St Café *(WC1)*
Ragam *(W1)*
Rasa *(W1)**
Savoy River Restaurant *(WC2)*
Woodlands *(SW1, W1)*

West
Blah! Blah! Blah! *(W12)**
Blue Elephant *(SW6)**
The Gate *(W6)**
Halcyon Hotel *(W11)**
Leith's *(W11)*

North
Chutneys *(NW1)*
Diwana Bhel-Poori House *(NW1)**
Geeta *(NW6)**
Manna *(NW3)**
Rani *(N3)*
Rasa *(N16)**
The Vegetarian Cottage *(NW3)*
Vijay *(NW6)**
Yum Yum *(N16)**

South
Bah Humbug *(SW2)*
Heather's *(SE8)**
Kastoori *(SW17)**
Le Pont de la Tour *(SE1)*
Rani *(TW9)*
Shree Krishna *(SW17)**

East
Carnevale *(EC1)**
Futures *(EC2)*
Futures *(EC3)**
The Place Below *(EC2)**

Wine lists for œnophiles

Central
Alastair Little
Andrew Edmunds
Au Jardin des Gourmets
Boisdale
Che
Cork & Bottle
1837 at Brown's Hotel
The Fifth Floor
Le Gavroche
Hardy's
Mirabelle
Sartoria
Les Saveurs
Shampers
The Square
La Tante Claire Berkeley Hotel
Tate Gallery
Teca

West
Bibendum
Clarke's
The Crescent
Hilaire
Leith's
Le Metro
Monkeys
192

North
Odette's

South
Cantinetto Venegazzú
Enoteca Turi
Le Pont de la Tour
Ransome's Dock
RSJ

East
Bleeding Heart
Reynier

CUISINES

An asterisk (*) after an
entry indicates exceptional
or very good cooking

EUROPE

Belgian

Central
Belgo Centraal (WC2)

North
Belgo Noord (NW1)

British, Modern

Central
a.k.a. (WC1)*
Alastair Little (W1)
Alfred (WC2)*
All Bar One (W1, WC1, WC2)
Andrew Edmunds (W1)
Atlantic Bar & Grill (W1)
Atrium (SW1)
Aurora (W1)
The Avenue (SW1)
Axis (WC2)*
Bank (WC2)
Blues (W1)
Boisdale (SW1)
Café de Paris (W1)
Café du Jardin (WC2)
Café Med (W1)
Le Caprice (SW1)*
Che (SW1)
Circus (W1)
Coast (W1)
Corney & Barrow (WC2)*
Cork & Bottle (WC2)
dell'Ugo (W1)
Drones (SW1)
Ebury Street Wine Bar (SW1)
The Fifth Floor (SW1)
French House (W1)
Goring Hotel (SW1)
Hodgson's (WC2)
Indigo (WC2)
Interlude (W1)*
The Ivy (WC2)*
Justin de Blank (W1)
The Lanesborough (W1)
Langan's Brasserie (W1)
Leith's Soho (W1)
The Lexington (W1)
Lindsay House (W1)*
The Marquis (W1)*
Mash (W1)

Mezzo (W1)
Museum St Café (WC1)
Nicole's (W1)
Nine Golden Square (W1)
No 1 Cigar Club (W1)
Oceana (W1)
Plummers (WC2)
Quaglino's (W1)
Rowley's (SW1)
Saint (WC2)
Scott's (W1)
Soho Brewing
  Company (WC2)
Sotheby's Café (W1)
Sound Republic (WC2)
Star Café (W1)
Stargazer (W1)
Stephen Bull (W1)*
Stephen Bull (WC2)*
The Sugar Club (W1)*
Tate Gallery (SW1)
Teatro (W1)
33 (SW1)
Thomas Goode (W1)
The Union Café (W1)
Zinc (W1)
Zoe (W1)

West
Alastair Little W11 (W11)
All Bar One (SW6, SW7, W11, W4)
Anglesea Arms (W6)*
Anonimato (W10)*
Bali Sugar (W11)
Belvedere (W8)
Bistrot 190 (SW7)
Bluebird (SW3)
Blythe Road (W14)
The Brackenbury (W6)*
Brinkley's (SW10)
Café Med (SW10, W11, W6)
The Canteen (SW10)*
Charco's (SW3)
Chelsea Ram (SW10)*
Chinon (W14)*
Chiswick (W4)*
Clarke's (W8)*
Coopers Arms (SW3)
The Cow (W11)*
The Crescent (SW3)
Dan's (SW3)
Dove (W6)
English Garden (SW3)
English House (SW3)
First Floor (W11)
Gilbert's (SW7)
Goolies (W8)*
Halcyon Hotel (W11)*
The Havelock Tavern (W14)*
Hilaire (SW7)

The Imperial Arms (SW6)
Joe's Brasserie (SW6)
Joe's Café (SW3)
Julie's (W11)
Kartouche (SW10)
Kensington Place (W8)
King's Brasserie (SW6)*
The Ladbroke Arms (W11)*
Launceston Place (W8)*
Leith's (W11)
Mas Café (W11)
Le Metro (SW3)
Min's Bar (SW3)
Nayab (SW6)*
192 (W11)
Patio (W12)
The Pen (SW6)
Pharmacy (W11)
The Prince Bonaparte (W2)*
Raoul's Café (W9)
755 (SW6)*
606 Club (SW10)
Snows on the Green (W6)
Stone Mason's Arms (W6)
The Tenth (W8)
The Terrace (W8)*
Vingt-Quatre (SW10)
The Westbourne (W2)
Wilson's (W14)
Wiz (W11)

North

All Bar One (N1, N6, NW8)
Bradley's (NW3)*
Byron's (NW3)
Café Med (NW8)
The Chapel (NW1)
Crown & Goose (NW1)
Cucina (NW3)
The Engineer (NW1)
Euphorium (N1)
Frederick's (N1)
Globe Restaurant (NW3)
Granita (N1)*
Gresslin's (NW3)*
Jindivick (N1)
Kavanagh's (N1)
Lansdowne (NW1)
Lola's (N1)
The Lord Palmerston (N19)
Mango Room (NW1)
Mesclun (N16)*
Odette's (NW1)*
The Queen's (NW1)
Quincy's (NW2)*
The Vine (NW5)*

South

All Bar One (SE1, SW11, SW18)
The Apprentice (SE1)*

Bah Humbug (SW2)
Belair House (SE21)
Blue Print Café (SE1)
Buchan's (SW11)
Chez Bruce (SW17)*
The Cook House (SW15)
The County Hall
  Restaurant (SE1)
The Depot (SW14)
Glaisters (SW11)
Helter Skelter (SW9)*
The Honest Cabbage (SE1)*
The Lavender (SW11, SW9)*
The Mason's Arms (SW8)*
Mezzanine (SE1)
Moxon's (SW4)*
Naked Turtle (SW14)
The North Pole (SE10)
On the Rise (SW11)
1 Lawn Terrace (SE3)
Oxo Tower (SE1)
The People's Palace (SE1)
Phoenix (SW15)
Le Pont de la Tour (SE1)
Putney Bridge (SW15)
Ransome's Dock (SW11)*
Rapscallion (SW4)
Redmond's (SW14)
RSJ (SE1)*
Scoffers (SW11)*
Sixty Two (SE1)
Snows by the Pond (SW13)
Sonny's (SW13)*
The Stable (SW13)
The Stepping Stone (SW8)*
The Sun & Doves (SE5)*
Vincent's (SW15)
The Waterloo Fire
  Station (SE1)
White Cross Hotel (TW9)

East

1 Lombard Street (EC3)*
Al's (EC1)
All Bar One (E14, EC1, EC2, EC3,
  EC4)
Bar Bourse (EC4)
Cantaloupe (EC2)
City Brasserie (EC3)
City Rhodes (EC4)*
The Circle (SE1)
The Fence (EC1)
Frocks (E9)
Gladwins (EC3)
Home (EC1)*
Hothouse Bar & Grill (E1)
The Peasant (EC1)
The Quality Chop
  House (EC1)
St John (EC1)

CUISINES – EUROPE

Searcy's Brasserie *(EC2)*
Sheekey's *(EC4)*
Stephen Bull *(EC1)*
Vic Naylors *(EC1)*
Whittington's *(EC4)*

British, Traditional

Central
Claridges Restaurant *(W1)*
Connaught *(W1)*
Dorchester Grill *(W1)**
Fryer's Delight *(WC1)**
Green's *(SW1)*
Greenhouse *(W1)*
Grenadier *(SW1)*
The Guinea *(W1)*
Odin's *(W1)**
Porters *(WC2)*
Rib Room *(SW1)**
The Ritz *(W1)*
RK Stanleys *(W1)*
Rules *(WC2)*
Savoy Grill *(WC2)*
Savoy River Restaurant *(WC2)*
Seafresh *(SW1)**
Shepherd's *(SW1)*
Simpsons-in-the-Strand *(WC2)*
Star Café *(W1)*
Wiltons *(SW1)**

West
Basil St Hotel *(SW3)*
Costa's Fish *(W8)**
Fat Boy's *(W4)*
Ffiona's *(W8)*
Geale's *(W8)**
Maggie Jones's *(W8)*
Monkeys *(SW3)**
Turner's *(SW3)**
Veronica's *(W2)*
Windsor Castle *(W8)*

North
Nautilus *(NW6)*
Seashell *(NW1)**
Toff's *(N10)**
Two Brothers *(N3)**
Upper St Fish Shop *(N1)**

South
Brady's *(SW18)*
The Butlers Wharf Chop-
house *(SE1)*

East
The Bow Wine Vaults *(EC4)*
Fox & Anchor *(EC1)**
George & Vulture *(EC3)*
Hope & Sir Loin *(EC1)**

The Quality Chop
House *(EC1)*
Reynier *(EC3)*
Simpson's of Cornhill *(EC3)*
10 *(EC2)*

Czech

North
Czech Club *(NW6)*

East/West

Central
The Birdcage *(W1)**
Mezzonine *(W1)*
Nobu *(W1)**
Vong *(SW1)**

West
I Thai *(W2)*
Rain *(W10)*

South
Bistrot 2 Riverside *(SE1)*

Fish & seafood

Central
Back to Basics *(W1)**
Bank *(WC2)*
Belgo Centraal *(WC2)*
Bentley's *(W1)*
Café Fish (Restaurant) *(W1)*
Cave *(W1)**
Fung Shing *(WC2)**
Green's *(SW1)*
Livebait *(WC2)**
Manzi's *(WC2)**
Motcomb's *(SW1)*
Le Palais du Jardin *(WC2)*
Quaglino's *(W1)*
Scott's *(W1)*
Sheekey's *(WC2)*
Wiltons *(SW1)**
Zilli Fish *(W1)*

West
L'Altro *(W11)*
La Belle Epoque *(SW3)*
Bibendum Oyster Bar *(SW3)**
Big Easy *(SW3)*
La Dordogne *(W4)**
Fishnets *(SW6)*
Ghillies *(SW6)**
Jason's *(W9)**
Lou Pescadou *(SW5)*
Mandarin Kitchen *(W2)**
Mediterraneo *(W11)**

Poissonnerie de
  l'Avenue *(SW3)**
Restaurant 190 *(SW7)*
Stratford's *(W8)*
Le Suquet *(SW3)**

North
Belgo Noord *(NW1)*
Bradley's *(NW3)**
Chez Liline *(N4)**

South
Ghillies *(SW17)**
Livebait *(SE11)**
Lobster Pot *(SE11)**
Moxon's *(SW4)**
Polygon Bar & Grill *(SW4)*
Le Pont de la Tour Bar &
  Grill *(SE1)**

East
Aquarium *(E1)*
Beauchamp's *(EC3)*
Gow's *(EC2)*
The Grapes *(E14)**
Rudland & Stubbs *(EC1)**
Sweetings *(EC4)**

French

Central
L'Artiste Musclé *(W1)*
Au Jardin des Gourmets *(W1)*
Beotys *(WC2)*
Boudin Blanc *(W1)**
Café Bohème *(W1)*
Café des Amis du Vin *(WC2)*
Café Flo *(SW1, W1, WC2)*
Café Rouge *(W1, WC2)*
Café Royal Grill *(W1)**
Cave *(W1)**
Chez Gérard *(W1, WC2)*
Chez Nico *(W1)**
Claridges Restaurant *(W1)*
Connaught *(W1)*
The Criterion *(W1)*
Cy *(W1)*
1837 at Brown's Hotel *(W1)*
Elena's L'Etoile *(W1)**
L'Escargot (brasserie) *(W1)**
L'Estaminet *(WC2)**
The Foundation *(SW1)*
Le Gavroche *(W1)**
Hyde Park Hotel
  Park Room *(SW1)*
Interlude *(W1)**
Kaspia *(W1)*
Magno's Brasserie *(WC2)*
Mirabelle *(W1)**
Mon Plaisir *(WC2)**
Le Muscadet *(W1)*

Nico Central *(W1)**
Oak Room MPW *(W1)*
L'Odéon *(W1)*
Odin's *(W1)**
L'Oranger *(SW1)**
Orrery *(W1)*
Le Palais du Jardin *(WC2)*
Pied à Terre *(W1)**
La Poule au Pot *(SW1)*
Quo Vadis *(W1)*
Randall & Aubin *(W1)**
The Ritz *(W1)*
Roussillon *(SW1)*
Les Saveurs *(W1)*
Savoy River Restaurant *(WC2)*
Simply Nico *(SW1)*
Soho Soho (Rôtisserie) *(W1)*
Le Soufflé *(W1)*
The Square *(W1)**
La Tante Claire
  Berkeley Hotel *(SW1)*
Townhouse Brasserie *(WC1)*
Villandry *(W1)*
Windows on the World *(W1)*

West
The Abingdon *(W8)*
Aubergine *(SW10)*
La Belle Epoque *(SW3)*
Bibendum *(SW3)*
La Bouchée *(SW7)*
Brass. du Marché *(W10)**
La Brasserie *(SW3)*
Brasserie St Quentin *(SW3)*
Café Flo *(SW6, SW7, W8)*
Café Rouge *(SW3, SW6, SW7, W11,
  W2, W4, W6, W8, W9)*
Capital Hotel *(SW3)*
Chavot *(SW3)*
Chez Gérard *(SW3)*
Chez Moi *(W11)*
Chezmax *(SW10)**
Chinon *(W14)**
Christian's *(W4)*
La Ciboulette *(SW3)*
Le Colombier *(SW3)*
La Dordogne *(W4)**
Emile's *(SW6)**
L'Escargot Doré *(W8)*
Francofill *(SW7)*
Gordon Ramsay *(SW3)**
Icon *(SW3)*
Langan's Coq d'Or *(SW5)*
Lou Pescadou *(SW5)*
Monkeys *(SW3)**
Novelli W8 *(W8)*
One-O-One *(SW7)*
Pelham Street *(SW7)*
Poissonnerie de
  l'Avenue *(SW3)**

Simply Nico Chelsea (SW10)
Stratford's (W8)
Le Suquet (SW3)*
Thierry's (SW3)
Turner's (SW3)*

North
Les Associés (N8)
L'Aventure (NW8)*
Café Delancey (NW1)
Café des Arts (NW3)
Café Flo (N1, NW3)
Café Rouge (N6, NW1, NW3, NW8)
La Cage Imaginaire (NW3)
Camden Brasserie (NW1)
Le Mercury (N1)
Mims (EN4)*
Oslo Court (NW8)*
Le Sacré-Coeur (N1)*
Soulard (N1)*
Village Bistro (N6)
The White Onion (N1)*

South
Le Bouchon Bordelais (SW11)
La Bouffe (SW11)
Café de la Place (SW11)
Café Rouge (SE1, SW11, SW14, SW15, SW19, SW4)
Côte à Côte (SW11)
Emile's (SW15)*
Gastro (SW4)
Le Gothique (SW18)
Lobster Pot (SE11)*
Monsieur Max (1W12)*
Newton's (SW4)
Le P'tit Normand (SW18)
Restaurant du Marche (SW11)
Le Versailles (SW9)

East
Ashtons (EC3)
Bleeding Heart (EC1)*
Bubb's (EC1)
Café du Marché (EC1)*
Café Flo (EC4)
Café Rouge (EC4)
Chez Gérard (EC1, EC2)
Club Gascon (EC1)
Coq d'Argent (EC3)
Luc's Brasserie (EC3)
Maison Novelli (EC1)*
Mange 2 (EC1)
MPW (E14)*
Novelli EC1 (EC1)
Saigon Times (EC3)

Game

Central
Dorchester Grill (W1)*

The Marquis (W1)*
Rules (WC2)
Wiltons (SW1)*

West
Monkeys (SW3)*

German

North
Café Mozart (N6)

Greek

Central
Beotys (WC2)

West
Café O (SW3)
Costa's Grill (W8)
Halepi (W2)
Kalamaras, Micro (W2)

North
Daphne (NW1)
Greek Valley (NW8)
Lemonia (NW1)
Nontas (NW1)
Vrisaki (N22)*

South
Beyoglu (SW11)*

Hungarian

Central
Gay Hussar (W1)

North
Café Mozart (N6)

Italian

Central
L'Arte (W1)
Bertorelli's (W1, WC2)
Bice (W1)
Café Pasta (WC2)
Caffè Uno (W1, WC2)
Caldesi (W1)
La Capannina (W1)
Caraffini (SW1)*
Cecconi's (W1)
Como Lario (SW1)
Diverso (W1)*
Il Faro (W1)
La Fontana (SW1)
Grissini (SW1)
The Halkin (SW1)
Ibla (W1)*
L'Incontro (SW1)

Italian Kitchen *(WC1, WC2)*
Little Italy *(W1)*
Luigi's *(WC2)*
Luna Nuova *(WC2)*
Mimmo d'Ischia *(SW1)*
Neal Street *(WC2)*
Oliveto *(SW1)**
Olivo *(SW1)**
Orso *(WC2)*
Pasta di Milano *(W1)*
Pollo *(W1)*
Purple Sage *(W1)**
Ristorante Italiano *(W1)*
Sale e Pepe *(SW1)*
Santini *(SW1)*
Sartoria *(W1)*
Signor Sassi *(SW1)*
La Spiga *(W1)*
La Spighetta *(W1)*
Teca *(W1)**
Toto's *(SW1)*
Uno *(SW1)**
Vasco & Piero's Pavilion *(W1)*
Il Vicolo *(SW1)*
Zafferano *(SW1)**
Zilli Fish *(W1)*

West
L'Accento Italiano *(W2)*
Al San Vincenzo *(W2)**
L'Altro *(W11)*
Assaggi *(W2)**
Bersagliera *(SW3)*
Boyd's *(W8)*
Café 206 *(W11)**
Café Milan *(SW3)*
Café Montpeliano *(SW3)*
Café Pasta *(W4, W8)*
Caffè Uno *(SW6, W2, W4, W8)*
Calzone *(SW10, W11)*
Cibo *(W14)**
Da Mario *(SW7)*
Da Pierino *(SW7)*
Daphne's *(SW3)*
De Cecco *(SW6)**
La Delizia *(SW3, SW5)**
Elistano *(SW3)**
Il Falconiere *(SW7)*
La Famiglia *(SW10)*
Formula Veneta *(SW10)*
Grano *(W4)*
The Green Olive *(W9)**
I Thai *(W2)*
King's Road Café *(SW3)*
Leonardo's *(SW10)*
Luigi's Delicatessen *(SW10)**
Made in Italy *(SW3)*
Mona Lisa *(SW10)*
Montpeliano *(SW7)**
Monza *(SW3)*

Orsino *(W11)*
Osteria Basilico *(W11)*
Palatino *(W4)*
Palio *(W11)*
Paparazzi Café *(SW3)*
Pasta di Milano *(W8)*
La Perla *(SW3)*
Il Portico *(W8)*
The Red Pepper *(W9)**
Riccardo's *(SW3)**
The River Café *(W6)**
Sabatino *(W8)*
Sambuca *(SW3)*
San Lorenzo *(SW3)*
San Martino *(SW3)*
Sandrini *(SW3)*
Scalini *(SW3)*
Spago *(SW7)*
Ziani *(SW3)*
Zucca *(W11)*

North
Billboard Café *(NW6)*
La Brocca *(NW6)*
Café Pasta *(N1, NW3)*
Caffè Uno *(N1, N6, NW1, NW8)*
Calzone *(N1, NW3)*
Cantina Italia *(N1)**
Casale Franco *(N1)*
Florians *(N8)*
Marine Ices *(NW3)*
La Porchetta Pizzeria *(N4)**
San Carlo *(N6)*
San Daniele *(N5)*
Vegia Zena *(NW1)**
Villa Bianca *(NW3)*

South
Antipasto & Pasta *(SW11)**
Arancia *(SE16)**
Bellinis *(SW13)*
Buona Sera *(SW11)*
Caffè Uno *(SW13)*
Cantina del Ponte *(SE1)*
Cantinetto Venegazzú *(SW11)**
Côte à Côte *(SW11)*
Del Buongustaio *(SW15)**
Enoteca Turi *(SW15)**
La Lanterna *(SE1)*
C Notarianni & Sons *(SW11)*
Ost. Antica Bologna *(SW11)*
Pizzeria Castello *(SE1)*
Pizzeria Franco *(SW9)**
Prego *(TW9)*
Riva *(SW13)**
Tentazioni *(SE1)**

East
Alba *(EC1)*
Caravaggio *(EC3)*
The Clerkenwell *(EC1)*

CUISINES – EUROPE

Gt Eastern Dining Rm *(EC2)*
Medina's *(EC1)*
Taberna Etrusca *(EC4)*
Terraza-Est *(EC4)*

Irish

Central
O'Conor Don *(W1)*

Mediterranean

Central
Drones *(SW1)*
Fifth Floor (Café) *(SW1)*
The Foundation *(SW1)*
Hujo's *(W1)*
Mediterranean Café *(W1)*
Mezzonine *(W1)*
Zoe *(W1)*

West
Boyd's *(W8)*
The Cross Keys *(SW3)*
Made in Italy *(SW3)*
Mediterraneo *(W11)*
Palio *(W11)*
Woz *(W10)*

North
Café des Arts *(NW3)*
Centuria *(N1)*

South
Newton's *(SW4)*
Oxo Tower *(SE1)*

East
The Eagle *(EC1)*

Polish

West
Daquise *(SW7)*
The Polish Club *(SW7)*
Wódka *(W8)*

North
Café Mozart *(N6)*
Zamoyski *(NW3)*

Portuguese

South
Café Portugal *(SW8)*

Russian

Central
Kaspia *(W1)*

West
Nikita's *(SW10)*

North
Troika *(NW1)*

Scandinavian

North
Anna's Place *(N1)*

Steaks & grills

Central
Café Coq *(WC2)*
Chez Gérard *(W1, WC2)*
Christopher's *(WC2)*
The Gaucho Grill *(W1)*
The Guinea *(W1)*
Kettners *(W1)*
Quaglino's *(W1)*
Rib Room *(SW1)*
Smollensky's *(W1)*
Smollensky's, Strand *(WC2)*
Soho Soho (Rôtisserie) *(W1)*
Wolfe's *(WC2)*

West
Chez Gérard *(SW3)*
El Gaucho *(SW3)*
Popeseye *(W14)*
Rôtisserie *(W12)*
Rôtisserie Jules *(SW3, SW7, W11)*

North
Camden Brasserie *(NW1)*
Gaucho Grill *(NW3)*
Rôtisserie *(N1)*

South
Polygon Bar & Grill *(SW4)*
Le Pont de la Tour Bar &
   Grill *(SE1)*

East
Arkansas Café *(E1)*
Chez Gérard *(EC1, EC2)*
Fox & Anchor *(EC1)*
Hope & Sir Loin *(EC1)*
Simpson's of Cornhill *(EC3)*

Spanish

Central
Goya *(SW1)*
Rueda *(W1)*

West
Albero & Grana *(SW3)*
Albero & Grana, Bar *(SW3)*
Cambio de Tercio *(SW5)*
Galicia *(W10)*

La Rueda (SW6)

North
Bar Gansa (NW1)*
Cuba Libre (N1)
Don Pepe (NW8)
La Finca (N1)

South
don Fernando's (TW9)
La Finca (SE11)
La Mancha (SW15)
Meson don Felipe (SE1)
Rebato's (SW8)
La Rueda (SW4)

East
Barcelona Tapas (E1, EC3)*
Fuego (EC3)
Gaudi (EC1)
Leadenhall Tapas Bar (EC3)
Moro (EC1)*

Swiss

Central
St Moritz (W1)

International

Central
Alphabet (W1)
Balans (W1)
Boulevard (WC2)
Browns (W1, WC2)
Café Emm (W1)
Deals (W1)
Dôme (W1, WC2)
Dover Street (W1)
Footstool (SW1)
Garlic & Shots (W1)
Gordon's Wine Bar (WC2)
Grumbles (SW1)
Hardy's (W1)*
Hyde Park Hotel
   Park Room (SW1)
Little Bay (SW1)
Motcomb's (SW1)
Oriel (SW1)
Pitcher & Piano (W1, WC2)
Pomegranates (SW1)
Sarastro (WC2)
Shampers (W1)
Stock Pot (SW1, W1)
Vendôme (W1)
The Waldorf Meridien (WC2)

West
Balans West (SW5)
Beach Blanket Babylon (W11)
Blakes Hotel (SW7)

Browns (SW3)
Café Grove (W11)
Café Laville (W2)
Chelsea Bun Diner (SW10)
Chelsea Kitchen (SW3)
The Collection (SW3)
Conrad Hotel (SW10)
Coopers Arms (SW3)
Deals (SW10, W6)
Dôme (SW3, SW5, W8)
Dove (W6)
The Enterprise (SW3)
Foxtrot Oscar (SW3)
Front Page (SW3)
The Gasworks (SW6)
Glaisters (SW10)
Julie's Bar (W11)
Mackintosh's Brasserie (W4)
Pitcher & Piano (SW10, SW3, SW6, W4)
PJ's (SW3)
The Scarsdale (W8)
Sporting Page (SW10)
Stock Pot (SW3)
Windsor Castle (W8)
Wine Gallery (SW10)

North
Banners (N8)
Dôme (N1, NW3)
The Fox Reformed (N16)
House on Rosslyn Hill (NW3)
The Landmark Hotel (NW1)
The Little Bay (NW6)
Pitcher & Piano (N1)

South
Alma (SW18)
Archduke Wine Bar (SE1)
Batt. Barge Bistro (SW8)
Côte à Côte (SW11)
Heather's (SE8)*
Hornimans (SW4)
Naked Turtle (SW14)
Pitcher & Piano (SW11, SW12, SW17)
The Secret Garden (SE5)
The Ship (SW18)

East
Brasserie 24 (EC2)
Brasserie Rocque (EC2)
Dôme (EC1, EC4)
Lunch (EC1)
Mustards Brasserie (EC1)
Pitcher & Piano (EC3)

'SNACK' FOOD

Afternoon tea

Central
Aurora *(W1)*
Fifth Floor (Café) *(SW1)*
Hyde Park Hotel
  Park Room *(SW1)*
The Lanesborough *(W1)*
Thomas Goode *(W1)*
Villandry *(W1)*
The Waldorf Meridien *(WC2)*

West
Basil St Hotel *(SW3)*
Daquise *(SW7)*
Julie's Bar *(W11)*

Burgers, etc

Central
Capital Radio
  Restaurant *(WC2)*
Deals *(W1)*
Ed's Easy Diner *(W1)*
Fashion Café *(W1)*
Football Football *(SW1)*
Hard Rock Café *(W1)*
Joe Allen *(WC2)*
Planet Hollywood *(W1)*
The Rainforest Café *(W1)*
Wolfe's *(WC2)*

West
Big Easy *(SW3)*
Deals *(SW10, W6)*
Ed's Easy Diner *(SW3)*
Foxtrot Oscar *(SW3)*
Luigi Malones *(SW7)*
Sticky Fingers *(W8)*
Tootsies *(SW6, SW7, W11, W4)*

North
Ed's Easy Diner *(NW3)*
Tootsies *(NW3)*

South
Tootsies *(SW13)*

East
Arkansas Café *(E1)*
Babe Ruth's *(E1)*

Fish & chips

Central
Fryer's Delight *(WC1)**
Seafresh *(SW1)**

West
Costa's Fish *(W8)**

Geale's *(W8)**

North
Nautilus *(NW6)*
Seashell *(NW1)**
Toff's *(N10)**
Two Brothers *(N3)**
Upper St Fish Shop *(N1)**

South
Brady's *(SW18)*

East
Faulkner's *(E8)**

Ice cream

Central
Häagen-Dazs *(WC2)*

West
Häagen-Dazs *(SW7, W2)*

North
Häagen-Dazs *(NW3)*
Marine Ices *(NW3)*

South
C Notarianni & Sons *(SW11)*

Pizza

Central
Ask! Pizza *(SW1, W1)*
Gourmet Pizza Co. *(W1)*
Kettners *(W1)*
Luna Nuova *(WC2)*
Mash *(W1)*
Oliveto *(SW1)**
Pizza On The Park *(SW1)*
PizzaExpress *(SW1, W1, WC1, WC2)*
Pizzeria Condotti *(W1)*
La Spiga *(W1)*

West
Ask! Pizza *(SW6, SW7, W11, W2, W4, W8)*
Calzone *(SW10, W11)*
Da Mario *(SW7)*
La Delizia *(SW3, SW5)**
Paparazzi Café *(SW3)*
Pizza Pomodoro *(SW3)*
Pizza the Action *(SW6)*
PizzaExpress *(SW10, SW3, SW6, W11, W14, W2, W4, W8)*
Pucci Pizza *(SW3)**
The Red Pepper *(W9)**
Spago *(SW7)*

North
Ask! Pizza *(N1, NW3)*
La Brocca *(NW6)*
Calzone *(N1, NW3)*

Cantina Italia (N1)*
Casale Franco (N1)
Marine Ices (NW3)
PizzaExpress (N1, N6, NW1, NW3, NW8)
La Porchetta Pizzeria (N4)*

South
Bellinis (SW13)
Buona Sera (SW11)
Eco (SW4)*
Gourmet Pizza Co. (SE1)
C Notarianni & Sons (SW11)
Pizza Metro (SW11)*
PizzaExpress (SE1, SW11, SW14, SW15, SW18, SW4)
Pizzeria Castello (SE1)
Pizzeria Franco (SW9)*
Zed (SW2)

East
Ask! Pizza (EC1)
Gourmet Pizza Co. (E14)
Medina's (EC1)
Pizza Pomodoro (E1)
PizzaExpress (EC2, EC4)

Sandwiches, cakes, etc

Central
Au Bon Pain (W1, WC2)
Bar Italia (W1)
Coffee Republic (W1, WC2)
EAT (SW1, WC2)
Maison Bertaux (W1)*
Pâtisserie Valerie (W1, WC2)
Pret A Manger (SW1, W1, WC1, WC2)
Seattle Coffee Co (SW1, W1, WC2)*

West
Café Grove (W11)
Coffee Republic (W11, W2)
Coins (W11)
Fileric (SW7)*
King's Road Café (SW3)
Lisboa Patisserie (W10)*
Manzara (W11)
Pâtisserie Valerie (SW3)
Pret A Manger (SW3, W6, W8)
Seattle Coffee Co (W8)*
Le Shop (SW3)
Tom's (W10)*
Troubadour (SW5)

North
Pret A Manger (N1, NW1)

South
Boiled Egg (SW11)
Fileric (SW8)*

East
Au Bon Pain (EC1)
Brick Lane Beigel Bake (E1)*
EAT (EC4)
Pret A Manger (EC1, EC2, EC4)

Vegetarian

Central
Chiang Mai (W1)*
Cranks (W1, WC2)
Dorchester Grill (W1)*
Food for Thought (WC2)*
India Club (WC2)
The Lanesborough (W1)
Malabar Junction (WC1)
Mandeer (WC1)
Mildreds (W1)*
Museum St Café (WC1)
Ragam (W1)
Rasa (W1)*
Savoy River Restaurant (WC2)
Woodlands (SW1, W1)

West
Blah! Blah! Blah! (W12)*
Blue Elephant (SW6)*
The Gate (W6)*
Halcyon Hotel (W11)*
Leith's (W11)

North
Chutneys (NW1)
Diwana Bhel-Poori House (NW1)*
Geeta (NW6)*
Manna (NW3)*
Rani (N3)
Rasa (N16)*
The Vegetarian Cottage (NW3)
Vijay (NW6)*
Yum Yum (N16)*

South
Bah Humbug (SW2)
Heather's (SE8)*
Kastoori (SW17)*
Le Pont de la Tour (SE1)
Rani (TW9)
Shree Krishna (SW17)*

East
Carnevale (EC1)*
Futures (EC2)
Futures (EC3)*
The Place Below (EC2)*

AMERICAS

American

Central
Christopher's (WC2)
Joe Allen (WC2)
Navajo Joe (WC2)
Planet Hollywood (W1)
Smollensky's (W1)
Smollensky's, Strand (WC2)
TGI Friday's (W1, WC2)

West
Big Easy (SW3)
Chicago Rib Shack (SW7)
Dakota (W11)
Montana (SW6)*
Shoeless Joe's (SW6)
TGI Friday's (W2)

East
Arkansas Café (E1)
Babe Ruth's (E1)

Argentinian

Central
The Gaucho Grill (W1)*

North
Gaucho Grill (NW3)*

Brazilian

West
Paulo's (W6)
Rodizio Rico (W11)

Cajun/creole

West
Cactus Blue (SW3)

Mexican/TexMex

Central
Café Pacifico (WC2)
Down Mexico Way (W1)
Football Football (SW1)
La Perla (WC2)
Texas Embassy Cantina (WC2)

West
Coyote Café (W4)
Texas Lone Star (SW7)

South
Dixie's Bar & Grill (SW11)

East
Al's (EC1)

South American

Central
Café Latino (W1)
Havana (W1)
Little Havana (WC2)

West
Cactus Blue (SW3)
El Gaucho (SW3)

North
Cuba Libre (N1)
La Piragua (N1)

South
Fina Estampa (SE1)*

AFRICA

Afro-Caribbean

Central
Calabash (WC2)

North
Cottons (NW1)
Mango Room (NW1)

South
Smokey Joe's (SW18)*

North African

Central
Momo (W1)
Oceana (W1)

West
Adams Café (W12)*
Pasha (SW7)

North
Laurent (NW2)*

East
Moro (EC1)*

South African

West
Springbok Café (W4)*

Sudanese

West
Mandola (W11)*

Tunisian

West
Adams Café *(W12)**

North
Laurent *(NW2)**

MIDDLE EAST

Egyptian

North
Ali Baba *(NW1)**

Israeli

North
Solly's Exclusive *(NW11)*

Kosher

Central
Reubens *(W1)*

North
Nautilus *(NW6)*
Solly's Exclusive *(NW11)*

Lebanese

Central
Al Bustan *(SW1)*
Al Hamra *(W1)**
Al Sultan *(W1)*
Beiteddine *(SW1)*
Fakhreldine *(W1)*
Ishbilia *(SW1)*
Maroush *(W1)**

West
Beirut Express *(W2)**
Maroush *(SW3, W2)**
Phoenicia *(W8)**
Ranoush *(W2)**

Middle Eastern

East
Moro *(EC1)**

Persian

West
Alounak *(W14)**
Isfehan *(W2)*
Yas *(W14)*

Turkish

Central
Café Sofra *(W1, WC1, WC2)*
Efes Kebab House *(W1)*
Sofra *(W1, WC2)*

West
Manzara *(W11)*

North
Iznik *(N5)**
Pasha *(N1)*
Sarcan *(N1)**

South
Beyoglu *(SW11)**

East
Café Sofra *(EC4)*

ASIA

Afghani

Central
Caravan Serai *(W1)*

North
Afghan Kitchen *(N1)**

Burmese

West
Mandalay *(W2)**

Chinese

Central
Cam Phat *(W1)*
China City *(WC2)*
Chuen Cheng Ku *(W1)*
Dorchester, Oriental *(W1)**
Fung Shing *(WC2)**
Golden Dragon *(W1)*
Harbour City *(W1)*
Hunan *(SW1)**
Jenny Lo's *(SW1)*
Joy King Lau *(W1)**
Ken Lo's Memories *(SW1)*
Mayflower *(W1)**
Mekong *(SW1)*
Mr Chow *(SW1)*
Mr Kong *(WC2)**
New World *(W1)*
Poons *(WC2)*
Poons, Lisle Street *(WC2)*
Royal China *(W1)**
Wong Kei *(W1)*
Zen Central *(W1)*

Zen Garden (W1)

West
The Four Seasons (W2)
Ken Lo's Memories (W8)
Mandarin Kitchen (W2)*
Mao Tai (SW6)
Mr Wing (SW5)*
Nanking (W6)
New Culture Rev'n (SW3, W11)
Royal China (W2)*
Zen (SW3)*

North
Cheng Du (NW1)
China Blues (NW1)
Feng Shang (NW1)
Gung-Ho (NW6)*
New Culture Rev'n (N1, NW1)
Singapore Garden (NW6)
The Vegetarian
   Cottage (NW3)
Weng Wah House (NW3)
Yoahan Plaza (NW9)
ZeNW3 (NW3)

South
Elvis Gracelands Palace (SE15)
Four Regions (SE1)
Royal China (SW15)

East
Imperial City (EC3)*
Shanghai (E8)*

Chinese, Dim sum

Central
Chuen Cheng Ku (W1)
Dorchester, Oriental (W1)*
Golden Dragon (W1)
Harbour City (W1)
Joy King Lau (W1)*
New World (W1)
Royal China (W1)*
Zen Central (W1)

West
Royal China (W2)*
Zen (SW3)*

South
Royal China (SW15)

East
Shanghai (E8)*

Indian

Central
Chor Bizarre (W1)
Gopal's of Soho (W1)*
India Club (WC2)

Kundan (SW1)*
Malabar Junction (WC1)
Mandeer (WC1)
La Porte des Indes (W1)
Ragam (W1)
Rasa (W1)*
Red Fort (W1)
Salloos (SW1)*
Soho Spice (W1)
Tamarind (W1)*
Veeraswamy (W1)
Woodlands (SW1, W1)

West
Anarkali (W6)
Bombay Brasserie (SW7)*
Bombay Palace (W2)*
Brilliant (UB1)*
Café Lazeez (SW7)
Chutney Mary (SW10)*
Khan's (W2)
Khan's of Kensington (SW7)*
Khyber Pass (SW7)*
Madhu's Brilliant (UB1)*
Malabar (W8)*
Memories of India (SW7)*
Nayab (SW6)*
Noor Jahan (SW5)*
Saffron (SW10)
Standard Tandoori (W2)
Star of India (SW5)*
Tandoori Lane (SW6)*
Tandoori of Chelsea (SW3)
Vama (SW10)*

North
Anglo Asian Tandoori (N16)
Chutneys (NW1)
Diwana Bhel-Poori
   House (NW1)
Geeta (NW6)*
Great Nepalese (NW1)*
Haandi (NW1)
Rani (N3)
Rasa (N16)*
Vijay (NW6)*

South
Babur Brasserie (SE23)*
Battersea Rickshaw (SW11)
Bengal Clipper (SE1)*
Bombay Bicycle Club (SW12)*
Café Spice Namaste (SW11)*
Indian Ocean (SW17)*
Kastoori (SW17)*
Ma Goa (SW15)*
Rani (TW9)
Shree Krishna (SW17)*
Zujuma's (SW19)

East
Café Indiya *(E1)**
Café Spice Namaste *(E1)**
Lahore Kebab House *(E1)**
Rupee Room *(EC2)*
Sri India *(EC2)*

Indian, Southern

Central
India Club *(WC2)*
Malabar Junction *(WC1)*
Mandeer *(WC1)*
Ragam *(W1)*
Woodlands *(SW1, W1)*

North
Chutneys *(NW1)*
Diwana Bhel-Poori
  House *(NW1)**
Geeta *(NW6)**
Rani *(N3)*
Rasa *(N16)**
Vijay *(NW6)**

South
Kastoori *(SW17)**
Rani *(TW9)*
Shree Krishna *(SW17)**

Indonesian

Central
Melati *(W1)**

South
Enak Enak *(SW11)*

Japanese

Central
Benihana *(W1)*
Hamine *(W1)*
Ikeda *(W1)*
Ikkyu *(W1, WC2)**
Japanese Canteen *(W1)*
Kulu Kulu *(W1)**
Masako *(W1)*
Matsuri *(SW1)**
Mitsukoshi *(SW1)**
Miyama *(W1)**
Nobu *(W1)**
Satsuma *(W1)*
Shogun *(W1)**
Suntory *(SW1)*
Tokyo Diner *(WC2)*
Wagamama *(W1, WC1)*
Yo! Sushi *(W1)*
Yoshino *(W1)**

West
Bar Japan *(SW5)*
Benihana *(SW3)*
Inaho *(W2)**
Japanese Canteen *(W10)*
Sushi Wong *(W8)*
t'su *(SW3)*

North
Benihana *(NW3)*
Bu San *(N7)**
Café Japan *(NW11)**
Sushi-Say *(NW2)**
Wakaba *(NW3)*

East
Aykoku-Kaku *(EC4)*
City Miyama *(EC4)**
Japanese Canteen *(EC1)*
Moshi Moshi Sushi *(EC2, EC4)**
Noto *(EC2, EC4)*
Tatsuso *(EC2)**

Korean

Central
Kaya Korean *(W1)*

North
Bu San *(N7)**

Malaysian

Central
Melati *(W1)**

North
Singapore Garden *(NW6)*

East
Café Spice Namaste *(E1)**
Singapura *(EC3, EC4)*

Misc oriental

Central
Mongolian Barbecue *(WC2)*
Wok Wok *(W1)*

West
Bonjour Vietnam *(SW6)*
Jim Thompson's *(SW6)*
Mongolian Barbecue *(SW7, W4)*
Sash *(SW6)*
Southeast *(W9)**
Tiger Lil's *(SW3)*
Wok Wok *(SW10)*

North
Mongolian Barbecue *(NW1)*
Tiger Lil's *(N1)*
Wok Wok *(N1)*

Yoahan Plaza *(NW9)*

South
Enak Enak *(SW11)*
Sash Oriental Bar *(SW4)*
Tiger Lil's *(SW4)*
Wok Wok *(SW11)*

East
Cicada *(EC1)*
East One *(EC1)*
Pacific Spice *(EC1)*
Suan-Neo *(EC2)*
Tao *(EC4)*

Thai

Central
Blue Jade *(SW1)*
Chiang Mai *(W1)**
Manorom *(WC2)*
Noho *(W1)**
Silks & Spice *(W1)*
Sri Siam *(W1)**
Thai Pot Express *(WC2)*

West
Bangkok *(SW7)**
Bedlington Café *(W4)**
Ben's Thai *(W9)**
Blue Elephant *(SW6)**
Busabong Too *(SW10)*
Busabong Tree *(SW10)*
Café 209 *(SW6)*
Churchill *(W8)**
Esarn Kheaw *(W12)**
Fat Boy's *(W4)*
I Thai *(W2)*
Krungtap *(SW10)*
Latymers *(W6)**
The Papaya Tree *(W8)*
S&P Patara *(SW3)**
Sabai Sabai *(W6)**
Sash *(SW6)*
Silks & Spice *(W4)*
Tawana *(W2)**
Thai Bistro *(W4)**
Thai Break *(W8)**
Thai on the River *(SW10)*
Topsy-Tasty *(W4)**
Tui *(SW7)**

North
Silks & Spice *(NW1, NW8)*
Tuk Tuk *(N1)*
Yum Yum *(N16)**

South
Chada *(SW11)*
Kwan Thai *(SE1)*
Newton's *(SW4)*
The Old School Thai *(SW11)*

The Pepper Tree *(SW4)**
Phuket *(SW11)*
Thailand *(SE14)**

East
Sri Siam City *(EC2)**
Sri Thai *(EC4)*

Tibetan

Central
Tibetan Restaurant *(WC2)*

Vietnamese

Central
Cam Phat *(W1)*
Mekong *(SW1)*

West
Nam Long *(SW5)*

East
Saigon Times *(EC3)*

AREA OVERVIEWS

CENTRAL

Soho, Covent Garden & Bloomsbury
(Parts of W1, all WC2 and WC1)

£60+	Savoy Grill	British, Traditional	❸②②
	Savoy River Restaurant	French	④②②
£50+	Neal Street	Italian	④⑤④
	The Waldorf Meridien	Afternoon tea	④②②
£40+	Atlantic Bar & Grill	European	⑤⑤❶
	Alastair Little	British, Modern	④⑤⑤
	Axis	"	②②②
	Bank	"	❸④❸
	Café de Paris	"	④④②
	Circus	"	④❸④
	The Ivy	"	②❶❶
	Leith's Soho	"	❸❸④
	Lindsay House	"	②❸②
	Mezzo	"	⑤⑤④
	The Sugar Club	"	②④②
	Teatro	"	❸❸④
	Rules	British, Traditional	❸❸❶
	Simpsons-in-the-Strand	"	⑤④❸
	Sheekey's	Fish & seafood	– – –
	Zilli Fish	"	❸④❸
	Café Royal Grill	French	②②❶
	The Criterion	"	❸⑤❶
	Luigi's	Italian	④④④
	Christopher's	American	❸❸❸
£35+	Café du Jardin	British, Modern	❸❸④
	dell'Ugo	"	⑤⑤④
	Indigo	"	④❸④
	Stephen Bull	"	②❸④
	Livebait	Fish & seafood	②❸④
	Manzi's	"	②❸❸
	Beotys	French	④❶❸
	L'Escargot	"	②②❸
	L'Estaminet	"	②②❸
	Le Palais du Jardin	"	❸❸②
	Quo Vadis	"	④④④
	Orso	Italian	④④④
	Planet Hollywood	Burgers, etc	⑤④❸
	Red Fort	Indian	④④⑤
	Kaya Korean	Korean	④❸④
£30+	Belgo Centraal	Belgian	④④❸
	Alfred	British, Modern	②②④
	Blues	"	❸❸②

French House	"	3 2 3
Hodgson's	"	3 3 3
The Lexington	"	4 5 3
Saint	"	3 4 2
Mezzonine	East/West	5 5 4
Au Jardin des Gourmets	French	3 2 3
Café Bohème	"	4 4 1
Café des Amis du Vin	"	4 3 3
Magno's Brasserie	"	5 4 5
Mon Plaisir	"	2 2 1
Gay Hussar	Hungarian	3 2 2
Bertorelli's	Italian	3 3 3
La Capannina	"	3 2 4
Little Italy	"	3 2 2
Luna Nuova	"	4 3 4
Vasco & Piero's Pavilion	"	3 1 3
St Moritz	Swiss	3 2 3
Browns	International	4 3 3
Fashion Café	Burgers, etc	5 5 5
Joe Allen	American	4 3 2
TGI Friday's	"	5 3 3
Fung Shing	Chinese	1 4 5

£25+			
	a.k.a.	British, Modern	2 2 3
	Andrew Edmunds	"	3 2 1
	Café Med	"	4 4 3
	Cork & Bottle	"	4 3 2
	Corney & Barrow	"	2 1 4
	Nine Golden Square	"	3 3 4
	Plummers	"	4 4 5
	Soho Brewing Company	"	3 3 4
	Sound Republic	"	4 4 4
	Café Flo	French	4 4 4
	Chez Gérard	"	4 4 3
	Randall & Aubin	"	2 3 2
	Soho Soho (Rôtisserie)	"	4 4 3
	Townhouse Brasserie	"	3 3 3
	Italian Kitchen	Italian	3 3 4
	Hujo's	Mediterranean	3 1 2
	Alphabet	International	3 2 1
	Balans	"	4 4 3
	Boulevard	"	5 4 4
	Deals	"	5 4 4
	Garlic & Shots	"	4 3 4
	Sarastro	"	5 4 1
	Shampers	"	3 2 2
	Capital Radio Restaurant	Burgers, etc	5 4 3
	The Rainforest Café	"	5 5 3
	Wolfe's	"	3 3 4

	La Spiga	*Pizza*	③③③
	Navajo Joe	*American*	④③②
	Smollensky's, Strand	"	④④③
	Café Pacifico	*Mexican/TexMex*	④④③
	Texas Embassy Cantina	"	⑤④④
	Little Havana	*South American*	③③④
	Sofra	*Turkish*	③④④
	China City	*Chinese*	③④④
	Chuen Cheng Ku	"	③④④
	Harbour City	"	③⑤⑤
	Mayflower	"	②④④
	Gopal's of Soho	*Indian*	②③④
	Malabar Junction	"	③③④
	Soho Spice	"	③③③
	Ikkyu	*Japanese*	②④④
	Wok Wok	*Misc oriental*	④④④
	Chiang Mai	*Thai*	①③⑤
	Sri Siam	"	②③③
£20+	All Bar One	*British, Modern*	④④③
	Aurora	"	③④①
	Porters	*British, Traditional*	④⑤⑤
	Café Rouge	*French*	⑤⑤④
	Café Pasta	*Italian*	④③④
	Caffè Uno	"	⑤④④
	Pasta di Milano	"	③③④
	Café Emm	*International*	③③③
	Dôme	"	⑤④④
	Pitcher & Piano	"	④④②
	Ed's Easy Diner	*Burgers, etc*	③②②
	Kettners	*Pizza*	⑤④②
	Pâtisserie Valerie	*Sandwiches, cakes, etc*	③③②
	Museum St Café	*Vegetarian*	③②④
	La Perla	*Mexican/TexMex*	③④②
	Café Latino	*South American*	④②②
	Calabash	*Afro-Caribbean*	③④⑤
	Golden Dragon	*Chinese*	③④④
	Mr Kong	"	②③⑤
	New World	"	③③④
	Poons	"	③④④
	Satsuma	*Japanese*	③②②
	Yo! Sushi	"	④②②
	Melati	*Malaysian*	②④④
	Mongolian Barbecue	*Misc oriental*	⑤④④
	Manorom	*Thai*	③③④
	Thai Pot	"	③④④
	Thai Pot Express	"	③④④
£15+	Star Café	*British, Modern*	③④③
	Pollo	*Italian*	④④③

	Mediterranean Café	*Mediterranean*	③②④
	Café Coq	*Steaks & grills*	③②④
	Gordon's Wine Bar	*International*	④③❶
	PizzaExpress	*Pizza*	③③③
	Cranks	*Vegetarian*	⑤⑤⑤
	Food for Thought	"	②③④
	Mildreds	"	②③③
	Joy King Lau	*Chinese*	②②③
	Poons, Lisle Street	"	③④⑤
	India Club	*Indian*	④④④
	Hamine	*Japanese*	③④④
	Kulu Kulu	"	②④⑤
	Tokyo Diner	"	③②③
	Wagamama	"	③③③
	Tibetan Restaurant	*Tibetan*	③②③
	Cam Phat	*Vietnamese*	④③④
£10+	Stock Pot	*International*	④③④
	Café Sofra	*Turkish*	④⑤④
	Wong Kei	*Chinese*	③⑤④
£5+	Fryer's Delight	*Fish & chips*	②③④
	Häagen-Dazs	*Ice cream*	③④⑤
	Au Bon Pain	*Sandwiches, cakes, etc*	④③④
	Bar Italia	"	④③❶
	Coffee Republic	"	③②③
	EAT	"	③②③
	Maison Bertaux	"	②③②
	Pret A Manger	"	③❶④
	Seattle Coffee Co	"	②③③

Mayfair & St James's
(Parts of W1 and SW1)

£100+	Oak Room MPW	*French*	③④④
£90+	Le Gavroche	*French*	②②③
£80+	Connaught	*British, Traditional*	③❶②
	Chez Nico	*French*	②④④
£70+	1837 at Brown's Hotel	*French*	③⑤③
	Suntory	*Japanese*	③③④
£60+	Dorchester Grill	*British, Traditional*	②❶②
	Claridges Restaurant	*French*	④②②
	The Ritz	"	④②❶
	Dorchester, Oriental	*Chinese*	②③④
	Mitsukoshi	*Japanese*	❶②⑤

AREA OVERVIEWS

Price	Restaurant	Cuisine	Ratings
£50+	The Lanesborough	British, Modern	④❷❶
	Wiltons	British, Traditional	❷❷❸
	Nobu	East/West	❶❸❷
	L'Odéon	French	④④④
	Les Saveurs	"	④④⑤
	Le Soufflé	"	❸❷⑤
	The Square	"	❷❸❸
	Windows on the World	"	⑤④❷
	Cecconi's	Italian	⑤⑤⑤
	Sartoria	"	④④❸
	Zen Central	Chinese	❸❷⑤
	Ikeda	Japanese	❸❷④
	Miyama	"	❷④⑤
	Shogun	"	❷④④
£40+	The Avenue	British, Modern	④④❸
	Le Caprice	"	❷❶❶
	Che	"	– – –
	Coast	"	❸④⑤
	Nicole's	"	④❸❸
	Rowley's	"	⑤④④
	Scott's	"	❸❸❷
	33	"	❸❸④
	Thomas Goode	"	④❸❷
	Green's	British, Traditional	❸❷❸
	Greenhouse	"	❸❷❸
	Bentley's	Fish & seafood	❸❸❷
	Cave	French	❷❷④
	Cy	"	④❸④
	Mirabelle	"	❷❷❷
	L'Oranger	"	❶❶❷
	Bice	Italian	④❸④
	Diverso	"	❷❷❸
	Teca	"	❷④④
	Kaspia	Russian	❸❸④
	The Guinea	Steaks & grills	❸④④
	Dover Street	International	⑤⑤❸
	Reubens	Kosher	❸❸④
	Zen Garden	Chinese	❸❷❸
	Benihana	Japanese	④④❸
	Matsuri	"	❷❷④
£35+	Langan's Brasserie	British, Modern	④❸❷
	Quaglino's	"	④④❸
	The Gaucho Grill	Steaks & grills	❷❷❷
	Vendôme	International	④❸❸
	Momo	North African	④④❶
	Al Hamra	Lebanese	❷④④
	Al Sultan	"	❸④④

			Rating		
	Fakhreldine	"	③	②	④
	Chor Bizarre	Indian	③	③	②
	Tamarind	"	②	②	②
£30+	The Marquis	British, Modern	②	①	④
	Sotheby's Café	"	③	②	③
	Zinc	"	⑤	④	④
	Café Fish (Restaurant)	Fish & seafood	③	④	③
	Boudin Blanc	French	②	②	①
	Il Vicolo	Italian	③	②	④
	Browns	International	④	③	③
	Veeraswamy	Indian	③	③	③
£25+	Café Flo	French	④	④	④
	Chez Gérard	"	④	④	③
	Ristorante Italiano	Italian	③	③	④
	Hard Rock Café	Burgers, etc	④	③	②
	Smollensky's	American	④	③	③
	Down Mexico Way	Mexican/TexMex	⑤	④	②
	Havana	South American	⑤	④	③
	Sofra	Turkish	③	④	④
	Rasa	Indian	①	②	③
	Yoshino	Japanese	②	③	④
£20+	All Bar One	British, Modern	④	④	③
	L'Artiste Musclé	French	④	②	②
	Caffè Uno	Italian	⑤	④	④
	Gourmet Pizza Co.	Pizza	③	④	③
	Pizzeria Condotti	"	③	③	②
	Woodlands	Indian	③	④	④
£15+	Ask! Pizza	Pizza	③	③	③
	PizzaExpress	"	③	③	③
£10+	Stock Pot	International	④	③	④
	Café Sofra	Turkish	④	⑤	④
£5+	Au Bon Pain	Sandwiches, cakes, etc	④	③	④
	Coffee Republic	"	③	②	③
	EAT	"	③	②	③
	Pret A Manger	"	③	①	④
	Seattle Coffee Co	"	②	③	③

Fitzrovia & Marylebone
(Part of W1)

			Rating
£50+	Orrery	French	④❸❸
	Pied à Terre	"	❷❸④
	Masako	Japanese	❸❷❸
£40+	Mash	British, Modern	⑤⑤④
	Interlude	French	❷❷❸
	La Porte des Indes	Indian	❸❸❷
£35+	No 1 Cigar Club	British, Modern	⑤❷❷
	Stephen Bull	"	❷❸④
	The Union Café	"	❸❸⑤
	Zoe	"	④④④
	Elena's L'Etoile	French	❷❶❶
	Le Muscadet	"	④④④
	Nico Central	"	❷④④
	Odin's	"	❷❶❶
	Il Faro	Italian	❸❷❸
£30+	Oceana	British, Modern	❸❸④
	Back to Basics	Fish & seafood	❶❸④
	Villandry	French	❸⑤④
	Bertorelli's	Italian	❸❸❸
	Caldesi	"	❸❷④
	Ibla	"	❶❷❸
	Purple Sage	"	❷❷❷
	O'Conor Don	Irish	❸❷❷
	Hardy's	International	❷❶❸
	Maroush	Lebanese	❷❷❸
£25+	Justin de Blank	British, Modern	④④④
	Stargazer	"	④❷④
	RK Stanleys	British, Traditional	④❸❸
	The Birdcage	East/West	❶❸❶
	Café Flo	French	④④④
	La Spighetta	Italian	❸④④
	Rueda	Spanish	④④❷
	Sofra	Turkish	❸④④
	Caravan Serai	Afghani	④❷❸
	Royal China	Chinese	❶❸❸
	Ikkyu	Japanese	❷④④
£20+	All Bar One	British, Modern	④④❸
	Café Rouge	French	⑤⑤④
	L'Arte	Italian	❸❸⑤
	Caffè Uno	"	⑤④④
	Pâtisserie Valerie	Sandwiches, cakes, etc	❸❸❷
	Efes Kebab House	Turkish	④❸❸
	Mandeer	Indian	❸④④

	Ragam	"	③④⑤
	Woodlands	"	③④④
	Noho	Thai	❷❷❸
	Silks & Spice	"	③④❸
£15+	Ask! Pizza	Pizza	❸❸❸
	PizzaExpress	"	❸❸❸
	Cranks	Vegetarian	⑤⑤⑤
	Japanese Canteen	Japanese	④❸⑤
	Wagamama	"	❸❸❸
£10+	Stock Pot	International	④❸④
	Café Sofra	Turkish	④⑤④
£5+	Pret A Manger	Sandwiches, cakes, etc	❸❶④
	Seattle Coffee Co	"	❷❸❸

Belgravia, Victoria & Pimlico
(SW1, except St James's)

£70+	La Tante Claire		
	Berkeley Hotel	French	– – –
£60+	One-O-One	French	④❷④
	The Halkin	Italian	④❸❸
£50+	L'Incontro	Italian	④④④
	Santini	"	⑤④⑤
	Rib Room	Steaks & grills	❷❶❷
£40+	The Fifth Floor	British, Modern	④❸❷
	Goring Hotel	"	④❶❸
	Vong	East/West	❶❷❸
	La Poule au Pot	French	❸❸❶
	Roussillon	"	– – –
	La Fontana	Italian	❸❸④
	Mimmo d'Ischia	"	❸❸❷
	Signor Sassi	"	❸❶❷
	Toto's	"	❸❷❸
	Motcomb's	International	④❷❷
	Ken Lo's Memories	Chinese	❸④④
	Mr Chow	"	❸❸❷
	Salloos	Indian	❶❸④
£35+	Atrium	British, Modern	⑤⑤④
	Drones	"	⑤④⑤
	Tate Gallery	"	④❸❷
	Grenadier	British, Traditional	④❸❷
	Boisdale	French	❸④❸
	Simply Nico	"	❸❸④
	Grissini	Italian	❸❷④

AREA OVERVIEWS

			Rating
	Sale e Pepe	"	❸❷❶
	Zafferano	"	❶❶❷
	Pomegranates	International	❹❸❷
	Al Bustan	Lebanese	❸❷⑤
£30+	Ebury Street Wine Bar	British, Modern	❸❹④
	The Foundation	French	❸❹⑤
	Caraffini	Italian	❷❶❷
	Como Lario	"	❸❷❷
	Olivo	"	❷❸❸
	Fifth Floor (Café)	Mediterranean	❹❹❷
	Goya	Spanish	❸❹❸
	Footstool	International	⑤❹❸
	Beiteddine	Lebanese	❸❷④
	Kundan	Indian	❷❸④
£25+	Uno	Italian	❷❸④
	Grumbles	International	❹④❸
	Oriel	"	⑤❹❸
	Football Football	Burgers, etc	⑤⑤⑤
	Oliveto	Pizza	❷❸❸
	Ishbilia	Lebanese	❸❸❸
	Hunan	Chinese	❶❸④
£20+	Shepherd's	British, Traditional	❸❷❷
	Pizza On The Park	Pizza	❹❸❷
	Blue Jade	Thai	❸❷④
£15+	Hyde Park Hotel		
	Park Room	Afternoon tea	❸❸❷
	Seafresh	Fish & chips	❷❸④
	Ask! Pizza	Pizza	❸❸❸
	PizzaExpress	"	❸❸❸
	Jenny Lo's	Chinese	❸❷④
	Mekong	Vietnamese	❸④④
£10+	Little Bay	International	❹❸❷
£5+	Pret A Manger	Sandwiches, cakes, etc	❸❶④
	Seattle Coffee Co	"	❷❸❸

WEST

Chelsea, South Kensington, Kensington, Earl's Court & Fulham (SW3, SW5, SW6, SW7, SW10 & W8)

£80+	Blakes Hotel	International	④④❶
£70+	Capital Hotel	French	❸②❸
£60+	Gordon Ramsay	French	❷❷④
£50+	Aubergine	French	— — —
	Bibendum	"	❸④❸
	Chavot	"	❸❸❸
	Turner's	"	❷❸❸
	San Lorenzo	Italian	④④❷
£40+	Bluebird	British, Modern	④④❸
	The Canteen	"	❶❷❷
	Clarke's	"	❶❶❷
	English Garden	"	❸❷❷
	English House	"	④❸❸
	Hilaire	"	❸❷❸
	Joe's Café	"	❸❸❸
	Kensington Place	"	❸❸❷
	King's Brasserie	"	❷❸⑤
	Launceston Place	"	❷❶❶
	The Tenth	"	❸❷❸
	Poissonnerie de l'Avenue	Fish & seafood	❷❸❸
	Restaurant 190	"	❸❷❸
	La Belle Epoque	French	④⑤④
	L'Escargot Doré	"	❸❷④
	Icon	"	❸❸❷
	Le Suquet	"	❷❸❸
	Daphne's	Italian	④④❷
	Montpeliano	"	❷❷❸
	San Martino	"	④❸❸
	Scalini	"	④❷❷
	Albero & Grana	Spanish	⑤⑤❸
	The Collection	International	④⑤❸
	Conrad Hotel	"	❸❷❸
	Zen	Chinese	❷❸④
	Bombay Brasserie	Indian	❷❸❷
	Benihana	Japanese	④④❸
	Blue Elephant	Thai	❷❷❶
£35+	Belvedere	British, Modern	❸❸❷
	Dan's	"	❸❷❶
	Min's Bar	"	⑤❸❷

755	"	②②④
606 Club	"	④④②
The Terrace	"	②②③
Fishnets	Fish & seafood	③②⑤
Stratford's	"	③②④
Brasserie St Quentin	French	④③④
Chezmax	"	①①②
Langan's Coq d'Or	"	④③④
Lou Pescadou	"	④④④
Novelli W8	"	④⑤⑤
Pelham Street	"	④④❸
Simply Nico Chelsea	"	③③④
Boyd's	Italian	⑤⑤④
Café Milan	"	– – –
La Famiglia	"	③④②
Sabatino	"	③②④
Sandrini	"	③②④
Nikita's	Russian	⑤④②
Montana	American	②③③
Ken Lo's Memories	Chinese	③③③
Mr Wing	"	②③❶
Chutney Mary	Indian	②③③
Star of India	"	②④③
Tandoori of Chelsea	"	③②④
Vama	"	②④③

£30+	Bistrot 190	British, Modern	④④❸
	Charco's	"	④④④
	Goolies	"	②❶②
	Joe's Brasserie	"	④④④
	Kartouche	"	④④❸
	Basil St Hotel	British, Traditional	④③❸
	Maggie Jones's	"	③②❶
	Bibendum Oyster Bar	Fish & seafood	❶②❸
	Ghillies	"	②③❸
	The Abingdon	French	③②❸
	La Brasserie	"	④④④
	Le Colombier	"	④❸❸
	Monkeys	"	②③②
	Thierry's	"	④③④
	Café O	Greek	③②④
	De Cecco	Italian	②④②
	Formula Veneta	"	③②❸
	Leonardo's	"	③②④
	Monza	"	③②❸
	La Perla	"	❸❸❸
	Il Portico	"	❸❸❸
	Sambuca	"	❸❶❸
	Ziani	"	❸②❶
	The Cross Keys	Mediterranean	❸❸②

	Wódka	Polish	④④❸
	Browns	International	④❸❸
	The Enterprise	"	❸❸❶
	PJ's	"	④④❸
	Big Easy	American	④❸❷
	Shoeless Joe's	"	⑤④❷
	Cactus Blue	South American	④④❷
	Pasha	North African	④❸❶
	Maroush	Lebanese	❷❷❸
	Phoenicia	"	❷❶❸
	Mao Tai	Chinese	❶❷❷
	Café Lazeez	Indian	④④❸
	Busabong Too	Thai	❸④④
	Busabong Tree	"	④❸④
	Thai on the River	"	④❸❷
	Nam Long	Vietnamese	❸④❷
£25+	Gilbert's	Modern European	⑤⑤⑤
	Brinkley's	British, Modern	④④❷
	Café Med	"	④④❸
	Chelsea Ram	"	❶❸❷
	Le Metro	"	❸❸❷
	The Pen	"	❸❸❸
	Ffiona's	British, Traditional	❸❷❷
	La Bouchée	French	④⑤❸
	Café Flo	"	④④④
	Chez Gérard	"	④④❸
	Bersagliera	Italian	❸❷❸
	Café Montpeliano	"	❸❸❷
	Da Mario	"	❸❸❸
	Elistano	"	❷❶❶
	Il Falconiere	"	❸❷❸
	Paparazzi Café	"	④④❷
	Riccardo's	"	❷④❷
	The Polish Club	Polish	❸❸❷
	Albero & Grana, Bar	Spanish	❸❸❷
	Cambio de Tercio	"	❸❷❷
	La Rueda	"	④④❷
	Balans West	International	❸❷❶
	Deals	"	⑤④④
	Foxtrot Oscar	"	④④④
	The Gasworks	"	⑤④❶
	Glaisters	"	④⑤④
	Chicago Rib Shack	American	❷❷④
	Nayab	Indian	❷④④
	Noor Jahan	"	❷④④
	Saffron	"	❸④❸
	Sushi Wong	Japanese	❸❶⑤
	t'su	"	❸❸❸
	Jim Thompson's	Misc oriental	④⑤❶

	Wok Wok	"	④④④
	Bangkok	Thai	❷④⑤
	The Papaya Tree	"	❸❷④
	S&P	"	❷❷④
	S&P Patara	"	❷❷④
	Tui	"	❷④⑤
£20+	All Bar One	British, Modern	④④❸
	The Crescent	"	❸❷❸
	The Imperial Arms	"	❸❷④
	Vingt-Quatre	"	④❷❸
	Café Rouge	French	⑤⑤④
	Emile's	"	❷❶❸
	Francofill	"	❸❸④
	Café Pasta	Italian	④❸④
	Caffè Uno	"	⑤④④
	Calzone	"	④❸④
	Da Pierino	"	❸❸④
	Made in Italy	"	❸❸❷
	Pasta di Milano	"	❸❸④
	Spago	"	❸④④
	Coopers Arms	International	❸❸❷
	Dôme	"	⑤④④
	Front Page	"	❸❷❷
	Pitcher & Piano	"	④④❷
	The Scarsdale	"	④❸❷
	Sporting Page	"	❸❷❷
	Wine Gallery	"	④❸❷
	Ed's Easy Diner	Burgers, etc	❸❷❷
	Luigi Malones	"	④⑤❸
	Sticky Fingers	"	④❸❸
	Tootsies	"	④④④
	Geale's	Fish & chips	❷❸④
	La Delizia	Pizza	❷④❸
	Pizza Pomodoro	"	④④❷
	Pâtisserie Valerie	Sandwiches, cakes, etc	❸❸❷
	Le Shop	"	❸❸❷
	Texas Lone Star	Mexican/TexMex	⑤❸❸
	El Gaucho	South American	❸❸❸
	Khan's of Kensington	Indian	❷❸④
	Khyber Pass	"	❷❷⑤
	Malabar	"	❶❷❷
	Memories of India	"	❷❷❸
	Tandoori Lane	"	❷❶❸
	Bar Japan	Japanese	❸❸❸
	Bonjour Vietnam	Misc oriental	⑤④④
	Mongolian Barbecue	"	⑤④④
	Sash	"	⑤④❸
	Tiger Lil's	"	④④❸
	Thai Break	Thai	❷❸④

			Ratings
£15+	King's Road Café	*Italian*	④❸❸
	Daquise	*Polish*	④❸④
	Rôtisserie Jules	*Steaks & grills*	❸❸⑤
	Chelsea Bun Diner	*International*	④❸❸
	Windsor Castle	*"*	④❸❶
	Ask! Pizza	*Pizza*	❸❸❸
	Pizza the Action	*"*	❸❸❸
	PizzaExpress	*"*	❸❸❸
	Pucci Pizza	*"*	❷④❶
	Troubadour	*Sandwiches, cakes, etc*	④⑤❶
	New Culture Rev'n	*Chinese*	④❸④
	Café 209	*Thai*	④❷❸
	Krungtap	*"*	④❸④
£10+	Costa's Grill	*Greek*	❸❷❸
	Luigi's Delicatessen	*Italian*	❶④❸
	Mona Lisa	*"*	❸❸⑤
	Chelsea Kitchen	*International*	④❷④
	Stock Pot	*"*	④❸④
	Costa's Fish	*Fish & chips*	❷❷④
	Churchill	*Thai*	❷④❸
£5+	Häagen-Dazs	*Ice cream*	❸④⑤
	Fileric	*Sandwiches, cakes, etc*	❷❷④
	Pret A Manger	*"*	❸❶④
	Seattle Coffee Co	*"*	❷❸❸

Notting Hill, Holland Park, Bayswater, North Kensington & Maida Vale (W2, W9, W10, W11)

			Ratings
£70+	I Thai	*East/West*	④④④
£60+	Halcyon Hotel	*British, Modern*	❷❸❸
£50+	Leith's	*British, Modern*	❸❸④
£40+	Bali Sugar	*British, Modern*	❸❸❸
	Julie's	*"*	④❸❶
	Al San Vincenzo	*Italian*	❶❶④
£35+	Alastair Little	*British, Modern*	❸❸⑤
	The Cow	*"*	❷❸❸
	First Floor	*"*	⑤⑤④
	192	*"*	④④❸
	Pharmacy	*"*	④④❸
	Jason's	*Fish & seafood*	❶❷❷
	Chez Moi	*French*	❸❶❷
	Assaggi	*Italian*	❶❶❷
	The Green Olive	*"*	❷❷❸

	Orsino	"	❸❹❸
	Beach Blanket Babylon	International	❺❹❷
	Dakota	American	❸❹❸
£30+	Anonimato	British, Modern	❷❷❸
	Veronica's	British, Traditional	❹❷❷
	Rain	East/West	❹❹❸
	L'Altro	Italian	❹❸❹
	Palio	"	❺❺❸
	Zucca	"	❹❸❹
	Woz	Mediterranean	❸❷❷
	Julie's Bar	International	❺❸❶
	TGI Friday's	American	❺❸❸
	Maroush	Lebanese	❷❷❸
	Mandarin Kitchen	Chinese	❶❹❹
	Bombay Palace	Indian	❷❷❸
£25+	Café Med	British, Modern	❹❹❸
	Mas Café	"	❸❸❷
	Raoul's Café	"	❸❸❸
	Brass. du Marché	French	❷❶❶
	L'Accento Italiano	Italian	❹❷❹
	Café 206	"	❷❷❸
	Osteria Basilico	"	❸❹❷
	The Red Pepper	"	❷❹❸
	Mediterraneo	Mediterranean	❷❷❷
	Café Laville	International	❹❹❷
	Royal China	Chinese	❶❸❸
	Inaho	Japanese	❶❹❺
£20+	All Bar One	British, Modern	❹❹❸
	The Ladbroke Arms	"	❷❸❷
	The Prince Bonaparte	"	❷❹❸
	The Westbourne	"	❹❺❶
	Wiz	"	— — —
	Café Rouge	French	❺❺❹
	Halepi	Greek	❸❶❸
	Kalamaras, Micro	"	❸❹❹
	Caffè Uno	Italian	❺❹❹
	Calzone	"	❹❸❹
	Galicia	Spanish	❸❹❸
	Tootsies	Burgers, etc	❹❹❹
	Coins	Sandwiches, cakes, etc	❸❸❷
	Rodizio Rico	Brazilian	❺❹❹
	Mandola	Sudanese	❷❸❶
	Isfehan	Persian	❸❸❸
	The Four Seasons	Chinese	❸❹❸
	Standard Tandoori	Indian	❸❸❹
	Southeast	Misc oriental	❷❹❹
	Ben's Thai	Thai	❷❹❸

			Ratings
	Tawana	"	②④④
£15+	Rôtisserie Jules	Steaks & grills	❸❸⑤
	Café Grove	International	④④②
	Ask! Pizza	Pizza	❸❸❸
	PizzaExpress	"	❸❸❸
	Tom's	Sandwiches, cakes, etc	❷❷❷
	Beirut Express	Lebanese	❷❷❸
	Ranoush	"	❶④④
	Manzara	Turkish	❸❸④
	Mandalay	Burmese	❷❶④
	New Culture Rev'n	Chinese	④❸④
	Khan's	Indian	④⑤❸
	Japanese Canteen	Japanese	④❸⑤
£5+	Häagen-Dazs	Ice cream	❸④⑤
	Coffee Republic	Sandwiches, cakes, etc	❸❷❸
	Lisboa Patisserie	"	❶❸④

Hammersmith, Shepherd's Bush Chiswick & Olympia (W4, W5, W6, W12, W14)

			Ratings
£40+	Cibo	Italian	❷❷❸
	The River Café	"	❷❸❷
£35+	Chiswick	British, Modern	❷❸④
	Chinon	French	❶④④
	La Dordogne	"	❷❷❷
£30+	The Brackenbury	British, Modern	❷❷❸
	Snows on the Green	"	④④④
	Wilson's	"	❸❷④
	Grano	Italian	– – –
	Springbok Café	South African	❷❶❸
£25+	Anglesea Arms	British, Modern	❷⑤❸
	Blythe Road	"	❸❷❷
	Café Med	"	④④❸
	Christian's	French	❸❸❸
	Palatino	Italian	❸❷④
	Popeseye	Steaks & grills	❶❷❸
	Rôtisserie	"	④❸⑤
	Deals	International	⑤④④
	Mackintosh's Brasserie	"	④④④
	Nanking	Chinese	❸❸❸
	Anarkali	Indian	❸④④
£20+	All Bar One	British, Modern	④④❸
	The Havelock Tavern	"	❷❸❷

	Name	Cuisine	Ratings
	Stone Mason's Arms	"	③④③
	Café Rouge	French	⑤⑤④
	Café Pasta	Italian	④③④
	Caffè Uno	"	⑤④④
	Pitcher & Piano	International	④④②
	Tootsies	Burgers, etc	④④④
	Blah! Blah! Blah!	Vegetarian	②③②
	The Gate	"	①①②
	Paulo's	Brazilian	③②③
	Coyote Café	Mexican/TexMex	③③③
	Adams Café	Tunisian	②②④
	Alounak	Persian	①②④
	Yas	"	④③③
	Madhu's Brilliant	Indian	②①④
	Mongolian Barbecue	Misc oriental	⑤④④
	Esarn Kheaw	Thai	②④④
	Fat Boy's	"	③③③
	Latymers	"	②③⑤
	Sabai Sabai	"	②②④
	Silks & Spice	"	③④③
	Thai Bistro	"	②②④
	Topsy-Tasty	"	②②④
£15+	Dove	British, Modern	③④②
	Patio	"	③②②
	Ask! Pizza	Pizza	③③③
	PizzaExpress	"	③③③
	Brilliant	Indian	①②④
	Bedlington Café	Thai	②⑤⑤
£5+	Pret A Manger	Sandwiches, cakes, etc	③①④

NORTH

**Hampstead, West Hampstead, St John's Wood,
Regent's Park, Kilburn & Camden Town
(NW postcodes)**

£50+	The Landmark Hotel	*International*	④❸❶
£40+	Benihana	*Japanese*	④④❸
	Wakaba	*"*	❸❸④
£35+	Bradley's	*British, Modern*	❷❷❸
	Odette's	*"*	❷❷❶
	L'Aventure	*French*	❶❷❶
	Oslo Court	*"*	❶❶❸
	Villa Bianca	*Italian*	④❸❷
	Gaucho Grill	*Steaks & grills*	❷❷❷
	China Blues	*Chinese*	④④❸
£30+	Belgo Noord	*Belgian*	④④❸
	The Engineer	*British, Modern*	❸⑤❷
	Gresslin's	*"*	❷❸⑤
	Quincy's	*"*	❶❶❸
	Café des Arts	*French*	④④❸
	Mims	*"*	❷⑤⑤
	House on Rosslyn Hill	*International*	④④❷
	Cheng Du	*Chinese*	❸❸❸
	Feng Shang	*"*	❸❷❷
	ZeNW3	*"*	❸❷❸
£25+	Byron's	*British, Modern*	④❷❷
	Café Med	*"*	④④❸
	The Chapel	*"*	❸❷❷
	Cucina	*"*	❸❷❸
	The Queen's	*"*	④④④
	The Vine	*"*	❷④❷
	Café Delancey	*French*	④④❷
	Café Flo	*"*	④④④
	La Cage Imaginaire	*"*	④❸❸
	Camden Brasserie	*"*	❸❷❷
	La Brocca	*Italian*	❸④❸
	Vegia Zena	*"*	❷❸④
	Cottons	*Afro-Caribbean*	④④❸
	Solly's Exclusive	*Israeli*	❸④❸
	Gung-Ho	*Chinese*	❷❸❸
	Sushi-Say	*Japanese*	❷❷④
	Singapore Garden	*Malaysian*	❸④④
£20+	Great Nepalese	*Nepalese*	❷❷⑤
	All Bar One	*British, Modern*	④④❸
	Crown & Goose	*"*	❸④❸

Globe Restaurant	"		④❷④
Lansdowne	"		④④❷
Czech Club	Czech		④④④
Café Rouge	French		⑤⑤④
Daphne	Greek		❸❷❸
Greek Valley	"		④❷❸
Lemonia	"		❸❷❶
Billboard Café	Italian		⑤❸④
Café Pasta	"		④❸④
Caffè Uno	"		⑤④④
Calzone	"		④❸④
Marine Ices	"		④❸❸
Zamoyski	Polish		④④❸
Don Pepe	Spanish		❸❸❸
Dôme	International		⑤④④
Ed's Easy Diner	Burgers, etc		❸❷❷
Tootsies	"		④④④
Nautilus	Fish & chips		❸④④
Seashell	"		❷❸④
Manna	Vegetarian		❷④❸
Mango Room	Afro-Caribbean		❸❷❶
Laurent	Tunisian		❷❷⑤
Weng Wah House	Chinese		❸❷❸
Café Japan	Japanese		❷❷④
Mongolian Barbecue	Misc oriental		⑤④④
Silks & Spice	Thai		❸④❸
£15+	Nontas	Greek	❸❸④
	Troika	Russian	④④❸
	Bar Gansa	Spanish	❷④❷
	Ask! Pizza	Pizza	❸❸❸
	PizzaExpress	"	❸❸❸
	Ali Baba	Egyptian	❷❷④
	New Culture Revolution	Chinese	④❸④
	The Vegetarian Cottage	"	❸❷❸
	Chutneys	Indian	❸④❸
	Haandi	"	❸④④
	Vijay	"	❷❸④
	Yoahan Plaza	Misc oriental	❸④⑤
£10+	The Little Bay	International	④❸❷
	Diwana B.-Poori Hs	Indian	❶④④
	Geeta	"	❷❸⑤
£5+	Häagen-Dazs	Ice cream	❸④⑤
	Pret A Manger	Sandwiches, cakes, etc	❸❶④

Islington, Highgate, Crouch End, Stoke Newington, Finsbury Park, Muswell Hill & Finchley (N postcodes)

Price	Restaurant	Cuisine	Ratings
£35+	Euphorium	British, Modern	③②③
	Frederick's	"	③②②
£30+	Granita	"	②②④
	Jindivick	"	④④③
	Lola's	"	③②③
	Village Bistro	French	③④③
	The White Onion	"	①①③
	Casale Franco	Italian	③④③
	Florians	"	④③②
	San Carlo	"	④④③
	Anna's Place	Scandinavian	③②②
£25+	Kavanagh's	British, Modern	③④②
	Mesclun	"	①①④
	Chez Liline	Fish & seafood	①③④
	Les Associés	French	③③③
	Café Flo	"	④④④
	Soulard	"	②②②
	Rôtisserie	Steaks & grills	④③⑤
	Banners	International	④④②
	Toff's	Fish & chips	①③⑤
	Cuba Libre	South American	⑤⑤③
	Rasa	Indian	①②③
	Wok Wok	Misc oriental	④④④
£20+	All Bar One	British, Modern	④④③
	The Lord Palmerston	"	④②③
	Café Rouge	French	⑤⑤④
	Le Sacré-Coeur	"	①②①
	Vrisaki	Greek	②②③
	Café Pasta	Italian	④③④
	Caffè Uno	"	⑤④④
	Calzone	"	④③④
	Cantina Italia	"	②③④
	San Daniele	"	③③④
	Centuria	Mediterranean	③⑤④
	Dôme	International	⑤④④
	The Fox Reformed	"	③③③
	Pitcher & Piano	"	④④②
	Two Brothers	Fish & chips	①②④
	Pasha	Turkish	③①②
	Anglo Asian Tandoori	Indian	③③③
	Rani	"	③②③
	Bu San	Korean	②③⑤
	Tiger Lil's	Misc oriental	④④③

AREA OVERVIEWS

	Tuk Tuk	*Thai*	④❸⑤
	Yum Yum	*"*	❷❷❸
£15+	Le Mercury	*French*	⑤⑤❸
	Café Mozart	*German*	❸❸④
	La Porchetta Pizzeria	*Italian*	❷❸❷
	La Finca	*Spanish*	❸④❷
	Upper St Fish Shop	*Fish & chips*	❷❸④
	Ask! Pizza	*Pizza*	❸❸❸
	PizzaExpress	*"*	❸❸❸
	La Piragua	*South American*	❸❷❷
	Iznik	*Turkish*	❷❶❶
	Sarcan	*"*	❷❸❸
	New Culture Rev'n	*Chinese*	④❸④
£10+	Afghan Kitchen	*Afghani*	❷④❸
£5+	Pret A Manger	*Sandwiches, cakes, etc*	❸❶④

SOUTH

South Bank
(SE1)

Price	Name	Cuisine	Rating
£50+	Le Pont de la Tour	British, Modern	4 4 2
£40+	Blue Print Café	"	3 3 2
	Oxo Tower	"	4 4 2
	The Butlers Wharf Chop-house	British, Traditional	4 3 3
£35+	County Hall	British, Modern	4 3 4
	The People's Palace	"	4 3 4
	Livebait	Fish & seafood	2 3 4
	Cantina del Ponte	Italian	5 5 5
	Le Pont de la Tour Bar & Grill	Steaks & grills	2 2 2
£30+	RSJ	British, Modern	2 2 3
	Bistrot 2 Riverside	East/West	3 4 4
	Tentazioni	Italian	1 1 4
	Bengal Clipper	Indian	2 3 4
£25+	The Apprentice	British, Modern	1 5 5
	The Honest Cabbage	"	2 4 3
	Mezzanine	"	3 3 4
	The Waterloo Fire Station	"	4 4 4
	Archduke Wine Bar	International	4 4 4
	Fina Estampa	South American	2 3 5
	Four Regions	Chinese	3 3 3
	Kwan Thai	Thai	3 2 4
£20+	All Bar One	British, Modern	4 4 3
	The Circle	"	– – –
	Sixty Two	"	3 4 4
	Café Rouge	French	5 5 4
	La Lanterna	Italian	3 2 3
	Meson don Felipe	Spanish	3 4 1
	Gourmet Pizza Co.	Pizza	3 4 3
£15+	PizzaExpress	Pizza	3 3 3
	Pizzeria Castello	"	3 3 3

AREA OVERVIEWS

Battersea, Clapham, Wandsworth, Barnes, Putney, Brixton & Lewisham
(All postcodes south of the river except SE1)

£40+	Putney Bridge	*British, Modern*	⑤⑤④
£35+	Belair House	*British, Modern*	❸❸❷
	Chez Bruce	"	❶❶❷
	Ransome's Dock	"	❷❷❷
	Lobster Pot	*Fish & seafood*	❶❷❸
	Prego	*Italian*	❸❸❸
	Riva	"	❷❸④
£30+	Buchan's	*British, Modern*	❸❸❷
	The Cook House	"	❸❷④
	1 Lawn Terrace	"	❸④❸
	Redmond's	"	❸❷❸
	Snows by the Pond	"	⑤⑤⑤
	Sonny's	"	❷❷❷
	The Stepping Stone	"	❷❶❸
	Ghillies	*Fish & seafood*	❷❸❸
	Le Gothique	*French*	❸❸❸
	Le Versailles	"	❸❸④
	Del Buongustaio	*Italian*	❶❷❷
	Enoteca Turi	"	❷❷❸
	Polygon Bar & Grill	*Steaks & grills*	❸❸❷
	Bombay Bicycle Club	*Indian*	❷❷❷
	Thailand	*Thai*	❷❷❸
£25+	Bah Humbug	*British, Modern*	④④❶
	The Depot	"	④④❷
	Glaisters	"	④⑤④
	Helter Skelter	"	❷❷④
	The North Pole	"	❸❷❸
	On the Rise	"	④❸④
	Phoenix	"	❸❷❷
	Rapscallion	"	❸❸④
	The Stable	"	❸④❸
	The Sun & Doves	"	❷❷❷
	Moxon's	*Fish & seafood*	❷❸④
	Le Bouchon Bordelais	*French*	④④❷
	La Bouffe	"	④❸❷
	Monsieur Max	"	❷❸❸
	Newton's	"	❸❸❸
	Le P'tit Normand	"	❸❷❸
	Antipasto & Pasta	*Italian*	❶❶❸
	Cantinetto Venegazzú	"	❶❷❸
	Ost. Antica Bologna	"	❸④❸
	Café Portugal	*Portuguese*	❷❷④
	La Mancha	*Spanish*	❸❸❷

		Rating		
La Rueda	"	4	4	2
Naked Turtle	International	4	2	2
Elvis Gracelands Palace	Chinese	4	4	3
Royal China	"	2	2	3
Babur Brasserie	Indian	1	1	3
Café Spice Namaste	"	2	2	2
Ma Goa	"	1	2	4
Zujuma's	"	4	3	4
Enak Enak	Indonesian	3	4	3
Wok Wok	Misc oriental	4	4	4
Chada	Thai	3	3	4

£20+

All Bar One	British, Modern	4	4	3
The Lavender	"	2	2	2
The Mason's Arms	"	2	4	2
Scoffers	"	2	2	2
Vincent's	"	3	2	3
Café de la Place	French	3	4	3
Café Rouge	"	5	5	4
Emile's	"	2	1	3
Gastro	"	4	3	1
Restaurant du Marche	"	3	3	4
Arancia	Italian	2	3	3
Buona Sera	"	3	3	2
Caffè Uno	"	5	4	4
don Fernando's	Spanish	3	2	2
Rebato's	"	3	1	2
Alma	International	4	4	3
Hornimans	"	3	4	3
Pitcher & Piano	"	4	4	2
The Ship	"	3	4	2
Tootsies	Burgers, etc	4	4	4
Eco	Pizza	1	4	3
C Notarianni & Sons	"	3	4	4
Pizza Metro	"	1	1	3
Zed	"	3	2	3
Battersea Rickshaw	Indian	3	3	4
Indian Ocean	"	2	2	4
Rani	"	3	2	3
Sash Oriental Bar	Misc oriental	5	4	3
Tiger Lil's	"	4	4	3
The Old School Thai	Thai	3	1	3

£15+

White Cross Hotel	British, Modern	3	4	2
La Finca	Spanish	3	4	2
Batt. Barge Bistro	International	4	3	2
Côte à Côte	"	4	4	3
The Secret Garden	"	3	3	2
Brady's	Fish & chips	3	4	4
Bellinis	Pizza	4	3	3

PizzaExpress	"	❸❸❸
Pizzeria Franco	"	❶❸④
Boiled Egg	Sandwiches, cakes, etc	❸④❸
Heather's	Vegetarian	❷④❸
Dixie's Bar & Grill	Mexican/TexMex	⑤④❸
Smokey Joe's	Afro-Caribbean	❷❷❸
Beyoglu	Turkish	❷❶④
Kastoori	Indian	❶❷④
Shree Krishna	"	❶❸④
The Pepper Tree	Thai	❷❷❸
Phuket	"	❸❷④

£5+	Fileric	Sandwiches, cakes, etc	❷❷④

EAST

Smithfield & Farringdon
(EC1)

£50+	Maison Novelli	*French*	②④④
£40+	Bubb's	*French*	④④④
	Novelli EC1	*"*	❸④④
£35+	Mange 2	*French*	④❸④
	Gaudi	*Spanish*	④④④
£30+	The Fence	*British, Modern*	❸❷❸
	The Peasant	*"*	❸❸❸
	The Quality Chop House	*"*	❸❸❸
	St John	*"*	❸❷❸
	Stephen Bull	*"*	④❸⑤
	Rudland & Stubbs	*Fish & seafood*	❷❸❸
	Café du Marché	*French*	❷❷❶
	Club Gascon	*"*	– – –
	Hope & Sir Loin	*Steaks & grills*	❷❸④
	Moro	*North African*	❷❷❷
	Pacific Spice	*Misc oriental*	❸❸④
£25+	Home	*British, Modern*	❷④❷
	Vic Naylors	*"*	④④❷
	Bleeding Heart	*French*	❷❷❶
	Chez Gérard	*"*	④④❸
	Alba	*Italian*	❸④④
	The Clerkenwell	*"*	❸❸④
	Mustards Brasserie	*International*	④❸④
	Carnevale	*Vegetarian*	❷❸④
	Cicada	*Misc oriental*	④④❷
	East One	*"*	❸❸❷
£20+	Al's	*British, Modern*	④④❸
	All Bar One	*"*	④④❸
	Fox & Anchor	*British, Traditional*	❷④❷
	The Eagle	*Mediterranean*	❷④❷
	Dôme	*International*	⑤④④
£15+	Medina's	*Italian*	④❷❸
	Ask! Pizza	*Pizza*	❸❸❸
	Japanese Canteen	*Japanese*	④❸⑤
£10+	Lunch	*International*	❸❷④
£5+	Au Bon Pain	*Sandwiches, cakes, etc*	④❸④
	Pret A Manger	*"*	❸❶④

227

The City & East End
(All E and EC postcodes, except EC1)

£60+	Tatsuso	*Japanese*	❶③④
£50+	City Brasserie	*British, Modern*	④④❸
	City Rhodes	"	❶②❸
	Gladwins	"	❸②④
	City Miyama	*Japanese*	❷②④
£40+	Sheekey's	*British, Modern*	– – –
	10	*British, Traditional*	❸④④
	Beauchamp's	*Fish & seafood*	④④④
	Ashtons	*French*	④④❸
	Coq d'Argent	"	⑤④❸
	Caravaggio	*Italian*	④④④
	Aykoku-Kaku	*Japanese*	❸④④
	Suan-Neo	*Misc oriental*	④⑤⑤
£35+	1 Lombard Street	*British, Modern*	❷❸❸
	Bar Bourse	"	❸④❸
	Searcy's Brasserie	"	❸④④
	Whittington's	"	④❸④
	Gow's	*Fish & seafood*	④④④
	Brasserie 24	*International*	④⑤④
	Brasserie Rocque	"	④④❸
£30+	Aquarium	*Fish & seafood*	❸❸❷
	The Grapes	"	❷❸❸
	Sweetings	"	❷❸❷
	Luc's Brasserie	*French*	❸❷❷
	MPW	"	❷❸⑤
	Saigon Times	"	❸❸❸
	Taberna Etrusca	*Italian*	④⑤④
	Imperial City	*Chinese*	❷❷❸
	Singapura	*Malaysian*	❸❸④
	Tao	*Misc oriental*	④④❸
	Sri Siam City	*Thai*	❷❸④
	Sri Thai	"	❸❸④
£25+	Cantaloupe	*British, Modern*	❸❸❶
	Frocks	"	❸④❷
	Hothouse Bar & Grill	"	④④④
	The Bow Wine Vaults	*British, Traditional*	④❸④
	George & Vulture	"	④❸❸
	Café Flo	*French*	④④④
	Chez Gérard	"	④④❸
	Gt Eastern Dining Room	*Italian*	– – –
	Terraza-Est	"	❸❸④
	Fuego	*Spanish*	❸④④
	Babe Ruth's	*American*	⑤⑤⑤

	Café Spice Namaste	*Indian*	②②②
	Rupee Room	*"*	③③④
£20+	All Bar One	*British, Modern*	④④③
	Simpson's of Cornhill	*British, Traditional*	③③②
	Café Rouge	*French*	⑤⑤④
	Barcelona Tapas	*Spanish*	②②②
	Leadenhall Tapas Bar	*"*	④④③
	Dôme	*International*	⑤④④
	Pitcher & Piano	*"*	④④②
	Faulkner's	*Fish & chips*	①③⑤
	Gourmet Pizza Co.	*Pizza*	③④③
	Pizza Pomodoro	*"*	④④②
	Futures	*Vegetarian*	③③③
	Shanghai	*Chinese*	②②③
	Café Indiya	*Indian*	②②④
	Sri India	*"*	④③③
£15+	Reynier	*British, Traditional*	④③②
	Arkansas Café	*Steaks & grills*	③④⑤
	PizzaExpress	*Pizza*	③③③
	The Place Below	*Vegetarian*	②⑤③
	Lahore Kebab House	*Indian*	①⑤⑤
	Moshi Moshi Sushi	*Japanese*	②③④
	Noto	*"*	③②⑤
£10+	Café Sofra	*Turkish*	④⑤④
£5+	EAT	*Sandwiches, cakes, etc*	③②③
	Pret A Manger	*"*	③①④
	Futures	*Vegetarian*	②③ –
£1+	Brick Lane Beigel Bake	*Sandwiches, cakes, etc*	②①④

MAPS

MAP 1 – LONDON OVERVIEW

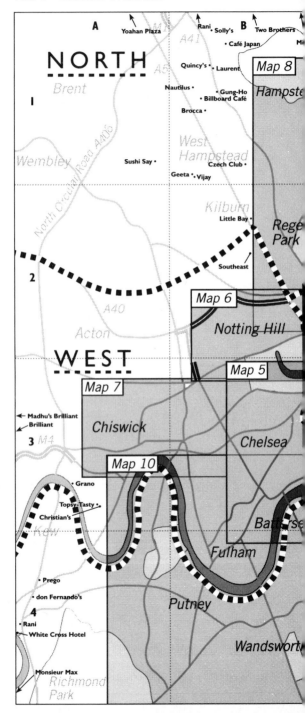

MAP 1 – LONDON OVERVIEW

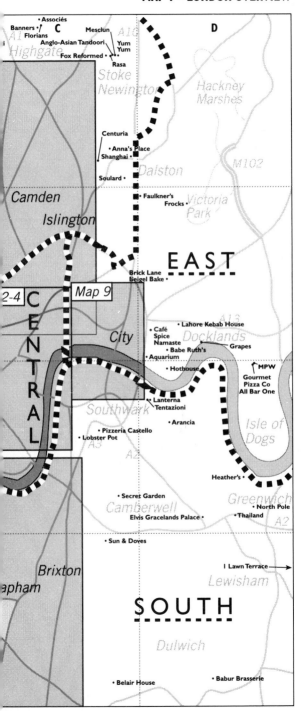

Associés
Banners • C
Florians
Anglo-Asian Tandoori
Fox Reformed •
Mesclun
Yum Yum
Rasa

D

Highgate

Stoke Newington

Hackney Marshes

Centuria
• Anna's Place
Shanghai •

Soulard •

Dalston

M102

Camden

Islington

• Faulkner's Frocks

Victoria Park

EAST

Map 9

Brick Lane
Beigel Bake •

2-4 C

City

CENTRAL

• Café
Spice
Namaste
• Aquarium
• Babe Ruth's

Lahore Kebab House

Docklands

Grapes

• Hothouse

MPW
Gourmet
Pizza Co
All Bar One

• Lanterna
Tentazioni

Southwark

• Arancia

Isle of Dogs

• Pizzeria Castello
• Lobster Pot

A3

A2

Heather's •

• Secret Garden
Elvis Gracelands Palace •

Camberwell

Greenwich

• North Pole
• Thailand

A2

• Sun & Doves

Brixton

apham

1 Lawn Terrace →

Lewisham

SOUTH

Dulwich

• Belair House

• Babur Brasserie

MAP 2 – WEST END OVERVIEW

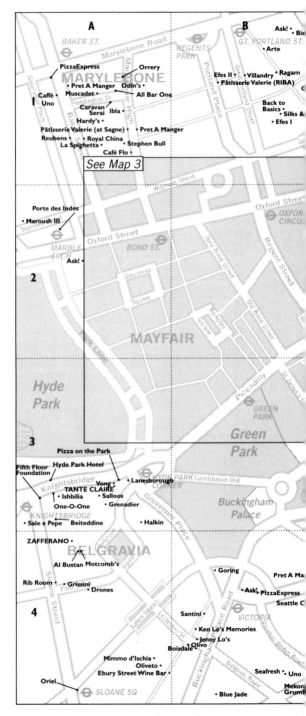

A

BAKER ST.

Marylebone Road

REGENTS PARK

B

Ask! • Bir

GT. PORTLAND ST.

• Arte

PizzaExpress • • Orrery

MARYLEBONE

• Pret A Manger   Odin's •

Muscadet •

Caffè •

Uno

1

Caravan
Serai

• Ibla

Hardy's •

Pâtisserie Valerie (at Sagne) •

Reubens •   • Royal China

La Spighetta •

• All Bar One

• Pret A Manger

Café Flo •

• Stephen Bull

Efes II •   • Villandry   • Ragam

• Pâtisserie Valerie (RIBA)

Back to
Basics •
• Silks &
• Efes I

C

See Map 3

Porte des Indes

• Maroush III

MARBLE
ARCH

• Ask!

2

Oxford Street

BOND ST.

Grosvenor
Square

Oxford Street

New Bond Street

Old Bond Street

Regent Street

Oxford Stree

OXFOR
CIRCU

Berkeley
Square

MAYFAIR

Hyde
Park

Piccadilly

St James's

GREEN
PARK

3

Green
Park

Pizza on the Park

Fifth Floor   Hyde Park Hotel
Foundation

Knightsbridge

Vong •

• Lanesborough

HYDE PARK Constitution Hill

TANTE CLAIRE

• Ishbilia   • Salloos

One-O-One •   • Grenadier

KNIGHTSBRIDGE

• Sale e Pepe   Beiteddine

ZAFFERANO •

BELGRAVIA

Al Bustan   Motcomb's •

Rib Room •   • Grissini

• Drones

4

Sloane Street

• Halkin

Grosvenor Place

Buckingham
Palace

• Goring

Pret A Ma

• Ask!   • PizzaExpress

Seattle C

VICTORIA

Santini •

• Ken Lo's Memories

• Jenny Lo's

Boisdale •   • Olivo

Mimmo d'Ischia •

Oliveto •

Ebury Street Wine Bar •

Oriel •

SLOANE SQ

• Blue Jade

Seafresh •   • Uno

Mekon
Grumb

MAP 2 –WEST END OVERVIEW

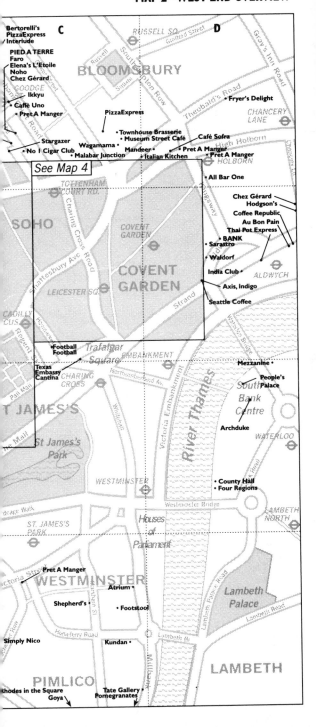

C

Bertorelli's
PizzaExpress
/ Interlude

PIED A TERRE
Faro
Elena's L'Etoile
Noho
Chez Gérard
GOODGE
Ikkyu
Caffè Uno
Pret A Manger

Stargazer
No 1 Cigar Club

D

RUSSELL SQ

BLOOMSBURY

Theobald's Road

Fryer's Delight

CHANCERY
LANE

PizzaExpress

Townhouse Brasserie
Museum Street Café
Wagamama
Mandeer
Malabar Junction
Italian Kitchen

Café Sofra
High Holborn
Pret A Manger
Pret A Manger
HOLBORN

All Bar One

See Map 4

TOTTENHAM
COURT RD

SOHO

Charing Cross Road

COVENT
GARDEN

COVENT
GARDEN

LEICESTER SQ

Shaftesbury Ave

CADILLY
LUS

Regent St

Football
Football

Texas
Embassy
Cantina

CHARING
CROSS

T JAMES'S

Ne Mall

St James's
Park

WESTMINSTER

ST JAMES'S
PARK

dge Walk

Trafalgar
Square

EMBANKMENT

Northumber...nd Av.

Chez Gérard
Hodgson's
Coffee Republic
Au Bon Pain
Thai Pot Express
BANK
Sarastro
Waldorf
India Club
ALDWYCH
Axis, Indigo

Seattle Coffee

Strand

Mezzanine

South
Bank
Centre

People's
Palace

Archduke

WATERLOO

River Thames

Victoria Embankment

Houses
of
Parliament

WESTMINSTER

Victoria Street

Pret A Manger

Atrium

Shepherd's

Footstool

Horseferry Road

Simply Nico

Kundan

PIMLICO

Rhodes in the Square
Goya

Tate Gallery
Pomegranates

County Hall
Four Regions

Westminster Bridge

LAMBETH
NORTH

Lambeth
Palace

Lambeth Palace Road

LAMBETH

Millbank

Lambeth Rd

MAP 3 – MAYFAIR, ST JAMES'S & WEST SOHO

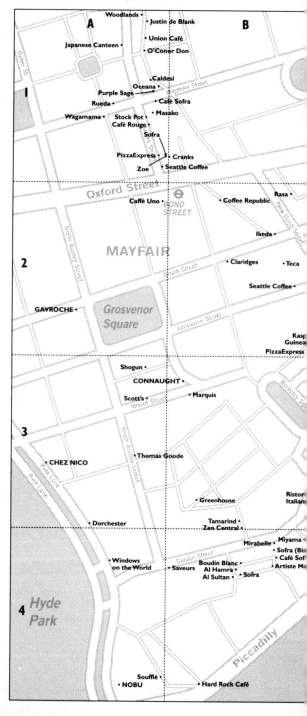

A   **B**

Woodlands •
• Justin de Blank
• Union Café
Japanese Canteen •
• O'Conor Don
• Caldesi
Oceana •
Purple Sage •
Rueda •
• Café Sofra
Wagamama •
• Masako
Stock Pot •
Café Rouge •
Sofra •
PizzaExpress •
• Cranks
Zoe •
• Seattle Coffee

1

Oxford Street

Caffè Uno •
BOND STREET

Rasa •
• Coffee Republic
Ikeda •

MAYFAIR

• Claridges
• Teca

2

Seattle Coffee •
GAVROCHE •
Grosvenor Square
Kasp
Guinea
PizzaExpress

Shogun •
CONNAUGHT •
Scott's •
• Marquis

3

• CHEZ NICO
• Thomas Goode

• Greenhouse
Ristor
Italian

• Dorchester
Tamarind •
Zen Central •

Mirabelle •
• Miyama
• Sofra (Bis
• Café Sof
• Windows on the World
• Saveurs
Boudin Blanc •
Al Hamra •
Al Sultan •
• Sofra
• Artiste M

4

Hyde Park

Soufflé •
• NOBU
• Hard Rock Café

Piccadilly

MAP 3 – MAYFAIR, ST JAMES'S & WEST SOHO

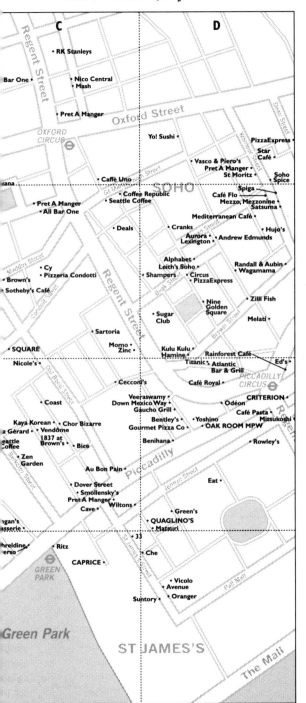

MAP 4 – EAST SOHO, CHINATOWN & COVENT GARDEN

A

B

All Bar One •

New Oxford Street

Dyott St

• Pret A Manger •

Oxford Street

1

TOTTENHAM CT. RD.

Soho St

Charing Cross Road

Soho Square

• Gay Hussar

• Au Jardin des Gourmets

Café Pasta •

SOHO

Shaftesbury Avenue

Mon Plai

Mildreds •
Café Rouge •

• Café Med
Quo Vadis
dell'Ugo •
• All Bar One

Frith St

2

Red
Fort

Dean St

• Gopal's

• Soho Soho
Escargot •
• Wok Wok
Garlic
& Shots •
• Café Emm

• Pasta di Milano
• PizzaExpress
Stock Pot •
Sri Siam
Pollo •

Café Coq •

Monmouth St

• Pitcher & Piano

Alastair Little •
Chiang Mai

• Little Italy
• Bar Italia
• Café Bohème

• Ed's

Cambridge
Circus

Blues •

Old Compton Street

Pâtisserie •
Valerie •
Café Sofra •

• Café Latino
Kettners •

Maison Bertaux •

Balans •

Teatro •

IVY •

• Dôme

Capannina •
French House

• Lindsay House

Shaftesbury Avenue

• New World

• Cam Phat
Ikkyu

• Harbour City

3

Mayflower •

CHINATOWN

Gerrard St

China City
Mr Kong •
Fung Shing •

• Poons, Lisle St

• Tokyo Diner

• Saint
Cranks

Charing Cross Road

Cranbourn St

Wong Kei •

Wardour Street

Lisle Street

• Pret A
Manger
Stephen Bu

• Café Fish
PizzaExpress

• Golden Dragon

LEICESTER
SQ.

Beotys •

Chuen Cheng Ku •

• Manzi's

Cork & Bottle •

Caffè Uno •

Sheekey's •
PizzaExpress

• Joy King Lau
• Poons

• Häagen-Dazs
• Little Havana

Planet Hollywood •
• Café de Paris

• Sound Republic

Leicester
Square

• Fashion Café

• TGI Friday's

All Bar One •

• Capital Radio
Restaurant

Sofra •

Browns

• Dôme

4

Haymarket

Whitcomb Street

Tibetan
Restaurant •

• Stock Pot
• Woodlands

• Café Flo

Corney & Barrow

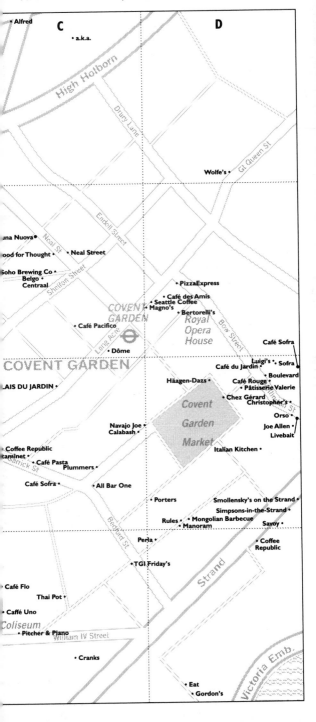

MAP 4 – EAST SOHO, CHINATOWN & COVENT GARDEN

C **D**

• Alfred
• a.k.a.

High Holborn

Drury Lane

Wolfe's •

Gt Queen St

Endell Street

una Nuova •
Neal St
ood for Thought •
• Neal Street

Shelton Street

Soho Brewing Co •
Belgo •
Centraal
• PizzaExpress

COVENT GARDEN
• Café des Amis
• Seattle Coffee
Magno's •
• Bertorelli's
Royal Opera House

• Café Pacifico
Long Acre
Café Sofra
Luigi's • Sofra
Café du Jardin •
• Boulevard
• Dôme
Café Rouge •
• Pâtisserie Valerie

COVENT GARDEN
Häagen-Dazs •
• Chez Gérard
Christopher's •

LAIS DU JARDIN •
Orso •

Navajo Joe •
Calabash •
Joe Allen •
Livebait

Bow Street

• Coffee Republic
taminet •
• Café Pasta
Plummers •
Italian Kitchen •

Café Sofra •
• All Bar One

Bedford St

• Porters
Smollensky's on the Strand •
Simpsons-in-the-Strand •
Rules • • Mongolian Barbecue
• Manoram
Savoy •

Perla •
• Coffee Republic

• TGI Friday's
Strand

• Café Flo
Thai Pot •

• Caffé Uno
Coliseum
• Pitcher & Piano
William IV Street

• Cranks

Victoria Emb.

• Eat
• Gordon's

MAP 5 – KNIGHTSBRIDGE, CHELSEA & SOUTH KENSINGTO

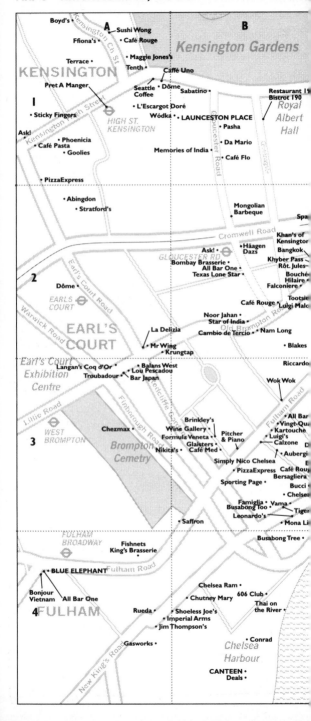

A

B

Boyd's •

• Sushi Wong

Ffiona's •

• Café Rouge

Kensington Gardens

Terrace •

• Maggie Jones's

KENSINGTON

Tenth •

Caffè Uno •

Pret A Manger

Seattle • Dôme •

Coffee Sabatino •

Restaurant 1

Bistrot 190

I

• Sticky Fingers

• L'Escargot Doré

Wódka •

• **LAUNCESTON PLACE**

Royal

Albert

Hall

Ask! •

HIGH ST.

KENSINGTON

• Pasha

• Phoenicia

• Café Pasta

• Da Mario

• Goolies

Memories of India •

• Café Flo

• PizzaExpress

• Abingdon

• Stratford's

Mongolian

Barbeque

Spa

Cromwell Road

Khan's of

Kensington

GLOUCESTER RD

Ask! •

• Häagen

Dazs

Bangkok

Bombay Brasserie •

All Bar One •

Khyber Pass

Rôt. Jules-

2

Dôme •

Texas Lone Star •

Bouché

Hilaire •

Falconiere •

Café Rouge •

Tootsie

Luigi Malc

EARL'S

COURT

Noor Jahan •

Star of India •

Nam Long

Cambio de Tercio •

Earl's Court

Exhibition

Centre

La Delizia •

• Mr Wing

• Krungtap

• Blakes

Langan's Coq d'Or •

• Balans West

Troubadour •

• Lou Pescadou

Bar Japan

Riccardo

Wok Wok

• All Bar

WEST

BROMPTON

Chezmax •

Brinkley's •

Wine Gallery •

Formula Veneta •

Pitcher

& Piano

• Vingt-Qu

• Kartouche

Luigi's •

3

Brompton

Cemetery

Glaisters •

Nikita's •

Café Med •

Calzone

D

Simply Nico Chelsea

• Auberg

E

• PizzaExpress

Café Rou

Bersagliera

Sporting Page •

Bucci

• Chelse

Famiglia •

Busabong Too •

Leonardo's •

• Vama

• Tiger

Mona Li

• Saffron

FULHAM

BROADWAY

Fishnets •

King's Brasserie •

Fulham Road

Busabong Tree •

• **BLUE ELEPHANT**

Bonjour

Vietnam

All Bar One

Chelsea Ram •

• Chutney Mary

606 Club •

Thai on

the River •

4 FULHAM

Rueda •

• Shoeless Joe's

• Imperial Arms

• Jim Thompson's

• Conrad

• Gasworks

Chelsea

Harbour

CANTEEN •

Deals •

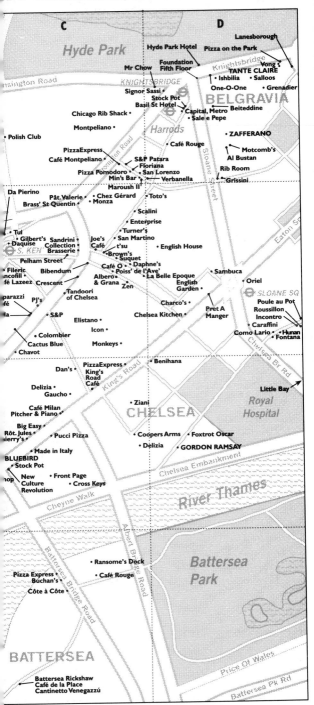

Hyde Park

C

D

Lanesborough

Hyde Park Hotel · Pizza on the Park

Mr Chow · Foundation · Knightsbridge · Vong
Fifth Floor · TANTE CLAIRE
KNIGHTSBRIDGE · Ishbilia · Salloos

Signor Sassi · One-O-One · Grenadier
Stock Pot
Basil St Hotel · Capital, Metro · Beiteddine

Chicago Rib Shack · Sale e Pepe

Montpeliano · **Harrods** · · ZAFFERANO

· Polish Club · Café Rouge · Motcomb's
Al Bustan

PizzaExpress · Rib Room
Café Montpeliano · S&P Patara
Floriana · Grissini
Pizza Pomodoro · San Lorenzo
Min's Bar · Verbanella
Maroush II

Da Pierino

Pât. Valerie · Chez Gérard · Toto's
Brass' St Quentin · Monza

· Scalini

· Enterprise

· Turner's
· Tul · Joe's · San Martino
· Gilbert's Sandrini Café
· Daquise Collection · t'su · English House
S. KEN Brasserie · Brown's
Pelham Street · Suquet

· Fileric Café O · Daphne's
ncofill · Bibendum Albero · Poiss' de l'Ave'
fé Lazeez Crescent & Grana Zen La Belle Epoque · Sambuca
English
Garden · Oriel
Tandoori
parazzi of Chelsea · SLOANE SQ
fé PJ's
Charco's · Pret A Poule au Pot
a · S&P Manger · Roussillon
Incontro
Elistano · Chelsea Kitchen · · Caraffini
Icon · Como Lario · Hunan
· Colombier Fontana
Cactus Blue Monkeys ·
Chavot

Dan's · PizzaExpress · Benihana
King's
Delizia · Road
Gaucho · Café · Little Bay

Café Milan · Ziani **Royal**
Pitcher & Piano **Hospital**
CHELSEA
Big Easy ·
Rôt. Jules · Pucci Pizza · Coopers Arms · Foxtrot Oscar
ierry's ·
· Delizia · GORDON RAMSAY
· Made in Italy
BLUEBIRD
· Stock Pot
hop New · Front Page · Chelsea Embankment
Culture · Cross Keys
Revolution
Cheyne Walk

River Thames

· Ransome's Dock
· Café Rouge

Pizza Express · **Battersea**
Buchan's · **Park**
Côte à Côte

BATTERSEA · Price Of Wales

Battersea Rickshaw
Café de la Place · Battersea Pk Rd
Cantinetto Venegazzú

MAP 6 – NOTTING HILL & BAYSWATER

MAP 7 – HAMMERSMITH & CHISWICK

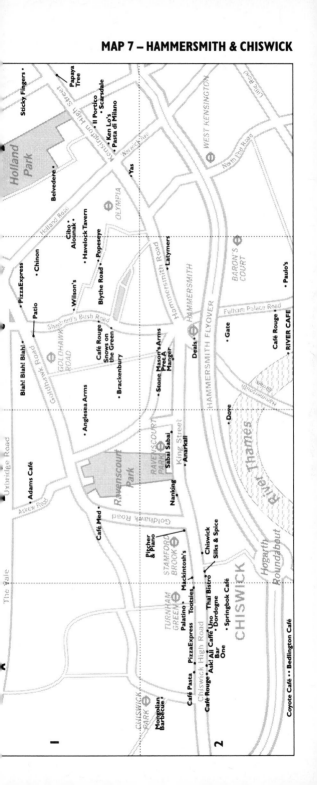

MAP 8 – HAMPSTEAD, CAMDEN TOWN & ISLINGTON

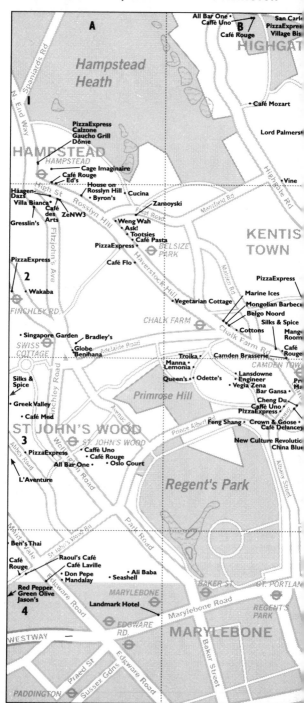

A

B

All Bar One •
Caffè Uno •
Café Rouge •

San Carl
PizzaExpress
Village Bis

HIGHGAT

Hampstead
Heath

1

• Café Mozart

Lord Palmersl

PizzaExpress
Calzone
Gaucho Grill
Dôme

HAMPSTEAD

HAMPSTEAD

Cage Imaginaire

Café Rouge •
Ed's

House on
Rosslyn Hill • Cucina
Byron's •

• Vine

Häagen-
Dazs
Villa Bianca •
Café
des
Arts
ZeNW3
Gresslin's •

Zamoyski

• Weng Wah
• Ask!
• Tootsies
• Café Pasta

PizzaExpress •

BELSIZE
PARK

**KENTIS
TOWN**

Café Flo •

PizzaExpress •

2

• Wakaba

FINCHLEY RD.

PizzaExpress

Marine Ices
Mongolian Barbec
Belgo Noord
Silks & Spice

• Vegetarian Cottage

CHALK FARM

• Cottons

Mang
Room

• Singapore Garden   Bradley's

*SWISS
COTTAGE*

Globe
Benihana

Adelaide Road

Café
Rouge

Camden Brasserie •

Troika •
Manna •
Lemonia •

CAMDEN TOW

Silks &
Spice

Queen's •   Odette's •

Lansdowne •
• Engineer
• Vegia Zena
Bar Gansa •

• Greek Valley

• Café Med

ST JOHN'S WOOD

Primrose Hill

Cheng Du •
Caffè Uno •
PizzaExpress •

Pri
Ma

Feng Shang • Crown & Goose •
Café Delancey

3

• PizzaExpress
All Bar One •

• Caffè Uno
• Café Rouge
• Oslo Court

New Culture Revolutic
China Blue

Regent's Park

L'Aventure

Ben's Thai

Café
Rouge

Raoul's Café
Café Laville
• Don Pepe
• Mandalay

• Ali Baba
• Seashell

Red Pepper
Green Olive
Jason's

MARYLEBONE

Landmark Hotel

MARYLEBONE

*EDGWARE
RD.*

*REGENT'S
PARK*

WESTWAY

PADDINGTON

Sussex Gdns.

Praed St.

MAP 8 – HAMPSTEAD, CAMDEN TOWN & ISLINGTON

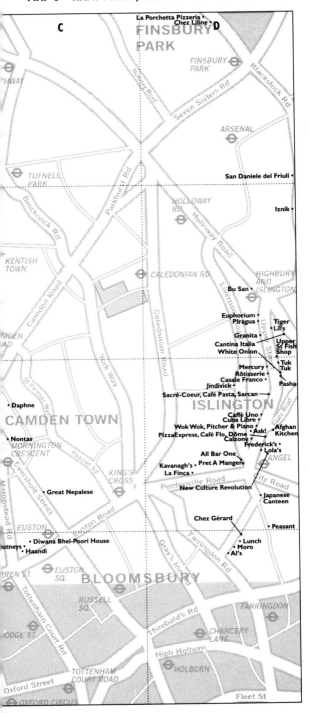

La Porchetta Pizzeria •
Chez Liline •

C   **D**

FINSBURY
PARK

FINSBURY
PARK

Blackstock Rd

Hornsey Road

Seven Sisters Rd

ARSENAL

TUFNELL
PARK

San Daniele del Friuli •

Parkhurst Rd

Brecknock Rd

HOLLOWAY
RD.

Iznik •

Holloway Road

KENTISH
TOWN

Camden Road

CALEDONIAN RD.

HIGHBURY
AND
ISLINGTON

DEN
AD

Fish Way

Caledonian Road

Liverpool Rd

Bu San •

Upper St

Euphorium •
Piragua •

Tiger
Lil's

Granita •

Upper
St Fish
Shop

Cantina Italia •
White Onion •

• Daphne

Mercury •
Rôtisserie •
Casale Franco •

Tuk
Tuk

York Way

St Pancras Wav

Jindivick •

Pasha

Sacré-Coeur, Café Pasta, Sarcan —

CAMDEN TOWN

ISLINGTON

• Nontas
MORNINGTON
CRESCENT

Caffè Uno •
Cuba Libre •

Wok Wok, Pitcher & Piano •

Afghan
Kitchen

St Johns Rd

St Pancras Rd

PizzaExpress, Café Flo, Dôme •
Calzone •

Ask! •

Frederick's •

Eversholt Street

• Great Nepalese

KING'S
CROSS

All Bar One •

Lola's

ANGEL

Kavanagh's •

Pret A Manger •

La Finca •

Hampstead Rd

New Culture Revolution

City Road

Pentonville Road

EUSTON

Euston Road

Japanese
Canteen

Chez Gérard

Farringdon Rd

• Peasant

utneys •
• Diwana Bhel-Poori House
• Haandi

EUSTON
SQ.

• Lunch
• Moro
• Al's

REN ST.

EUSTON
SQ.

BLOOMSBURY

Gray's Inn Rd

RUSSELL
SQ.

FARRINGDON

Tottenham Court Rd

Theobald's Rd

ODGE ST.

CHANCERY
LANE

High Holborn

HOLBORN

TOTTENHAM
COURT ROAD

Oxford Street

Fleet St

OXFORD CIRCUS

MAP 9 – THE CITY

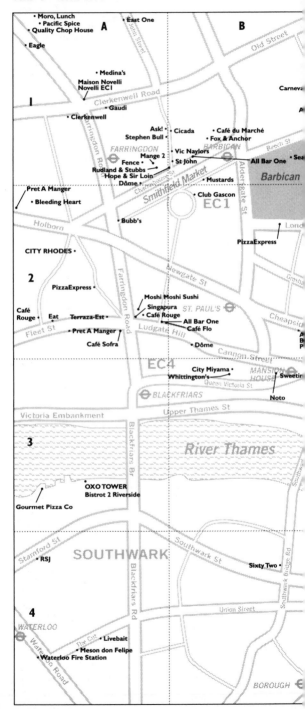

A
- Moro, Lunch
- Pacific Spice
- Quality Chop House
- East One
- Eagle

B

Old Street

- Medina's
- Maison Novelli
- Novelli EC1

Clerkenwell Road

Carneva

- Gaudi
- Clerkenwell

FARRINGDON

Beech St

- Ask!
- Stephen Bull
- Cicada
- Café du Marché
- Fox & Anchor
- Vic Naylors

BARBICAN

- Mange 2
- St John

Aldersgate St

- All Bar One
- Sea
- Fence
- Rudland & Stubbs
- Hope & Sir Loin
- Dôme

Smithfield Market

Barbican

- Mustards

EC1

- Club Gascon

Lond

- Pret A Manger
- Bleeding Heart

Holborn

- Bubb's

- PizzaExpress

CITY RHODES

Newgate St

Gresh

2

- PizzaExpress

Farringdon Road

- Moshi Moshi Sushi
- Singapura

ST. PAUL'S

Cheapsi

- Café Rouge
- Eat
- Terraza-Est

- Café Rouge
- All Bar One
- Café Flo

- A
- B

Fleet St

- Pret A Manger
- Café Sofra

Ludgate Hill

- Dôme

Cannon Street

EC4

- City Miyama
- Whittington's

MANSION HOUSE

- Sweetin

- Noto

BLACKFRIARS

Queen Victoria St

Upper Thames St

Victoria Embankment

Blackfriars Br

River Thames

Southw

3

- OXO TOWER
- Bistrot 2 Riverside

- Gourmet Pizza Co

Stamford St

Southwark St

SOUTHWARK

- RSJ

Blackfriars Rd

Southwark Bridge Rd

- Sixty Two

4

Union Street

WATERLOO

The Cut

- Livebait
- Meson don Felipe
- Waterloo Fire Station

Waterloo Road

BOROUGH

MAP 9 – THE CITY

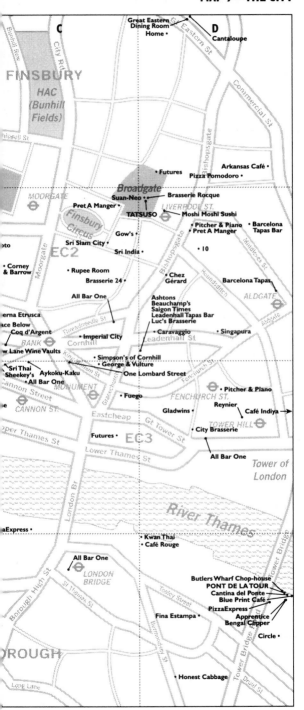

Great Eastern
Dining Room •
Home •
Cantaloupe

FINSBURY

HAC
(Bunhill
Fields)

• Futures

Arkansas Café •
Pizza Pomodoro •

Broadgate
Suan-Neo • Brasserie Rocque
Pret A Manger • *LIVERPOOL ST.*
TATSUSO • Moshi Moshi Sushi
Pitcher & Piano •
Gow's • • Pret A Manger
Sri Siam City •
Sri India •

Barcelona
Tapas Bar

• Corney
& Barrow

• Rupee Room
Brasserie 24 •

• 10

All Bar One •

Chez
Gérard •

Barcelona Tapas •

ALDGATE

erna Etrusca
ace Below
Coq d'Argent
BANK
w Lane Wine Vaults

• Imperial City

Ashtons
Beauchamp's
Saigon Times
Leadenhall Tapas Bar
Luc's Brasserie

• Caravaggio

• Singapura

Sri Thai
Sheekey's •
•All Bar One
MONUMENT

• Simpson's of Cornhill
• George & Vulture
Aykoku-Kaku One Lombard Street

• Fuego

Gladwins •

• Pitcher & Piano

Reynier
Café Indiya →

FENCHURCH ST.

TOWER HILL

Futures • *EC3*

• City Brasserie

Lower Thames St

All Bar One •

Tower of
London

River Thames

aExpress •

• Kwan Thai
• Café Rouge

All Bar One •
*LONDON
BRIDGE*

Butlers Wharf Chop-house
PONT DE LA TOUR
Cantina del Ponte
Blue Print Café
PizzaExpress •
Apprentice
Bengal Clipper

Fina Estampa •

Circle •

ROUGH

• Honest Cabbage

MAP 10 – SOUTH LONDON (AND FULHAM)

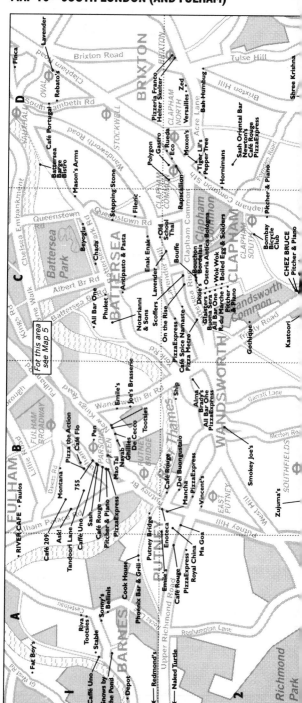

NOTES